Math

Compiled by
Marlene Peterson

Well-Educated Mother's Heart Learning Library
Libraries of Hope

Math

Compiled from:
Number Stories of Long Ago, by David Eugene Smith, Boston: Ginn & Co., (1919).

The Teaching of Arithmetic, by David Eugene Smith, Boston: Ginn & Co., (1909).

Arithmetic for Young Children, by Horace Grant, Boston: Lee and Shepherd, (1880).

The Teaching of Geometry, by David Eugene Smith, Boston: Ginn & Co. (1911).

The Teaching of Elementary Mathematics, by David Eugene Smith, New York: The MacMillam Co., (1900).

Mathematician's Delight, by W.W. Sawyer, Baltimore: Penguin Books, (1943). (In public domain.)

Libraries of Hope, Inc.
Appomattox, Virginia 24522

Website www.librariesofhope.com
Email: librariesofhope@gmail.com

Printed in the United States of America

CONTENTS

Number Stories of Long Ago 1

The Teaching of Arithmetic 155

Arithmetic for Young Children 175

The Teaching of Geometry 187

The Teaching of Elementary Mathematics..................... 239

Mathematician's Delight... 271

NUMBER STORIES OF LONG AGO

BY

DAVID EUGENE SMITH

CHING AND HIS THREE TURTLES

PREFACE NUMBER ONE

JUST BETWEEN US, AND WORTH READING

These are the stories that were really told in the crisp autumn evenings, the Story-Teller sitting by the fire that burned in the great fireplace in the cottage by the sea. These are the stories as he told them to the Tease and the rest of the circle of friends known as the Crowd. Sitting by the fire and listening to the stories, in the lights and shadows of the dancing flames they could see the forms of Ching and Lugal and all the rest with their curious dress of long ago.

Night after night he told these tales of the ages past, stories unlike the make-believes they had often heard, stories of what might really have happened when the world was young, stories that the Crowd said were " different " because they told of much that was new, much that was curious, and much that was interesting.

So the Crowd learned many strange things that have happened in Number Land, but they learned much more than this ; for the Story-Teller told them much that was interesting about the way in which boys and girls used to write in centuries long past — how Ching wrote on palm leaves, and Lugal on bricks, and Hippias on parchment. He also told them about many of the number puzzles that have delighted boys and girls for thousands of years, so that the Tease found new tricks to play on all her friends, and the Crowd found much to think about as the stories were related by the great log fire.

And you who read these stories should imagine yourselves sitting by the great log fire and listening to the Story-Teller. You should seem to see in the flames and the shadows the moving pictures of those who played their parts in Number Land when the world was learning as you do.

Is this history? Never mind. What is history but a story, and is not every story a history of something? Why bother our heads over history? For us the story is the important thing.

PREFACE NUMBER TWO

FOR THE GROWN-UPS, AND NOT WORTH READING

The story of our numbers, of the world's attempts to count, of the many experiments in writing numerals, and of the difficulties encountered through the ages in performing our everyday computations — all this is so interwoven with the history of humanity as to have an interest for every thinking person. As the world has grown, so the work with numbers has grown ; when the world has faced the mysteries of the universe, numbers have assisted in solving its problems ; when commerce and science have shown new needs in computation, arithmetic has always been ready to lend a hand. The history of mathematics is no small part of the history of civilization.

This being the case, it seems proper to relate at least some portion of the story of numbers to the pupils in our schools. It can be made quite as interesting as any other story of civilization, for it touches upon a subject with which the pupils in our schools are in daily contact, adding new values to the problems of arithmetic and giving a new perspective to the whole study of mathematics.

5

This book is intended for supplementary reading in the elementary school. It is written in nontechnical language, and the effort has been made to connect with the history enough of the human element to make it more interesting than any mere recital of facts. With it there is also joined something of the history of writing materials, this being connected naturally with the story of our numbers. Chapters I–VIII can easily be read aloud, and the Question Box at the end of each chapter can be used as a basis for conversation or for written work.

The facts stated in the book are as nearly exact as the circumstances permit. It is not to be expected, however, that changes in the form of various numerals will be considered. Such changes are of no moment in a work of this nature and do not contradict the statement that the historical facts are presented with substantial accuracy.

It is the author's hope that this little series of human incidents will create a new interest not merely in the study of arithmetic but in the story of the development of our civilization.

DAVID EUGENE SMITH

There is no knowledge that is not power. — EMERSON

There is no Past, so long as books shall live. — BULWER-LYTTON

They who lived in history only seemed to walk the earth again. — LONGFELLOW

Do not then train boys to learning by force and harshness; but direct them to it by what amuses their minds, so that you may be the better able to discover with accuracy the peculiar bent of the genius of each. — PLATO

AN-AM, BEL, AND THEIR SHEEP.

NUMBER STORIES
OF LONG AGO

CHAPTER I

HOW CHING AND AN-AM AND MENES
COUNTED

The logs are burning in the great stone fireplace in the cottage by the sea. The Story-Teller sits in his easy-chair looking at a book of curious pictures and still more curious letters. She of the teasing ways is dancing through the open door, and with her are the others who make up what she calls the Crowd, tired with the hours of play upon the beach.

" Just one little story before bedtime," says the Tease.

" Just one," chime in the others.

" Not a single word," says he of the book with the curious pages.

" Oh, just one," says the Tease.

" Just one," begs the Crowd.

" Well, just one," says the Story-Teller, who knew all the time that he would submit. "Take your chairs, then, put a new log on the fire, and listen to the story of Ching and An-am (än äm) and Menes (mē′nēz)."

The logs burned, the Crowd sat by the fire, and he of the curious book told this story:

It is so very, very long ago that not even the wisest men of China can tell the year or the century in which little Ching, the king's oldest son, played in the forests at the foot of Mount Yu, and painted a face on the shell of his biggest turtle, and told the soldier who guarded him what a lot of turtles he had. To be sure, Ching had only three turtles, but he did n't know a word for " three," and the soldier did n't, and not even the king could do more than say, "Yes, there are a lot of turtles."

For all this was so long ago that even in the oldest parts of the earth, of which China was one, most people could not count. It was before kings had palaces or crowns or royal robes, and when they were little more than savages. So we do not wonder that Ching, even though he was the son of a king, could only count "one, two," everything beyond that being a "lot." This was as far as people needed to count when Ching was playing in the forest at the foot of Mount Yu, for money was not invented, and we use our numbers to-day chiefly in buying the things we need. But in those days kings had many slaves and made them work, and sent them to kill animals, and made them bring back skins for clothing and meat for food. Few people needed to count, and only these few ever learned. Even the wisest men did not know much about the numbers that we use every day, because they had no need to do so.

At the time that Ching was growing up in China there lived on the plains of Mesopotamia (měs'ō pō tā'mǐ à), in southern Asia, a boy named An-am. He was the son of Bel, a shepherd of the country afterwards called the land of Babylon. Bel tended the sheep, and drove away the wolves that prowled about at night, and kept a careful watch to see that not one of his flock should wander away. One day Bel called out to An-am, " There

are many sheep out there; drive them back."
But really there were only a few sheep, for
neither An-am nor Bel could count beyond
three, and all larger numbers were called
" many." Nevertheless Bel and An-am knew
the sheep so well that they could tell if one
was missing, just as a good shepherd dog
to-day knows if one of his flock has gone
astray. So An-am and Bel could count " one,
two, three, many," and that was all they
needed to know about arithmetic.

While Ching was playing in the forest at
the foot of Mount Yu, and An-am was help-
ing to watch the flocks that fed near the
Euphrates (ū frā'tēz), another boy was living
on the banks of the Nile in ancient Egypt.
This boy's name was Menes, and he lived
not far from the place where now the enormous dam holds back the waters of the great
river. The little hut in which Menes lived
was the grandest house that he or his father
or his mother ever saw, and yet it had only
a single room, and this was smaller than the
schoolroom in which you study arithmetic.

For this was thousands of years ago, long
before people had real houses, long before

anyone knew how to read or write, long before the world had learned how to weave fine cloth, and long before men knew any other way to make a light than to rub two pieces of wood together until one of them was set on fire. Menes was proud of what he thought was the magnificent house in which he lived, although it was only a little hut, and he was glad to be able to say, " We have a great many palm trees about our house," although there were only six. For Menes had heard his father and mother speak of one tree, of two trees, of three trees, and of four trees, but beyond that they simply said "a great many trees," for they had names for numbers only up to four, and all beyond that was a great many, just as we might speak of a great many apples.

When Ching and An-am and Menes grew to be men, and Ching became a king, and An-am became a manager of the Babylonian king's estates, and Menes became a great captain in the wars against the savages who lived in the south, Ching could only count to two, and An-am to three, and Menes to four, because this was as far as people in their countries could count in the days when the world was only just coming out of savagery, when money was unknown, and when no one measured land or buildings or the things which they traded with one another.

But many hundreds of years later other boys played in the forest at the foot of Mount Yu, and they counted "one, two, two and one, two twos, two twos and one, a lot." The world was growing, and people needed larger numbers, and so they counted as far as "two twos and one," which we call "five," and all beyond that was simply called a "lot."

And other boys helped to tend the flocks of Babylon, and their fathers taught them to count by threes, — "one, two, three, three and one, three and two, two threes, two threes and one, two threes and two, three threes, three threes and one, three threes and two, many," for they did not know a word for four, so they could n't say "four threes," and they just said "many"; but of course they said another word, using the language of ancient Babylon. The world of Mesopotamia was growing older, and people needed more number names; but they still had no money, and a few such names were quite enough.

While the boys were counting to " two twos and one " in China and to " three threes and two " in Mesopotamia, Egyptian boys played under the palms where long before their time Menes had looked with pride upon his father's hut. No longer, however, was there just a hut with a single room, for the world was growing still older, and the descendants of the Menes of long ago had now a house with two rooms, and the Menes of this time had learned a new way of counting. The people along the Nile had found that the fingers of one hand would help them with their numbers, and so they made new names as far as five, and Menes now counted " one, two, three, four, five, five and one, five and two," and so on to " five fives and four "; and then he gave up and said " a great many." He could count farther than the Chings and the An-ams, but " five fives and four " is only twenty-nine, and this does not seem very far to us. But this was long before people could read and write, when they used knives made of stone, and when they thought the world was growing old, while to us it seems to have been very young.

Hundreds of years again went by, and still new Chings and An-ams and Meneses played in the forests of Yu, or on the plains of Mesopotamia, or on the banks of the Nile; but now the world began to feel that "five fives and four" was not large enough, even in ancient Egypt. Then it was that someone thought that if people could count to five on one hand, they might as well count to ten on two hands, and so the Ching and An-am and Menes of that day counted the trees and sheep by learning number names to ten, and then saying "one and ten, two and ten, three and ten," and so on to "ten tens, ten tens and one," and as much farther as they wished to go. The world had discovered that its ten fingers were useful in counting, and so it learned to count by tens; and this was one of the greatest discoveries that the world ever made. Although boys and girls speak different languages, they all have ten fingers, and so all civilized people to-day count by tens.

Near the equator, where the climate is

hot, and where people did not wear shoes, they counted their toes as well as their fingers, learning separate number names to twenty, — not "one and ten," "two and ten," and "three-ten" (thir-teen), but "eleven," "twelve," and so on, with special names, to twenty, which they sometimes called "man finished," and beyond that they counted by twenties. Some of these people wandered to other countries and carried along with them their way of counting. But most of the people of the world did as the children of Ching and An-am and Menes did, — they counted by tens. When we hear of "three-score years and ten," and when the French speak of "four twenties" instead of eighty, we have two remaining bits of the old way of counting by twenties.

Thus the world learned from Ching and An-am and Menes, and from their children and their children's children, and so on for hundreds and hundreds of years, first to count by twos or threes, and then by fives, and then by tens, and sometimes by twenties. A few people tried to count by twelves, and so we have twelve inches in a foot, twelve ounces in the ancient pound, and twelve things in a dozen, but the reason why the world came to count by tens was because Ching and An-am and Menes and you and I have just ten fingers on our two hands.

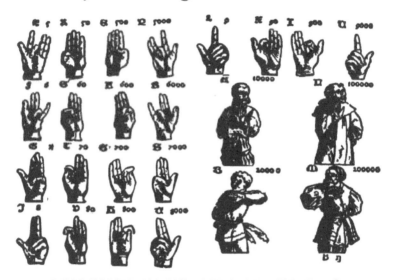

REPRESENTING NUMBERS BY THE HAND

From a book printed nearly four hundred years ago. It shows the way in which numbers were represented by the hand

Long after the early days of which we have been speaking, the world learned how to write numbers. Because different races wrote them in different ways, the merchants who traded with others whose language they did not speak represented numbers by their fingers. For at least two thousand years the merchants of different countries made number signs with their fingers in bargaining at the great fairs where they met to buy and sell the goods that thus went from country to country, — spices from India, silks from the land of Ching, wool from the ancient home of An-am, and dates from the palm trees under which Menes played many centuries before.

" Did they really count like this? " asked the Tease.

" Really," replied he of the curious book.

" I think it is funny," said the Tease.

" No funnier than your way would seem to Ching," said the Story-Teller.

" Do we have another story to-morrow night? " asked one of the Crowd.

" Not another story ever," replied the Story-Teller, " unless you go to bed."

" And then? "

" To-morrow we must all fill a question box, and each must answer every question."

" And then? " asked the Tease.

" And then? Well, then we shall see," replied the Story-Teller.

THE QUESTION BOX

1. How far could the first Ching mentioned in the story count?

2. Why did Ching not learn to count as we do?

3. What need have we for counting that Ching did not have?

4. Where did Ching live?

5. How far could the first An-am count?

6. If An-am could count no farther, how could he tell if one sheep was missing out of twenty sheep?

7. Why was it unnecessary for An-am to count farther?

8. Where did An-am live?

9. What name did the first Menes give for numbers beyond four?

10. Where did Menes live?

11. How did people come to count by tens?

12. By what other numbers than ten did the world sometimes count?

13. Why did people use one of the numbers referred to in Question 12?

14. What practical use did the world make of representing numbers on the fingers?

AHMES AND THE PRIEST
AT THE TEMPLE GATE

CHAPTER II

HOW AHMES AND LUGAL AND CHANG
WROTE THEIR NUMBERS

" Just one little story," whispered the Tease.

" Not a single word," said the Story-Teller.

" We filled the Question Box," said Maude.

" Just one," pleaded Gertrude.

" I will put on a big log," said Charles.

" And we will all keep still," said Fanny.

" Well, then, just one, but it must be short," remarked he of the curious book.

" What is the story about? " asked George.

" This," replied the Story-Teller, " is to be about Ahmes (ä'mĕs) and Lugal (loo'gäl) and Chang (chäng) and the way in which they wrote their numbers."

This, then, is what the Story-Teller related about these boys of long ago:

23

It was many a long century after the last of the little Chings had learned to count by tens that there lived on the banks of the Hwangho (hwänghō′), or Yellow River, a potter whose plates and cups were known all over Shantung (shän′tŏong′) as the best to be found anywhere in that great province.

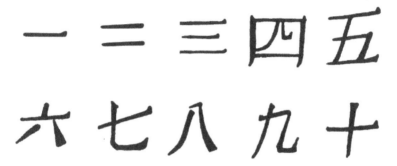

CHINESE FIGURES

Modern Chinese figures for the numbers from 1 to 10. These developed from those used by Chang

One day Chang watched his father write with a brush on a palm leaf some marks which showed how many cups there were upon the top shelf in his workshop.

Chang had learned to count the cups, but he could write ten only by making ten marks. So he said to his father, " I want to learn how to write the numbers as you do."

24

Then his father took the brush and wet it, rubbed it on a small cake of black paint, and painted some strange figures on a piece of palm leaf. These figures did not look at all like ours, for Chang's father did not know how to write numbers as we write them, and, indeed, no one in all the world at that time knew anything whatever about them.

七　百　八　十　九

CHINESE NUMBER

The number 789 in modern Chinese. The symbols mean 7 hundred 8 ten 9. The number is commonly written from the top down instead of from left to right

While Chang was learning the Chinese figures on the banks of the Yellow River, another boy was learning to write numbers in a far-distant country. This boy's name was Lugal, and his father was a merchant in Mesopotamia, not far from the place where An-am had lived so many years before.

Lugal's father did not use a brush and a palm leaf as Chang's father did. He took a piece of damp clay, just as you may have done when you made mud pies as children, and in this damp clay he wrote his numbers.

All this was still long before money was invented and long before paper was made. The few people who could write at all made letters by pressing with a pointed stick on pieces of damp clay, the clay being then dried in the sun.

BABYLONIAN NUMERALS

Babylonian figures for the numbers from one to ten as they appear on the ancient clay tablets

Because the signs looked like little wedges they were called cuneiform (kŭ nē'ĭ fôrm) signs, a word meaning "wedge-shaped."

This does not seem to us a very good way to write numbers, but it was the only way that Lugal knew. There was no book about arithmetic in those days, and boys and girls worked hard all day in the fields or shops instead of going to school.

While Chang and Lugal were learning their curious ways of writing numbers in China and Babylon, there lived in the valley of the Nile a boy named Ahmes. Near his home was a large temple, and on the walls were many curious signs that puzzled him.

EGYPTIAN NUMERALS

Numerals from the walls of a temple at Luxor

One day when Ahmes saw a priest looking at the temple wall he asked him what the curious signs meant.

The priest replied, " These are figures stating the number of days in the king's last war."

Then Ahmes said he wished that he knew how to write numbers, and the priest told him that he would teach him how to do so if he would get some papyrus (på pī'rŭs).

ANCIENT EGYPTIAN PAPYRUS

From a papyrus roll, showing the ancient manner of writing and illustrating. (From Breasted's " Ancient Times ")

Ahmes went home and asked his father to tell him what papryus was, and in this way he learned about a kind of paper on which the priests of Egypt used to write. In early times they had written on stone, brick, or pieces of pottery, but as the centuries went on they had invented something better.

There was a water plant growing in Egypt that looked like the bulrush in our own swamps, only it was much larger and taller. People found that if they cut this plant in thin strips, laid these strips close together, placed another layer crosswise over the first one, pressed these all down, and then allowed them to dry, they would have something on which they could write. This substance looked like our coarse brown paper. The water plant was the papyrus reed, and so the substance was called papyrus, and this is the word from which our word "paper" comes.

The papyrus was made in long strips, often about ten inches wide. On these strips the Egyptians wrote their books. They then rolled up the papyrus as we roll up a strip of wall paper. This is the reason that we speak of papyrus rolls instead of papyrus books. When you speak of the attendance roll at school you are simply using this ancient name.

Ahmes asked his father for a piece of papyrus and a brush and some black ink, and with these he went to the temple gate the next morning. The priest then showed Ahmes how to write numbers, and said to him, "If I should write twenty-seven thousand five hundred twenty-nine, I should write a number larger than anyone in the world would ever need to use." The priest thought this was true, for the world was still young, no one knew about money, and no one thought that large numbers would ever be needed.

EGYPTIAN NUMBER

The number 27,529 as the priest wrote it for Ahmes. The order and shape of the figures vary greatly in different inscriptions

Ahmes lived nearly four thousand years ago, and although he grew up and became a great man, and wrote the oldest book on mathematics that now exists, he never needed to use large numbers. The world was still too young to know much about arithmetic.

"Really, couldn't people multiply and divide numbers then?" asked the Tease.

"The answer to that question is another story," said the Story-Teller.

"Then there is another story to-morrow night?" asked Maude.

"That depends on the Question Box," replied he of the curious book.

"And then what happens?" asked Herbert.

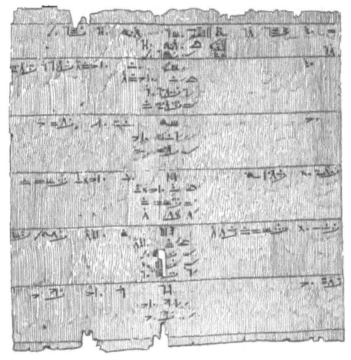

ANCIENT BOOK ON ARITHMETIC

From the oldest book on mathematics in the world, a papyrus roll written by Ahmes about 1700 B.C.

"There isn't any 'then,'" replied the Story-Teller, mysteriously. "What we call 'then' passed away long ago. There is only a 'now,' and now is the time for bed."

THE QUESTION BOX

1. Why did Chang write such strange numbers as he did instead of writing numbers as we do?

2. Why did Lugal not use a zero and thus write a number like seventy with two figures as we do, instead of writing seven times the sign for ten?

3. What materials did Chang and Lugal use for writing? Why did they not use paper?

4. What materials did the priest use when he explained the numerals to Ahmes?

5. How was papyrus made and what did it look like?

6. From what word does our word " paper " come?

7. When you speak of calling the roll, what does the word " roll " suggest to you?

8. What kind of a book did Ahmes write when he grew up and became a great man?

9. In what way are our numerals better than those of Chang and Lugal and Ahmes?

10. Could you add, subtract, multiply, and divide with the numerals of Chang and Lugal and Ahmes? What difficulties would you meet if you tried to do so?

11. Why do we call the numerals used by Lugal by a name meaning wedge-shaped?

12. Which numerals seem to you the easiest, those of Chang, those of Lugal, or those of Ahmes?

HIPPIAS
ON THE ACROPOLIS OF ATHENS

IΠΠIAΣ | דָּנִיֵּאל | TITVS

CHAPTER III

HOW HIPPIAS AND DANIEL AND TITUS
WROTE THEIR NUMBERS

"What is the story to-night?" asked the Tease as she came into the long room and stood before the fire, while the Crowd drew up the chairs.

"Story? Who said there was to be any story at all?" asked he of the curious book as he turned a new page.

"We always have a story," replied the Tease. "We have n't missed a single evening since we began."

"But we began only two nights ago."

"Yes, and this will make the third story," said George.

"But we must stop sometime," replied the Story-Teller, "and this is a good place."

"Oh, there is a great deal more that we want to know," said the Tease.

"What is it you wish to know?"

"The thing you are going to tell us," answered the Tease.

"Then," said the Story-Teller, "it must be about Hippias (hĭp'ĭ ås) and Daniel and Titus (tī'tŭs)."

And this is the story he told:

Many years after Chang had learned to write numbers in his home on the banks of the Yellow River, and Lugal to do so in

Mesopotamia, and Ahmes to do so by the temple on the Nile, there lived in Greece a boy who was known as Hippias.

ANCIENT COINS

Coins found in Asia Minor. They are among the earliest known, dating from about 550 B.C. (From Breasted's "Ancient Times")

The world was now getting old enough to have money for use in the shops, so that merchants not only traded their wares as they did in the days of Chang and Lugal and Ahmes but they sold them for copper and silver coins. This is the reason why there was more need for numbers than in the centuries before Hippias played about the Acropolis (à krŏp'ŏ lĭs) at Athens and learned how the merchants wrote their numbers on a parchment roll. For not only had the people invented new ways of writing numbers but they had invented something new on which to write. They tried for a time to use long strips of leather sewed together and rolled up, and on these they wrote with a brush dipped in black ink. They then found that they could whiten and toughen the skins of sheep and calves so as to make them better suited for writing. This was first done in a city called Pergamon (pûr'gà mŏn), in Asia Minor, and from the name of this city comes the word "parchment." It was many centuries after Hippias lived before the world began to use paper.

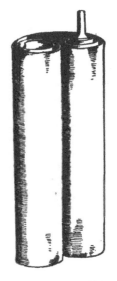

PARCHMENT ROLL

It was on such rolls that people wrote in the time of Hippias

Hippias learned to write his numbers on parchment, using Greek characters that were very different from our numerals.

If Hippias wished to write a number like 2977, he had to use fifteen Greek letters, so you see that arithmetic must have been much harder for the Greek boys than it is for us.

I Γ Δ H X

GREEK NUMERALS

The Greek numerals for 1, 5, 10, 100, and 1000 as Hippias wrote them on parchment

As the years went on there came a time when people felt the need of some easier way of writing numbers for use in the shops of Athens. So it came to pass that another little Hippias, not long before the days when

XXΓHHHHΓΔΔΓII

NUMBER WRITTEN IN GREEK

This is the way that Hippias wrote the number 2977

Paul preached at Athens nearly two thousand years ago, wrote on his parchment roll the letters of the Greek alphabet to represent numbers. The Greek name for the first letter was *alpha* (ăl'fā), and the second letter had the name *beta* (bā'tà). When Hippias learned his A B C's he learned his *alpha-betas*, and from this name we get our word "alphabet."

While Hippias was learning to write numbers in Athens, a boy named Daniel was living on the slope of the Mount of Olives. This boy went daily to Jerusalem with fruit which his father sold in the market place. He

A' B' Γ' Δ' E' F' Z' H' Θ' I'

GREEK LETTER-NUMERALS

The first ten numbers as the Greeks represented them by letters about two thousand years ago. For larger numbers they used other letters: K' for 20, Λ' for 30, and so on. They placed a mark (/ or ') by each letter to show that it stood for a number

needed to know how to write numbers, for the prices of the melons and figs were written on small boards and put upon his father's fruit stall. It was for this reason that Daniel's father taught him the smaller numbers that everyone needed to know. In those days, however, a man would work for a penny a day, and so most people had little need for numbers higher than ten, and numbers above a few thousand were rarely used by anyone.

The numerals which Daniel learned were only the first few letters of the Hebrew alphabet, just as those learned by Hippias were the first few letters of the Greek alphabet.

א ב ג ד ה ו ז ח ט י

HEBREW LETTER-NUMERALS

The first ten numerals as learned by Daniel, being the first ten letters of the Hebrew alphabet. They read from right to left, the Hebrew language being written in that way

You can see that such a way of writing numbers must have made multiplication and division very hard.

While Hippias was playing in the streets of Athens, and Daniel was carrying fruit from

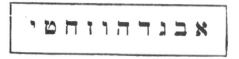

EARLY ROMAN NUMERALS

These nine characters represent the numbers 1, 5, 5, 10, 50, 100, 500, 500, and 1000 as written by the early Romans. Notice the two ways of writing 5 and 500

the Mount of Olives to Jerusalem, Titus was playing about the streets of Rome and attending a school near the great forum of the city.

The teacher showed the boys the way in which the ancient Romans wrote their numbers and also taught them the numerals that were then used in the shops of Rome.

IVXLC DⅭⅮ ∞

LATE ROMAN NUMERALS

Number forms for 1, 5, 10, 50, 100, 500, 1000, and 1000 used by the Romans about the beginning of the Christian era. Notice the two ways of writing 1000

If Titus had wished to write a number greater than a million he would have been very much puzzled, for in those days people rarely had any need for numbers above a few hundreds

CIƆCIƆDCCLCIƆCIƆDCCCLXXXXVIIII

ROMAN NUMBER

One of several ways of writing 2,752,899 at the time when Titus lived. The Romans themselves were not uniform in writing such large numbers

or a few thousands. Titus would probably have written such a large number in words.

When we see the Roman numerals on a watch or a clock we should know that Europe used them commonly until after America was discovered, that they were of no value in multiplying and dividing, but were fairly convenient for writing the small numbers needed in everyday business affairs.

Titus liked to puzzle a chum of his named Caius (kā'yŭs), and one day he asked him this question: "What is the number that becomes one more when one is taken away from it?"

"Your head," replied Caius, "must be just plain wood."

But when Titus wrote IX on the stone pavement and said to Caius, "Now take away the I and tell me what you have left," Caius saw that the wooden head had something in it after all.

Then Caius, remarking that he could think of many other numbers that would answer just as well, asked this question: "What is the number that becomes ten more when ten is taken away?"

Titus then asked Caius if he knew that half of nine was four, and Caius replied that he must be dreaming. But Titus pointed again to IX and asked Caius to take the upper half of it and see if it was not IV. Then Caius said that he could show that half of twelve was seven.

"That is nothing," said Titus; "half of thirteen is eight."

"That is easy," said Caius; "but can you take one hundred from four hundred and have five hundred left?"

"I think I have now told you enough for to-night," said the Story-Teller. "How many of you can show that half of twelve is seven?"

"I can," said Emily.

"And I," said half a dozen others.

"How many of you can show that half of thirteen is eight?"

"We all can," said the Crowd.

"Who can show how Caius took one hundred from four hundred and had five hundred left?"

Not everyone could do this. Can you do it?

"Who can tell me some other curious puzzle about the Roman numerals?"

"We all can," said the Crowd.

"Then," said the Story-Teller, "I think you had better fill the Question Box."

"If we fill it do we have another story to-morrow night?" asked Charles.

"Well, if you don't fill it you certainly will not have the story," said the Story-Teller.

THE QUESTION BOX

1. In the days of Hippias what was used instead of paper for writing purposes?

2. Why did the invention of money make it necessary for people to know more about counting and about working with numbers?

3. Why were the numerals used by Hippias not so convenient as those which you use?

4. What does the word "alphabet" mean, and how is it connected with the expression "Learn your A B C's"?

5. Was Daniel's way of writing numbers more nearly like that of Hippias or like the one used by Titus? Why was it not so good as ours?

6. Where have you seen the Roman numerals practically used, outside of your school work?

7. Why are the Roman numerals not so good for computing purposes as ours?

8. How many ways do you know of writing the number four in Roman numerals?

9. If you could not use our numerals, which numerals that you have read about would you prefer to use?

10. Titus and Caius found some amusing things connected with their numerals. Caius said he could show that half of twelve is seven. How did he do it? Can you, in the same way, show that half of thirteen is eight?

CHAPTER IV

HOW GUPTA AND MOHAMMED AND GERBERT WROTE THEIR NUMBERS

"No Story To-Night," wrote the Story-Teller in large letters on a piece of paper, smiling as he did it. Then he pinned the notice on the edge of the shelf just above the fireplace, went back to his easy-chair, opened his curious book, and pretended to read.

A few minutes later a certain small lady tiptoed in and then tiptoed out again. There was the sound of whispering and quiet laughing in the hall, and then the door opened softly, the Tease once more tiptoed in, crossed out the " No," and with her pencil wrote above it the words " A Real Good."

Then the Crowd rushed in and all read aloud, " A real good story to-night."

" What is the use in arguing with the Crowd ? " asked the Story-Teller.

" No use at all," answered the Crowd.

A Real Good

~~No~~ Story To-Night

THE STORY-TELLER'S NOTICE AND HOW IT WAS
CHANGED

But all this time the Story-Teller was just as anxious to begin as the Crowd was to listen. This, then, is the story he told:

It was a hot day, and Gupta (goop'tä), brown of skin and brown of dress, played under the shade of the bamboo on the banks of the Indus (ĭn'dŭs), the great stream that gives the name to India.

Gupta was glad to be out of the hot sun, glad to splash in the water with a branch of bamboo, glad to be living in that ancient land — ancient even when he played by the Indus two thousand years ago. Gupta had never been to school, for there were no schools like ours to attend, and so he could neither read nor write, and he had little idea of Europe and none whatever of America.

Of all the people he knew, only the priests in the temple near his home could read and write, and no one in all Europe or Asia or Africa had ever heard of America —for this was many hundred years before Columbus was born.

The priests soon noticed that Gupta was brighter than the other boys in the village, and so they took him to the temple and taught him to read and write. They also taught him to write the numbers to four, which was as far as they themselves were certain how to write them, but these numbers did not look at all like most of ours.

ANCIENT HINDU NUMERALS

The first four numerals, for 1, 2, 3, and 4, as Gupta learned them more than two thousand years ago

The first three numerals were simply straight marks, like those the Romans used, and the four looked like our plus sign.

Gupta learned to write numbers with a sharp iron pencil which scratched slightly into a piece of palm leaf. Books were always

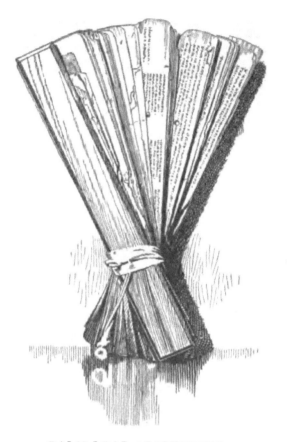

PALM-LEAF ARITHMETIC

An old arithmetic from India, written on strips made from the
leaf of a kind of palm

written in this way in India at the time that
Gupta lived, and indeed for many years thereafter, and they looked very different from the
book which you are reading.

When Gupta grew a little older he learned
of another kind of numerals. Some priests
had seen these numerals cut on the walls of

EARLY NUMERALS

Probable number forms from inscriptions on stone made in the
third century B.C.

a cave where pilgrims often rested for the
night. It is here that we have almost the

EARLY NUMERALS

Probable number forms from inscriptions made in a cave in India
in the second century B.C.

first traces of our present system of writing
numbers, and they are more than two thousand years old. There was no zero, however;

no one could write a number like 207 in the way that we write it, and so the figures were no better than those of Hippias, Daniel, or Titus, or even of Lugal, Ahmes, or Chang.

Long after Gupta died, and about a thousand years ago, someone had the wisdom to invent the zero, and after that it was easy to write numbers as we write them to-day.

About the time that the zero was invented there was born in the country near the Caspian Sea a boy whose parents named him after Mohammed (mṓ hăm′ĕd), the great religious leader of the Arabs.

Little Mohammed was a very bright boy, and Moses his father let him study with one of those wise men who watched the stars and thus told the time, for clocks and watches were then unknown.

Mohammed became so well known as a scholar that while still a young man he was called to Bagdad (băg däd′) to be the caliph's (kā′lĭf) astronomer. The caliphs were the kings of the country about the Tigris (tī′grĭs) River, and many stories are told about them in the Arabian Nights Tales. These tales describe Bagdad at about the time that our

Mohammed lived there, and they tell of
Harun-al-Rashid (hä rōōn' är rà shēd'), a name
which means Aaron the Just. Mohammed

١ ٢ ٣ ٤ ٥ ٦ ٧ ٨ ٩.

ARABIC NUMERALS

Numerals from 1 to 9, with a dot for zero, as used by the Arabs.
They are not like the numerals that we sometimes call Arabic

the son of Moses knew Harun's son, and the
two used to study and work together in the
caliph's observatory at Bagdad.

Mohammed the son of Moses found the
Arabs of Bagdad using numerals that were
quite different from those used by us to-day.
From certain wise men who came to Bagdad

HINDU NUMERALS

Numerals from 1 to 9, with zero, used by the Hindus and taken to
Bagdad about 1150 years ago

from India about this time, however, Mohammed learned the numerals used in that
country, and these were somewhat like ours.
He believed that they were better than the

ones the Arabs used, and so he wrote a book about them. This book was taken to Europe by some traveler and assisted in making known in that part of the world the numerals that we use. Because the numerals came to Europe from Arabia they were called Arabic numerals, but they were not used by the Arabs then nor have they been generally used by them since that time.

OLD EUROPEAN NUMERALS

Oldest example of our numerals known in any European manuscript. This manuscript was written in Spain in 976 A.D.

In France nearly a thousand years ago there lived a boy named Gerbert (zhĕr bâr'). He was so promising as a student that the priests whose school he attended sent him to Spain with a nobleman whom they knew, so that he might learn still more from travel. There he probably met with Arabs who knew about the Hindu numerals, because part of Spain was then under Arab rule, and when he went to Rome he explained these numerals to others. He became one of the most learned men of his time and was elected pope, taking the name of Sylvester II. In this way the numerals that we often call Arabic were brought to the attention of

CHANGES IN OUR NUMERALS

This shows some of the changes made in our numerals from about the time of Gerbert to the time when Europe began to print books. After printing was invented there were few changes

learned men in Europe about the year 1000, although they had been known a little before this time in Spain and possibly in Italy.

The handwriting of people changes so much from century to century and from country to country that the numerals which Gerbert used were very different from those which we study in school and which everyone in Europe and America uses to-day. Little by little, however, they came more nearly to resemble those which we now see in our arithmetics.

Printing from movable type was invented in Europe about 1450, although printing from engraved blocks was known much earlier. After the numerals were first printed they did not change very much. We use about the same figures that Columbus used. This is because printed letters and figures do not change as rapidly as written letters and figures.

An Italian boy named Leonardo (lä ō när′dō), who was born about seven centuries ago in Pisa (pē′zä), learned about these numerals in an Arab school in northern Africa, where his father was working. When he became a man he described them in a book which he wrote, and this assisted in making them known. But of course the book was not printed then, because printing was not yet known in Europe. He left the book in manuscript, and many people read it, especially in Italy, where it was written, and in this way they learned about these numerals.

"Did all these boys really live?" asked George.

"Really; every one of them."

"What are the funny marks under the picture of Gupta?" asked Clara.

"That is the way he wrote his name in his language. People in India did not know our alphabet in those days. They had a curious one of their own."

"But the marks don't look like those under Mohammed's picture," said Helen.

"That is because Mohammed wrote his name in Arabic," said the Story-Teller.

"Gerbert was a French boy," said Edward, "so why did n't he use French letters?"

"That is because the French use Latin letters. Did you ever think how odd it seems that Americans speak English and write in Latin letters?"

"How did they ever work with such curious figures?" asked Maude.

"That is another —"

"So there is another story!" interrupted the Crowd.

"That depends on the Question Box," said the Story-Teller.

THE QUESTION BOX

1. How did Gupta learn the numerals?

2. Describe the appearance of books in Gupta's time and country.

3. Why were the numerals used by Gupta no better than the others about which you have heard? What important symbol was lacking? About when was this symbol invented?

4. When Mohammed the son of Moses went to Bagdad, did he find the Arabs using our numerals? About when did our numerals reach Bagdad?

5. What did Mohammed the son of Moses do to make our numerals known in Bagdad and also in Europe?

6. About when did Gerbert live, and how did he come to know about our numerals? What prominent position did he hold?

7. About when did Leonardo of Pisa live, and what did he do to make our numerals known?

8. Why did Leonardo not have the book printed which he wrote when he became a man?

9. About when was printing from movable type invented in Europe?

10. What kind of printing was known before the invention of movable type? Why is it better for the printers to use movable type?

ROBERT RECORD LEARNING THE USE OF COUNTERS

CHAPTER V

HOW ROBERT AND WU AND CAIUS ADDED NUMBERS

"I don't see how they ever added numbers when they wrote them as the Romans did," said Irene, just to get the Story-Teller started.

"The numerals that Hippias used were worse," said Edward.

"But Daniel's were still worse," said Will.

"Ahmes and Lugal had the worst of all," added Dorothy.

"I see," said the wise old Story-Teller, "that the Crowd has planned all this talk just to get me started"; at which the Tease smiled significantly.

"Well, it is true that they all had trouble with their numerals," he continued, "and to-night I am going to tell you a story about some of the troubles of three boys who found ways of adding numbers in spite of their awkward numerals."

When Caius was a boy he attended a kind of business school. There he learned how to write, to read the parchment rolls that told of business customs, and to perform the only two operations with numbers that were then considered absolutely necessary. These operations were addition and subtraction, and when we come to think of it they cover a large part of our business arithmetic to-day. It is not often that we need a long multiplication or a long division.

If you are asked to add 257 and 369 you find the work so easy that you can hardly imagine that it would ever trouble anyone. But when his teacher told Caius to add these numbers written in the Roman numerals, the problem did not seem so simple. It is really easier, however, than one would at first think, and if arithmetic required only adding, the Roman numerals would not be very difficult. In the first place the Romans usually wrote IIII instead of IV, VIIII instead of IX, and so on, and if you do this you will find it about as easy to add with Roman numerals as with our own.

After learning to add, which he found quite easy, Caius learned to subtract, and that was also easy; but when he came to multiplying or dividing with Roman numerals he at once found himself in a great deal of trouble.

HOW CAIUS ADDED 257 AND 369

Caius had six I's, so he wrote VI below; he had two V's, so he wrote X below; he had one X, so he wrote X below that; he had two L's, so he wrote C below; and he had five other C's, so he wrote D below them

Although Caius learned how to add and subtract with Roman numerals, there was another method that was more common. He learned that pebbles were used in working with numbers. He found that he could draw lines on a board,— one to represent units, another to represent tens, and so on,— and that he could then place pebbles on these lines.

61

By placing the pebbles on the lines for units, tens, and so on, he could add quite rapidly. Of course he could not add as rapidly as we

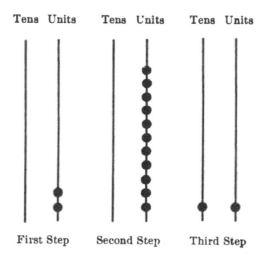

HOW CAIUS ADDED WITH PEBBLES

If Caius wished to add XXII and CXXXVIIII, he first placed 2 pebbles on the units' line, as shown in the First Step. He then placed 9 more, as shown in the Second Step. He then took away 10 of these pebbles, and added one pebble to the tens' line, as shown in the Third Step. The rest of the work is shown on page 49

do, but no one could work very quickly with numbers in those days, and Caius did as well as anyone else. People did not have much work to do with numbers, and they were not in as great a hurry as we are.

Of course Caius spoke Latin, and so he did not use the word "pebble," but used the Latin word *calculus* (kăl′kŭ lŭs), which means

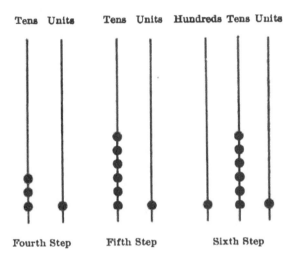

| Tens | Units | Tens | Units | Hundreds | Tens | Units |

Fourth Step   Fifth Step   Sixth Step

HOW CAIUS ADDED WITH PEBBLES

After the Third Step, as shown on page 48, Caius added 2 pebbles to the tens' line because of the XX in XXII, as shown in the Fourth Step. He then added 3 more because of the XXX in CXXXVIIII, as shown in the Fifth Step. Finally he drew a line for hundreds, and on this he placed one pebble because of the C in CXXXVIIII. His answer was CLXI

"pebble." So instead of saying that Caius pebbled the answer, we say that he calculated it, using a word that sounds more like Latin, and so we see what our words "calculate" and "calculation" originally meant.

Besides using pebbles, as he sometimes did and as was usually done in earlier times, Caius also used small circular disks like our checkers or button molds, and these he

GREEK WAX TABLET

This tablet was used by a Greek schoolboy early in the Christian era. The boy wrote part of the multiplication table upon it, and it can still be read. It is now in the British Museum

called *calculi* (kăl'kū lē), which is the plural of *calculus*. When he and the other boys went to school they did not carry notebooks, for paper was unknown, nor did they carry slates; but they sometimes carried small boards covered with wax, and on this wax they wrote with pointed sticks that looked somewhat like our pencils, erasing their work by simply smoothing the wax. They always carried their calculi, however, if they were studying

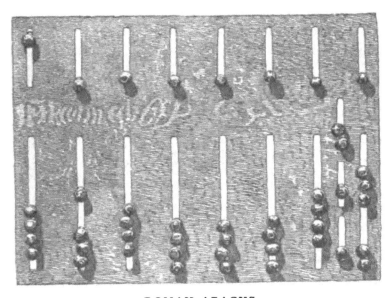

ROMAN ABACUS

Ancient bronze abacus used by the Romans. This is now in the British Museum

arithmetic. Indeed, practically everyone who did any work with numbers had at hand a small box or bag of these calculi.

Sometimes the merchants used a little calculating machine called an abacus (ăb'à kŭs) in which the calculi moved in grooves.

While Caius was learning to add and subtract with the Roman numerals and with calculi, a Chinese boy, whom we may know as Wu (woo), was learning to add and subtract with the numerals which Chang had studied many years before. He too found it necessary to use something like the calculi which

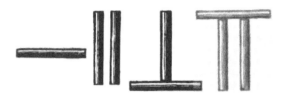

ANCIENT CHINESE STICK NUMERALS

The number 1267 expressed by means of rods or sticks by the old Chinese method

Caius had worked with, but instead of pebbles or small disks he used rods made of bamboo.

Wu thought he was doing something remarkable if he added two large numbers in two minutes. You would probably add them in a few seconds, but think how much longer it would take if you had only a little pile of sticks with which to work. It took Wu some time to lay the sticks out to represent a number and still longer to represent two numbers and then to find their sum.

This plan of computing by bamboo rods was carried by the Chinese to Korea, but

KOREAN RODS

Computing rods made of bone. Until quite recently these were used in the schools of Korea. The numbers were represented somewhat as the Chinese numerals were, as shown on page 52

the Koreans used rods made of bone, and continued to do this in their schools and in business calculations until quite recently.

It was more than a thousand years after Wu learned to add with the bamboo rods that the Chinese adopted the old Roman idea of having the calculi fastened to an abacus, and so they invented their reckoning board,

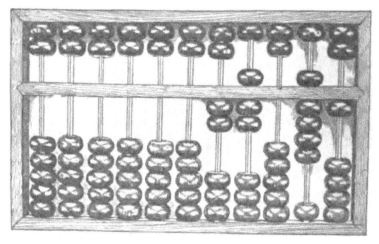

CHINESE ABACUS

Chinese abacus, or *suan pan*. This instrument is used everywhere in China to-day

or *suan pan* (swän pän). This they use in the schools, banks, and shops throughout all of China even to this day, and they often calculate more rapidly in this way than we can with pencil and paper. You have probably seen the *suan pan* used if you have ever visited a Chinese laundry in any of our cities.

About three hundred years ago there went to school in Japan a boy named Seki (sā kē), whose teacher had recently learned about an improvement which the Japanese had made on the Chinese abacus.

So Seki learned how to compute on the *soroban* (sō'rŏ bän'), which is the Japanese form

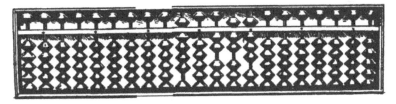

JAPANESE ABACUS

Japanese abacus, or *soroban*. This instrument is used everywhere in Japan to-day

of the *suan pan* of China, and this instrument is used everywhere in Japan to-day.

Seki grew up and became the greatest mathematician of Japan, and his name is known everywhere in that country and is also familiar to many mathematical scholars in other parts of the world.

Many Japanese can add and subtract more rapidly with the *soroban* than we can with pencil and paper.

About four hundred years ago there was born in England a boy named Robert Record (rĕk'ŏrd). When he went to school he was taught to use the Roman numerals, and he added, subtracted, multiplied, and divided numbers very much as Caius had learned to

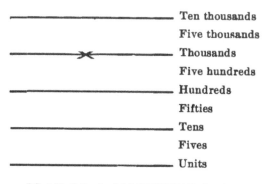

PLAN OF A COMPUTING TABLE

This plan shows the arrangement of lines on the kind of computing table used in most parts of Europe in the Middle Ages. It was still extensively used when Columbus made his voyages to America

do when he computed with the aid of calculi about fifteen hundred years earlier.

Two important changes, however, had been made in that length of time. Instead of having places on the computing table for only units, tens, hundreds, and so on, the spaces between the lines were used for fives, fifties, five hundreds, and similarly for all other fives, and the lines were now horizontal. We do not know when these changes were made, but they came in what are called the Dark Ages.

Because Robert cast the calculi down on the board, he spoke of "casting an account," and

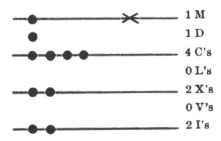

HOW ROBERT WROTE 1922 WITH COUNTERS

This shows how Robert Record represented MDCCCCXXII, or 1922, by counters. We sometimes see the number written MCMXXII, but this is not the old way of writing it. The cross was always placed on the 1000's line so as to aid the eye in reading the number. It finally suggested the use of the comma in writing a number like 47,256

this expression is sometimes used to-day. The board on which he counted was generally called a "counter." We buy goods over the counter to-day, not thinking what the word originally meant. Robert also called the calculi "counters," and if you have read Shakespeare you may have seen the expression "a counter

71

ADDITION.
Maſter.

The eaſieſt way in this arte, is to adde but two ſummes at ones togyther: howe be it, you maye adde moze, as I wil tel you anone. therefore whenne you wylle adde two ſummes, you ſhall fyrſte ſet downe one of them, it foꝛceth not whiche, and then by it draw a lyne croſſe the other lynes. And afterwarde ſette doune the other ſumme, ſo that that lyne maye be betwene them: as if you woulde adde 1659 to 8342, you muſt ſet your ſumes as you ſee here.

And then if you lyſt, you maye adde the one to the other in the ſame place, oꝛ els you may adde th:m boꝛhe togither in a new place: which way, bycauſe it is moſt plyneſt

3

PAGE FROM ROBERT RECORD'S BOOK

This page from Robert Record's "Ground of Artes" was printed nearly four hundred years ago

caster," meaning a man who could calculate only with counters and not with pencil and paper as we do. We sometimes use counters to-day in keeping the score in games.

Robert added numbers much as Caius did, placing the counters on the lines and in the spaces. When he had five counters on a line or in a space he took them up and carried one counter to the next place. You now see how we came to say "carry one" when we add, a counter being actually carried to the next place in the days of Robert Record.

A MODERN ADDING MACHINE

This kind of machine is used in banks and in many large establishments

When Robert became a man he wrote several books and used his influence to have the English people give up the Roman numerals.

We are apt to smile at Robert's use of counters and to think that we are much wiser than he because we use pencil and paper. But it is well to know that most of the world to-day finds it better not to use pencil and paper for computing. The Russians very generally use an abacus, many Persians use one, the Chinese use the *suan pan*, and the Japanese use the *soroban*. Even in Europe and America our most important computation is done by machinery, our banks all using adding machines, and our large corporations using machines for multiplying and dividing. Workmen in shops of various kinds often use a slide rule. Probably all of you have seen such an instrument,

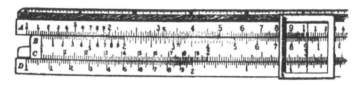

PART OF A SLIDE RULE

Such slide rules are extensively used in many industries to-day

and some of you may have learned how to multiply by sliding part of it along to the right or left.

This shows how Caius and Wu and Robert and many other boys in various parts of the world met the difficulties arising from poor numeral systems and overcame these difficulties by machinery, and how we are to-day coming to use machinery to help us in our work with numbers, especially in banks and workshops.

"It must have taken a long time to get an arithmetic lesson in those days," said Emily.

"No longer than it takes now," said the Story-Teller.

"How could that be?" asked Charles.

"It is just as easy as anything. All you have to do is to make the arithmetic lesson shorter, and that is just what was done."

"I wish they would do that in my school," remarked Margaret.

"Do you really?" asked the Story-Teller, "and do you want to do your work with counters on a board?"

"Well, that's different," Margaret answered, "and I think after all that our way is better than theirs."

"I don't see yet how they multiplied with the Roman numerals," said Helen.

"You are just trying to get me to promise another story," said the wily old Story-Teller. "Don't forget the Question Box. Now all of you get off to bed and don't bother me any more to-night."

"What about to-morrow night?" asked the Tease.

"To bed!" ordered the Story-Teller.

THE QUESTION BOX

1. How could Caius have added the numbers XXVII and LXXXVIII without using calculi?

2. What were the calculi and what is the origin of our word "calculate"?

3. How could Caius have added the numbers XXVII and LXXXVIII by using calculi?

4. What did Roman schoolboys take to school to help them in performing their calculations?

5. What were the wax tablets of the Greek and Roman schoolboys, and how were they used?

6. What people computed with bamboo rods in ancient times, and later with a *suan pan*?

7. In what country did the people compute with rods made of bone? Where is that country?

8. How did Robert Record compute?

9. What is the origin of our word "counter" as used in stores?

10. What nations still make much use of the abacus?

11. What kinds of machines or instruments are used for purposes of calculating in many of the most civilized countries to-day?

12. Of all the different ways of calculating that have been mentioned, which would you rather use if you were multiplying one large number by another?

CHAPTER VI

HOW CUTHBERT AND LEONARDO AND JOHANN MULTIPLIED NUMBERS

"So you wonder how people multiplied numbers, do you?" asked the Story-Teller, as the Crowd marched into the room, and George put another log on the fire, and the Tease stood wondering how it happened that the story was coming so easily. "Well, you see they just multiplied, and that's all."

"But how did they do it? That's the question," said the Tease. "How could anyone multiply with the Roman numerals, or how did anyone ever learn how to multiply, anyway?"

"When Ching was a boy no one could multiply at all," said the Story-Teller.

"I wish I could have gone to school then," said Fanny.

"There were n't any schools," said Charles.

"So much the better," remarked the Tease.

"As I have told you, those who did not go to school had to work all day, and how would you like that?" asked the Story-Teller.

The Crowd agreed that, after all, schools and multiplication and arithmetic were easier than digging and planting all day long, and so the Story-Teller continued:

"When Caius and Titus multiplied they did not use the Roman numerals; they used calculi, or counters, as they did when they added numbers. This story is too long, however, so I shall only tell you about the way in which the world learned to multiply as we do. Listen then to the story of Cuthbert (kŭth'-bẽrt) and Leonardo and Johann (yō hän')."

When Leonardo of Pisa went to school to the Moorish teacher on the northern coast of Africa, over seven hundred years ago, and learned how to write the numerals which we now use, the first great advantage that he found was in multiplying. Some of his boy friends in Pisa were probably using counters, or calculi, for this purpose, but his old Moorish schoolmaster could multiply much faster than any of them. He used the numerals that had come from the East, and so Leonardo was anxious to learn the new way.

If you have never seen a modern calculating machine, you would be interested to see how it works. You would watch the setting down of the multiplicand on certain keys, then you would see the multiplier set down, and then, on one of these modern machines, you would simply touch an electric button and the machine would make a little buzzing sound, after which you would read the answer upon it.

Some such curiosity and interest must have been Leonardo's when he first saw his old Moorish schoolmaster multiply one number of three figures by another number of three figures. With the counters this would have taken him several minutes, but his teacher did it in only one minute. Can we wonder, then, that Leonardo was anxious to learn what seemed to him to be a wonderful trick in the multiplication of numbers?

How do you think the Moorish schoolmaster proceeded? Of course we do not know exactly, but we know how Leonardo gave the work in the book which he wrote more than seven centuries ago. He first wrote the multiplicand; above that he placed the multiplier; and above that he wrote the product. This is our plan turned upside down. If you could ask Leonardo why he turned the work

```
392
  8
 49
```

HOW LEONARDO MULTIPLIED

From Leonardo's arithmetic of 1202. It represents the multiplication of 49 by 8, the product being 392

upside down, he would say that his work was right, but ours is upside down. It all depends on how we are taught.

It was about three hundred years after Leonardo that Cuthbert Tonstall (tŭn'stăl) was born in England. In those days it was still the custom in most countries to compute by counters, but Cuthbert went to a school where they taught the new method. In 1522 he published the first arithmetic printed in England. Although this was about a hundred years before the Pilgrims landed at Plymouth, it is interesting to know that only thirty-four years later, in 1556, an arithmetic was printed in the City of Mexico.

We do not know how Cuthbert was taught to multiply, but his book tells us what he thought was the best method. This was very

```
    60503
     4020
    00000
   121006
   00000
  242012
 243222060
```

HOW CUTHBERT MULTIPLIED

From Cuthbert Tonstall's arithmetic of 1522, showing the method of multiplication used by him

much like our own except that he did not know our short way of multiplying by zero, or, as he called it, " by a circle."

Thus we see that this great man could not multiply as easily as you can.

Just before Cuthbert's time there was a boy named Johann Widman (yō hän′ vĭd′män) attending an arithmetic school in Germany. In those days it was not the custom in that

PAGE FROM JOHANN WIDMAN'S BOOK

This shows two multiplication tables from Johann's arithmetic

country to teach arithmetic in all schools. Those who were going into business went to an arithmetic school and learned from an arithmetic teacher. In this school Johann learned how to multiply in the way that Cuthbert did, although he also learned how to multiply with counters as the German merchants did at that time.

When Johann became a man he wrote an arithmetic, and in this he used the signs for plus (+) and minus (−). This was the first time these signs were ever printed.

The way in which Cuthbert and Johann multiplied was not the only one followed in those days. Some teachers ruled the paper in squares like a chessboard, writing a figure in each square, and they called their plan the chessboard method. Others ruled the paper so that it looked like an iron grating, and they called this the grating method.

These are some of the ways in which the world tried its hand at multiplying, and that is all the story we shall have to-night about Cuthbert and Leonardo and Johann.

" I don't see," said the Tease, " how they ruled the paper in the grating plan. I don't see what it means."

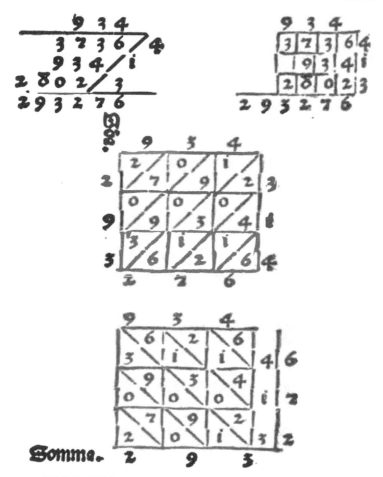

FROM THE FIRST PRINTED ARITHMETIC

This book was printed in Treviso, Italy, in 1478, a short time before America was discovered. This page shows four kinds of multiplication

"I will show you some pictures of it," answered the Story-Teller. "If you had studied it in school as Cuthbert did, you would see that it is about as easy as ours."

" How is the work done ? " asked Maude.

" That," said the Story-Teller, " is for you to work out some rainy day when you have

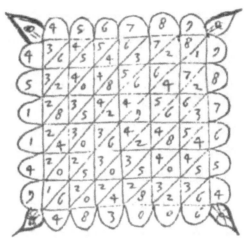

MULTIPLICATION FIVE HUNDRED YEARS AGO

From a manuscript of the fifteenth century

nothing else to do. What is much better than the grating plan at this time of the night is going to bed."

" And what do we have to-morrow night ? " asked Charles.

" Think of the Question Box," mysteriously answered the Story-Teller.

THE QUESTION BOX

1. What aids in multiplying were used in ancient times by people who had numeral systems that were something like the Romans?

2. Can you tell why the ancients had less use for multiplication than we have?

3. About how long ago did Leonardo of Pisa live, and what was there peculiar about his arrangement of the work in multiplication?

4. About when was the first printed arithmetic published, and in what country?

5. Show on paper one of the ways in which they multiplied 934 by 314 when the first arithmetic was printed.

6. In what respect did Cuthbert Tonstall's work in multiplication differ from ours?

7. How did Johann Widman arrange the multiplication tables in his book?

8. Why was one kind of multiplication called the chessboard method?

9. Why was one kind of multiplication called the grating method?

10. How do you think large corporations that have a great deal of multiplying to do proceed to find products of numbers?

11. What short methods in multiplication have you learned in school?

MICHAEL STIFEL
AND HIS TEACHER

CHAPTER VII

HOW FILIPPO AND ADRIAEN AND MICHAEL DIVIDED NUMBERS

" Since this is the last story," began the Story-Teller —

" But it is n't the last," broke in the Crowd.

" Positively the last," said the Story-Teller with great emphasis, " unless — "

" Unless what ? " asked two or three voices.

" Well, you know there 's the Question Box," replied the Story-Teller, " and I don't believe one of you has answered all the questions."

" But we *can* answer them, you know, and we have three or four nights before we go home," said the Tease.

" Three or four! Do you think I am an encyclopedia? At any rate, let us finish up our addition, subtraction, multiplication, and division to-night. Listen, then, to the story of the way in which Filippo (fḗ lēp'pō) and Adriaen (äd'rē än) and Michael (mī'kȧ ĕl) divided numbers."

About the time that Christopher Columbus was born, a boy by the name of Filippo

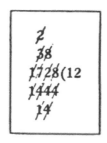

HOW FILIPPO DIVIDED MDCCXXVIII BY CXLIV

He first wrote the numbers in modern figures. The rest of the work is quite different from ours

Calandri (kä län'drē) was going to school in a small Italian town. His teacher one day asked Filippo to write two numbers on a small board that he used for his arithmetic work, and he told him to write them in Roman numerals. The teacher then told him to divide the first of the numbers by the second, and of course Filippo could not do it; but he said, " I can do it if you will let me write them in our common figures."

If you had been there to watch Filippo, you would have been just as much puzzled as you would be if you saw someone dividing by the aid of counters, for the work looked very different from that used in school to-day.

HOW FILIPPO PROVED HIS WORK

He proved that his work was right by dividing 1728 by 12 and finding 144 as the result

Filippo crossed out each figure when he was through with it, and so the work looks very strange to us.

We must not think that Filippo's way was altogether bad. He used fewer figures than we do, and if you should learn his method you might like it just as well as the one you learned in school.

After Filippo had shown that he knew how to divide, his teacher said, " Now show me how you would divide 1728 by 144, using the new method," and Filippo then divided almost the same way that we do.

Filippo lived just as Europe was beginning to pass from the old "scratch method," in which the figures were scratched out, or canceled, after they had been used, and was

```
144)1728(12
     144
   ─────
      28
     288
     288
     ───
```

FILIPPO'S NEW METHOD OF DIVIDING 1728 BY 144

Notice that Filippo used one more number (28) than we should and that he did not write the quotient above the dividend as we do. This was the second important step towards our modern method of long division

about to adopt a method very much like ours. The "scratch method" was called in Italy the "galley method" because the figures were arranged to look like a galley — a kind of boat — with its sail set. Schoolboys often showed the galley in the drawings they made in their notebooks, just as you made drawings in your books when you first went to school.

DIVISION THREE HUNDRED YEARS AGO

Page from a schoolboy's notebook written about three hundred years ago. The picture is supposed to resemble an old-fashioned galley with sails set

In using the method which his teacher called the new one, Filippo saw that it was unnecessary to write as many figures as the

PAGE FROM FILIPPO'S BOOK, 1491

This division of 53,497 by 83 is the first example in long division
by the modern method that ever was printed

teacher did, and so he decided that some day, when he grew up, he would write an arithmetic of his own and make the work in division still more simple.

When Filippo became a man he did what he had planned; he wrote an arithmetic containing our plan of dividing, and this was published in Florence just a year before Columbus discovered America.

In the time of Filippo Calandri, about the year 1500, Italy was much in advance of other

HOW ADRIAEN DIVIDED

The division of 150 by 6, from a work by Adriaen van Roomen, printed about three hundred years ago

European countries, and so we may expect that Filippo's improvement in division was not at once adopted outside of his country. This is the reason why a boy named Adriaen van Roomen (văn rō'mĕn), who lived in Holland one or two hundred years later, was still dividing by the old method.

For the same reason that Adriaen, going to school in Holland, was dividing by the old galley method, Michael Stifel (stē'fĕl), going to school in a little German town about the same time, also learned this same old-fashioned way, and so we see that Filippo's new method, the one that we use to-day, was not known to boys living in Holland and Germany one or two centuries later.

HOW MICHAEL DIVIDED

The division of 9552 by 12, from a work by Michael Stifel, printed about four hundred years ago

If you had lived when the Pilgrims came to America, you might all have learned division by the scratch method, because many people still used it then. Only a few years ago the Story-Teller found it still in use in Morocco, and the people who used it thought that it was better than ours. What do you think about it?

"I don't see why they ever used the 'scratch method,'" said Fanny. "Why did n't they use our way at first?"

"Why did n't they use electric lights instead of candles?" asked the Story-Teller, "and why did n't they have moving pictures and automobiles and airplanes?"

"Because they did not know about such things," answered Fanny.

"That is just the reason. They did not know about electric lights and railways, and neither did they know our way of dividing. As to dividing by machinery, they had never even dreamed of such a thing. Now this is enough for to-night, so get off to bed."

"But you have not mentioned the Question Box," said the Tease.

"To bed," growled the Story-Teller.

"You have n't told us how they divided with the Roman numerals," said the Tease.

"How do you think they did?" half growled the Story-Teller, trying to keep from smiling.

"Counters," said Charles.

"Right," said the Story-Teller, "and it was so hard that few could do it. And now —"

"To bed!" laughed the Crowd.

THE QUESTION BOX

1. What did Titus and Caius use to help them divide one number by another?

2. Why was the first method of dividing used by Filippo called the scratch, or galley, method?

3. How did Filippo's second method of dividing differ from the one that we use?

4. How did Filippo prove that his work in division was correct?

5. In whose book is to be found the first printed example in long division, substantially by our method?

6. Count the number of figures used by Adriaen and Michael in the galley method of dividing 1728 by 12, and

```
 34           144
1728(144   12)1728
1222         12
 11          52
             48
             48
             48
```

then count the number used by us in our method. Then compare the space required in the two cases. Can you see why the world refused so long to use our method?

AHMES STUDYING FRACTIONS

CHAPTER VIII

AHMES AND HERON AND JAKOB DESPAIR OF EVER LEARNING FRACTIONS

" Now we are getting near the end of our number stories," said the Story-Teller as the Crowd rushed into the room.

" Which end? " asked the Tease. " A line has two ends."

" Never mind which is the end of a line. One thing is sure, that I am near the end of my stories."

" Yes, but *which* end of the stories? " persisted the Tease.

" The end that we are near," said the Story-Teller, "and to-morrow night we shall be a great deal nearer."

" Then there is to be another story to-morrow night? " said the Tease.

" That depends," replied he of the curious book. " Remember the Question Box. What shall it be to-night? "

" I hope that it will be something that we all like," answered Maude.

" Then it must be fractions," guessed the Story-Teller, with a smile.

" Fractions! " gasped the Crowd.

" Fractions," smiled the Story-Teller. " Just listen to the story of Ahmes and Heron (hē'rŏn) and Jakob (yä'kŏp), and see if there is not something interesting about fractions in spite of the fact that you once found them hard."

The Crowd looked doubtful, but the curious book was closed, a new log was put on the fire, and the Story-Teller began:

When Ahmes had learned from the priest in the temple by the Nile how to read and write numbers, he felt that he knew a great deal about arithmetic; and when the priest had taught him to add and subtract, he felt that there was not much more to learn. As he grew older, however, he found that he needed to know about fractions. But no one in Egypt at that time used any fractions with a numerator greater than 1, with the single exception of $\frac{2}{3}$. Instead of thinking of $\frac{3}{4}$ as we do, the priest and Ahmes thought of $\frac{1}{2}+\frac{1}{4}$; and instead of thinking of $\frac{7}{8}$, they thought of $\frac{1}{2}+\frac{1}{4}+\frac{1}{8}$.

So it is no wonder that Ahmes had a great deal of trouble in learning fractions, and it is no wonder that he never learned how to work with fractions as we work with them.

Not only did the people of that time use only fractions with numerators 1, like $\frac{1}{2}$, $\frac{1}{3}$, $\frac{1}{4}$, and $\frac{1}{5}$, but for more than two thousand years after Ahmes died these fractions were commonly used in Egypt. They were also used in Babylon and in various other countries.

Nearly two thousand years after Ahmes studied in the temple on the banks of the great river which makes Egypt the fertile country that it is, there lived in Alexandria, at the mouth of the Nile, a boy named Heron. He was interested in machines and in measuring heights and distances, and he made friends with the scholars in Alexandria who studied the stars. He visited the Great Pyramid, listened to the stories of its building and its purpose, and came in contact with many travelers at this great port on the Mediterranean. So Heron grew up in very interesting surroundings and at an interesting time in the world's history — about the beginning of the Christian era.

When Heron went to school he found that he needed another kind of fraction than the one used by Ahmes. When he came to the very careful measurements used in making machines or in finding the position of the stars, he found that he needed certain other fractions that had come into use in Alexandria long after the time of Ahmes. These fractions had 60, or 60×60, or $60 \times 60 \times 60$ for their denominators, and since everyone knew this, it was not necessary to write the denominators. When we write 0.5 we mean $\frac{5}{10}$, and it is not necessary to write the denominator. To use our modern terms we may say that 23 minutes meant $\frac{23}{60}$ of something that was being measured, and 23 seconds meant $\frac{23}{60}$ of a minute, or $\frac{23}{3600}$ of the thing that was being measured. In the same way the next 23 meant $\frac{23}{60}$ of a second, and so on. In this way it was possible to have fractions without writing the denominators at all.

Do you think that this is about the most impractical thing you ever heard of? If you do, just remember that you use these fractions whenever you speak of the time of day. If it is 2 hr. 25 min. 47 sec. past noon, it is really 2 hr. $+\frac{25}{60}$ hr. $+\frac{47}{3600}$ hr. past noon. In other words, you are using the awkward fractions found in the writings of all who needed to use arithmetic for very accurate computation in the time of Heron of Alexandria, one of the great writers of Egypt at the beginning of the Christian era.

There have been many other ways of writing fractions, and I will tell you of one used by a boy named Jakob who lived in Germany about four hundred years ago.

Jakob went to school to an arithmetic teacher and tried his best to learn the new Arab way of writing fractions. The Arabs seemed to have learned these fractions from the Hindus. So Jakob learned how to write $\frac{3}{4}$ and $\frac{1}{8}$ and thought he knew a great deal about fractions.

Jakob's teacher did not think very highly of what he called " the new-fangled numerals," meaning the common ones that we use. He thought that the old Roman numerals, which were commonly used in Germany at that time, would continue to be used.

So Jakob learned how to write the Arabic fraction, but he then did a very funny thing —

Dieſe figur iſt vñ bedeüt ain ſtertel von ainez gantzen/alſo mag man auch ain fünfftail/ayn ſechſtail/ain ſybentail oder zwai ſechſtail 2c. vnd alle ander brüch beſchreiben/Als 2c.

Diß ſein Sechs achtail/das ſein ſechstail der acht ain gantz machen.

Diß Sigur betzaigt ann newn ayilfftail das ſeyn IX tail/der XI. ain gantz machen.

Diß Sigur betzaichet/zwentzigk ainundreyſſigt tail /das ſein zwentzigt tail .der ainsundreiſſigt ain gantz machen.

Diß ſein zwaihundert tail/der Sierhundert vnd ſechtzigt ain gantz machen

A PAGE FROM JAKOB KÖBEL'S BOOK

This shows Jakob's strange way of writing fractions

he made up his mind that he would write an Arabic fraction with Roman numerals, and you can imagine how strange it must have looked.

No Roman ever wrote a fraction like that, and no one ever put such an awkward fraction in a book until Jakob wrote an arithmetic himself. He thought he had done something very great, but no one else thought so.

It was nearly a hundred years after Jakob's time that a boy named Simon went to school in the city of Bruges (broo'jĕz), in Belgium. Like Ahmes and Heron and Jakob, he wrestled with fractions; but while these three boys despaired of ever learning how to conquer them, Simon made up his mind that he could come out the victor, and he did.

Simon saw that the Arabic fractions, which had then come to be called common fractions, were all right for cases like $\frac{3}{4}$, $\frac{7}{8}$, and $\frac{5}{12}$, but that they were not good for much when very fine measurements were required. So he set about to get a better kind of fraction for such work, and when he became a man he wrote a book on decimal fractions, printed more than three hundred years ago. You will hardly think that he knew much about decimals when you look at a page from his book, but he was the first man to write a work upon the subject.

It was not long before Simon's ideas were improved, so that the world soon came to write decimal fractions about as we do to-day. We have not yet agreed upon the decimal point, however, for children who go to school in England write decimal fractions with the point halfway up (3·14), and in the rest of Europe they use a comma for a decimal point (3,14).

HOW SIMON STEVIN WROTE DECIMALS

This is the first book ever published on decimal fractions. The first number is 27.847

So the world's ideas grow just as yours grow, and fashions change as the years go on. For this reason the fashion of decimal points varies from time to time and from country to country very much like the fashions of men's collars, of women's hats, of cutting boys' hair, and the ways of wearing belts on a girl's dress.

"Do you mean that we have fashions in arithmetic just as we have fashions in clothes?" asked Emily.

"Certainly; why not? We have been seeing fashions in reading and writing numbers, in adding, subtracting, multiplying, and dividing. Why do you call the answer in multiplication a product and not a sum? Nothing but fashion! It was once the fashion to use the word 'product' for the answer in addition, and the word 'sum' for the answer in subtraction. It is the fashion in school to speak of a dividend as a number to be divided, but it is not the fashion with business men to use it in this way. It is the fashion for you all to go to bed at this time, and —"

"But you say that fashions change," said the Tease.

"This fashion does n't change at all," replied the Story-Teller.

"And the fashion of telling us number stories at night does n't change, either," said the Tease.

"Neither does the fashion of the Question Box," laughed the Story-Teller as the Crowd started for bed.

THE QUESTION BOX

1. The kind of fraction used by Ahmes is called the unit fraction. Why does it have this name?

2. Ahmes used a fraction which we might write with our symbols $\frac{1}{2} + \frac{1}{4} + \frac{1}{8}$. What single fraction is this?

3. What single fraction is $\frac{1}{2} + \frac{1}{3}$?

4. About when did Heron live? What new kind of fraction did he use?

5. When we write 4 hr. 10 min. 30 sec. we mean 4 hr. $+ \frac{10}{60}$ hr. $+ \frac{30}{3600}$ hr. How do you express this as 4 hr. plus a single common fraction in lowest terms?

6. In hours, minutes, and seconds given in Question 5 how do you express the result as a decimal fraction to the nearest thousandth of an hour?

7. In what curious way did you find that Jakob wrote common fractions?

8. Who wrote the first book on decimal fractions? This was about how long ago?

9. In the first printed book on decimal fractions how was 27.847 represented?

10. In what part of the world do they write 3.14 for $3\frac{14}{100}$? Where is this written 3·14? Where is it written 3,14?

11. Which fractions do you find the easier to work with, decimals or common fractions? Think of the case of $\frac{29}{125}$ and 0.232; then of the case of $\frac{1}{8}$ and 0.125.

110

CHAPTER IX

NUMBER PUZZLES BEFORE THE LOG FIRE[1]

"So this is to be our last night," began the Story-Teller.

"The last but one," said the Tease.

"Are you sure?" asked the Story-Teller.

"Sure!" answered the Crowd, not intending to miss what would come by the asking.

"Well, what shall it be to-night? How would you like a nice long story about square root or cube root?"

"Cube root does n't sound very interesting," said Charles.

"Logarithms?" asked the Story-Teller.

"We never heard of them," said Maude. "Tell us something interesting."

[1] Chapters IX and X are not intended to be read aloud.

"Well, since we have a good log fire here, perhaps you would all like to hear the story of 'Number Puzzles before the Log Fire.' Listen, then, and look for Ching and Chang and An-am and all our friends, for they are all coming to visit us to-night.

"A curious thing happened one cold night, the place being the edge of a dense forest not many miles from here, the house being built of logs, the room being low and having a huge fireplace, the furniture consisting of a number of comfortable chairs arranged about the fire, and the time being early candlelight.

. "It may well be thought that there was developed in the forest a certain amount of curiosity in the fact that a fire burned brightly in a house which contained no living soul and that plenty of candles lighted up a room for no apparent purpose; for the animal life of the forest has quite as much curiosity as you and I and most other people have, and this is the reason that into the window there looked the squirrels, the owls, and the rabbits that made their homes in the trees or in the burrows of the woods.

" Over the heavy door of the log house someone had written in the years gone by these words: 'Let no one without imagination enter here.' And so the door is closed to you and me and all the world unless we have imagination. For us the log fire is cold and the candles do not burn and the heavy door is barred if we belong to that humdrum class that never has any daydreams. You, then, who are without imagination and who belong with those unfortunates who believe only what they see, stop on the threshold. For you the log fire has no attraction and the empty chairs will have no occupants. "

From out of the Great Unknown of Time and Space there come, one by one, into the room of the house of logs, each taking a chair in front of the great fire, our friends of long ago: Ching and Chang and Wu from the Land of the Yellow Dragon; An-am and Lugal from the Tigris and Euphrates; Menes and Ahmes from the banks of the Nile; Hippias from Greece; Titus and Caius from the Seven Hills of Rome; Daniel from the Mount of Olives; Gupta, Mohammed, Gerbert, and most of the others of whom we have read in our stories of Number Land, — strangers to each other, strangers to our present civilization, but drawn together by their interest in the puzzles of the world of number.

For this is to be a night of number puzzles, and each is to bring his contribution, each is to add to the interest of boys and girls in some of the curious things that have grown up in the thousands of years during which the world has played as well as worked in the realm of arithmetic. Imagine, therefore, Ching in his dress of leopard skin, and An-am with his cloak of sheepskin, and Ahmes with his roughly woven linen robe, and Gupta with his brown skin and his brown garb, and Mohammed with his long white robe, and all the rest, each in the dress of his land and time, all seated in front of the blazing logs, all intent upon hearing some of the number puzzles of the ages.

"In my land," said Ching, "there is an ancient book, perhaps the oldest book in all the world, and the name of this is Yih King (yē kĭng). It was written thousands of years ago and records one of the earliest of all the

curious things connected with number, for it
says that once upon a time there came out of

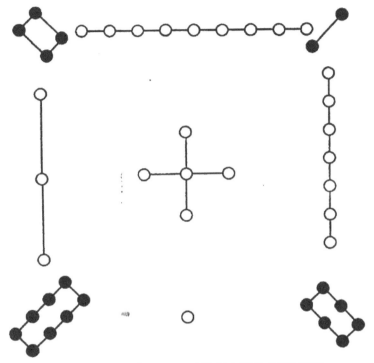

THE WORLD'S OLDEST MAGIC SQUARE

From the Yih King, one of the oldest Chinese books, written
perhaps three thousand years ago

the Yellow River a large turtle, and on its
back were some strange marks which puzzled
everyone who saw them. These I have written
on paper for you to see."

Then Ching passed around, that all might see it, a paper with some very curious figures written upon it.

"I know what it is," said Gupta; "it is a magic square, and the dots are numbers. The columns add to 15 and so do the rows and so do the diagonals. It is the world's oldest

4	9	2
3	5	7
8	1	6

A MAGIC SQUARE

The numbers of the dots in the magic square in the Yih King

number mystery. It is used as a charm all through the East; and in the Middle Ages, long after I died, it was used in many parts of Europe to drive away disease and to bring good fortune."

Gupta was right, for in the magic square is one of the oldest and most interesting curiosities of number to be found anywhere in the world.

"When I was living in the early days of Egypt," said Menes, "we did not have many number puzzles, but since then I have watched the world and have seen some strange things happen. One of the most curious relates to the numbers that are now used in Europe and America and in all places under their influence. If you take any number, say 3476, and reverse it, 6743, and then take the difference, $6743 - 3476 = 3267$, this difference will always be exactly divisible by 9. Whatever number you take, this will always be true. You may think that you can find a number with which this is not true, like 2222, but you will see that the difference will always be divisible by 9."

$$\begin{array}{r} 6743 \\ 3476 \\ \hline 3267 \end{array}$$

All the company tried to find out if Menes was right, using different numbers, but in every case the result was exactly divisible by 9. Chang, however, made a mistake. Having started with 3827, he simply mixed up the figures and obtained 2783, but he found that the difference was still divisible by 9.

$$\begin{array}{r} 3827 \\ 2783 \\ \hline 1044 \end{array}$$

"Yes," said Menes, "you may mix up the figures in any way and the rule still holds."

Some of the company knew the reason; some of you may know it; all of you will easily see it after you have studied a little algebra, for algebra is like a great electric light — it reveals many of the strange secrets of arithmetic.

"One of the most curious things that I have noticed in looking at the world for the past two thousand years," said Heron, "is seen in a simple example in addition. If you write any three numbers, say numbers of four figures each, I will at once write three numbers underneath them and will tell you before I do so the sum of all six numbers. It does not make any difference what numbers you take, nor does it make any difference whether they are all different or all alike."

This struck the company as a very curious thing, especially as Heron added, "Whatever three numbers you write, the sum of the six numbers will be 29,997."

```
2376
4152
3804
```

Adriaen then wrote on a piece of paper the three numbers 2376, 4152, and 3804.

118

Underneath these numbers Heron at once wrote the numbers 7623, 5847, and 6195.

He then told the company to add the six numbers, and, to the surprise of all, the sum was what Heron had prophesied.

Cuthbert Tonstall said he knew the trick. Do you know it?

If Adriaen had written four numbers, Heron would have written four, but he could have done the trick just the same, although he would have stated another sum.

2376
4152
3804
7623
5847
6195

" A strange thing was shown to me when I went as a boy to Barcelona," said Gerbert, " more than nine hundred years ago, and I will show it to you because it may prove to be interesting. If you will write on paper any number of as many figures as you please, I will write a single figure at the end of your number, and the number will then be exactly divisible by 11."

This did not seem a possibility, and so Jakob wrote 74,289.

Gerbert simply glanced at the number, wrote 6 after it, and said, " You will now find that 742,896 is exactly divisible by 11, and I have given you good measure, for I have also made it divisible by 22, 33, and 99."

The company all tried it and found that Gerbert was right.

Titus then wrote 66,742, and Gerbert wrote 5 at the end, saying, "You will find that 667,425 is exactly divisible by 11, and this time I have made it also divisible by 33 and 55."

The question now is, How did Gerbert do the trick?

"I think," said Hippias, "that you may be interested in a curious thing that I noticed a few hundred years ago. Two boys were giving each other puzzles, and one said, 'Think of any number you wish, multiply it by 2, add 18, divide the result by 2, and subtract the original number of which you thought.'

'I have done all this,' said the other.

'Then the result is 9,' said the first boy.

"Now," continued Hippias, "I suggest that all the company try this trick."

Then each one took a number, and each

did as directed, and to the surprise of all, the result in every case was 9.

"I know the trick," said Jakob. Of course he did, for he knew algebra. "I will give you a still better one," he continued. "Take any number, multiply it by 6, add 12, divide by 3, subtract 2, divide by 2, subtract the original number, and add 9."

"Well," said Adriaen, "what of it?"

"The result is 10," said Jakob.

At this the whole company laughed, for each had started with a different number, and yet each had ended with 10.

"I remember," said Leonardo, "that an old schoolmaster used to ask the new pupils which was correct, '6 and 7 *are* 14' or '6 and 7 *is* 14'"; but the rest of the boys were too quick to be puzzled by anything like this.

"Did you ever run across this ridiculous problem?" said Filippo. "If 6 cats eat 6 rats in 6 minutes, how many cats will it take to eat 100 rats in 100 minutes, at the same rate? It used to puzzle us down in Florence four or five hundred years ago."

"I know," said Wu; "it will take 100 cats." Was he right?

"When I was a boy," said Michael Stifel, "we had a couplet which ran like this:

> Ten fingers have I on each hand
> Five and twenty on hands and feet.

You know we used to say 'five and twenty' for twenty-five. The statement is perfectly true, but how do you explain it?"

At this the company lapsed into silence for a time.

"But I don't have 'five and twenty' fingers on my hands and feet," insisted Wu.

"You must think of your toes as fingers," said Robert.

"It is easy enough if you only know how," said Michael.

Then Heron said, "The explanation is—"

"Don't give it!" called out several voices. "We want to think it out for ourselves."

And so I shall have to leave it for you.

"Can any of you write an even number, using only odd digits?" asked Adriaen.

"I can," said Cuthbert. "It is just as easy as writing a hundred without using zero."

"Well, don't tell us," said Gupta. "We also want to think this out for ourselves."

" I believe," said Jakob, " that one of the oddest things I ever saw in numbers is a set of products that I have written here on paper"; and saying this he passed the paper around the room so that all might see it:

$$3 \times 37 = 111, \quad \text{and} \quad 1 + 1 + 1 = 3$$
$$6 \times 37 = 222, \quad \text{and} \quad 2 + 2 + 2 = 6$$
$$9 \times 37 = 333, \quad \text{and} \quad 3 + 3 + 3 = 9$$
$$12 \times 37 = 444, \quad \text{and} \quad 4 + 4 + 4 = 12$$
$$15 \times 37 = 555, \quad \text{and} \quad 5 + 5 + 5 = 15$$

" Now," he said, "how many can tell me the product of 18 and 37 and what the sum of the three digits is in the answer? Also, what are the products of 21 and 37, of 24 and 37, and of 27 and 37, and what are the sums of the digits in the various answers? "

Can you answer these questions?

Wu now wrote the following on paper:

$$7 \times 15{,}873 = 111{,}111$$
$$14 \times 15{,}873 = 222{,}222$$
$$21 \times 15{,}873 = 333{,}333$$

He then passed the paper around the room so that all the boys might look at it.

"And now I ask," he said, "the results of 28 × 15,873, of 35 × 15,873, of 42 × 15,873, and of 49 × 15,873."

Several could tell the results. Can you tell what they are?

Wu let them think for a few minutes and then asked: "Can any of you tell by what I should multiply 15,873 to have 888,888? to have 999,999?"

About half of the company could give the answers. Can you?

"While you are talking about such curious things," said An-am, "I will show you something interesting."

$$1 \times 8 + 1 = 9$$
$$12 \times 8 + 2 = 98$$
$$123 \times 8 + 3 = 987$$
$$1234 \times 8 + 4 = 9876$$
$$12345 \times 8 + 5 = 98765$$
$$123456 \times 8 + 6 = 987654$$
$$1234567 \times 8 + 7 = 9876543$$
$$12345678 \times 8 + 8 = 98765432$$
$$123456789 \times 8 + 9 = 987654321$$

He then wrote the above figures on a piece of paper and passed it around the room.

"Yes," said Menes, "that is interesting, but I will show you something that seems to me even more curious."

He then took a piece of paper and wrote:

$$1 \times 9 + 2 = 11$$
$$12 \times 9 + 3 = 111$$
$$123 \times 9 + 4 = 1111$$
$$1234 \times 9 + 5 = 11111$$
$$12345 \times 9 + 6 = 111111$$
$$123456 \times 9 + 7 = 1111111$$
$$1234567 \times 9 + 8 = 11111111$$
$$12345678 \times 9 + 9 = 111111111$$

"It seems to me," said Ahmes, "that these figures which were invented many hundred years after I died are very funny things. You could never do that with the numerals that I learned in Egypt four thousand years ago."

"No," answered Cuthbert, "and everyone knows that you couldn't do anything else with them, they were so bad!"

"Well," replied Ahmes, "you need not be so proud of your numerals; try writing twelve thousand twelve hundred and twelve."

This interested the company, and you will find it worth trying.

"Speaking of twelves," said Leonardo, "which is greater, six dozen dozen or a half dozen dozen?" Which is it?

"When I was a boy," said Titus, "I was given a puzzle problem which I will change a little so as to give it in English. Take nine from six, ten from nine, and fifty from forty, and show that the remainder is six."

This puzzled the company for a few minutes. Then Caius said, "It is very easy; all you have to do is to —"

"Don't tell us," cried the company.

"I have something that is as curious as those multiplications of An-am and Menes," said Lugal. "Look at this," and he wrote the following numbers and signs on paper:

$$9 \times 9 + 7 = 88$$
$$98 \times 9 + 6 = 888$$
$$987 \times 9 + 5 = 8888$$
$$9876 \times 9 + 4 = 88888$$

This struck all the company as very strange, because the left-hand numbers were 9, 98, 987, and 9876, and the numbers added were 7, 6, 5, and 4, while the products were always made up of 8's.

"Can you tell me," Lugal added, "the values of each of the sets of numbers which I will now write on paper?"

Saying this he wrote the following numbers:

$$98,765 \times 9 + 3 \qquad 9,876,543 \times 9 + 1$$
$$987,654 \times 9 + 2 \qquad 98,765,432 \times 9 + 0$$

Several of the company could tell the results at once. Can you do so?

"I ran across a curious thing about the number 45 when I was living in Spain a few hundred years ago," said Gerbert.

"What is it?" asked several.

"Well, 45 is equal to $8 + 12 + 5 + 20$, and these four numbers, 8, 12, 5, and 20 have curious combinations with 2, thus:

$$8 + 2 = 10, \quad 12 - 2 = 10, \quad 2 \times 5 = 10, \quad 20 \div 2 = 10,$$

the result of each of these four different operations being 10. Did you ever know anything more curious?"

"That is certainly very odd," replied Leonardo; "but I know another strange thing about 45. If you take the number 987,654,321, made up of the nine digits, reverse it, and subtract like this, you will have three numbers, — the minuend, the subtrahend, and the remainder,— and the sum

987,654,321
123,456,789
864,197,532

of the digits of each of the three is exactly 45."

The whole company thought that 45 was certainly a very curious kind of number.

"Here is a good one," said Adriaen. "Show how to write one hundred, using only the nine digits and the signs of arithmetic."

This puzzled everyone, and so Adriaen showed the company the following:

$$100 = 1 + 2 + 3 + 4 + 5 + 6 + 7 + 8 \times 9$$

"Easy enough, isn't it?" said Adriaen. "I know another way, too. Just take — "

"Don't tell us! Give us time to think about it," cried out several.

"While some of you are thinking about Adriaen's problem," said Johann, "perhaps others who are here would like to find a number of two digits which is equal to twice the product of those digits."

"I know," said Ching, "it is 12."

"No," said Johann, "for 12 is not equal to twice the product of 1 and 2."

"Well, I know," said Chang. "It is —"

"Don't tell us," said several who were figuring it out on paper.

Wu found the answer first. What is it?

"Here is a nice little problem for you," said Michael: "A snail crawling up a pole 10 feet high climbs 3 feet every day and slips back 2 feet every night. How long will it take to reach the top?"

"Ten days," said Wu — but he was wrong.

"Here is a little trick," said Jakob:

I C C	I N U
I N	N U
N T T	L N U
I C C	N U S
I A N T	O I N U

"Write figures in place of these letters so as to make the multiplications correct. Since it will take you some time to find these figures, here are two tricks in division also:"

E M A	M T
M A)U E M A	E M A)U U S S
M A	M A S
T M	O S S
A S	I A S
E M A	A S
E M A	

"These will take a great deal of time," continued Jakob, "so you had better let them go until to-morrow. In place of them you may take this little puzzle: A watermelon weighs $\frac{4}{5}$ of its weight and $\frac{4}{5}$ of a pound. How many pounds does it weigh?"

"That reminds me," said Lugal, "of this problem: If a herring and a half costs a cent and a half, how much will a dozen and a half herrings cost?"

"I wonder," said Gupta, "how many of you can write nineteen, using only four 9's."

"That is too easy," said Hippias. "It is no harder than to write two with four 9's. Why don't you ask how many of us can write twenty, using only four 9's? That is a puzzle worth thinking about."

"And that reminds me of one which I heard many years ago," said Titus. "A bottle and a cork cost $1.10, and the bottle costs $1 more than the cork. How much does each cost?"

"The bottle costs $1, and the cork costs 10 cents," said Ching.

"Wrong," said Titus. "I don't think you could even tell which is the heavier, a pound of gold or a pound of feathers."

"They weigh just the same," said Ching.

"I told you that you couldn't tell," said Titus. "I don't believe you could even tell how many minutes it would take to cut a strip of cloth 50 yards long into strips 1 yard long if each cut takes one minute."

"It would take," began Ching; but then he remembered that the other time he had spoken without thinking, so he stopped.

"This problem," said Caius, "reminds me of one which I heard many years ago. After cutting off $\frac{1}{10}$ of a piece of cloth, a merchant had 100 yards left. How many yards did he have at first?"

"He had 110 yards," said Ching. But Ching spoke again before he really solved the problem.

"You had better take a little more time," remarked Caius.

While Ching was thinking, Hippias told a story about himself.

"I was caught," said he, "about two thousand years ago by a simple little question. My teacher in Athens asked me how many quarter-inch squares it would take to make an inch square. I got this all right; but when he asked me how many quarter-inch cubes it would take to make an inch cube, I could n't tell. Can you tell?"

"While I am thinking," said Daniel, "you may care for this little problem: If an apple just balances in weight with ¾ of an apple of the same weight and ¾ of an ounce, how much does the apple weigh?"

"Speaking of apples," said Ahmes, "two fathers and two sons divided three apples among themselves, each receiving exactly one apple. How was this possible?"

"It is n't," said several.

"Oh yes, it is," said Ahmes, "if you—"

"Don't tell us," cried the whole company.

"It reminds me," said Mohammed, "of a puzzle I heard about a thousand years after I lived in Bagdad. In a family party there were 1 grandfather, 2 fathers, 1 grandmother, 2 mothers, 4 children, 3 grandchildren, 1 brother, 2 sisters, 2 sons, 2 daughters, 2 married men, 2 married women, 1 father-in-law, 1 mother-in-law, and 1 daughter-in-law. How many were there in the party?

"Let me see," said Wu; "$1+2+1+2+4+3+1+2+2+2+2+2+1+1+1$ is 27."

"You have come nowhere near it," replied Mohammed.

"Then how many do you say there were?" asked Wu.

"I know how many there were," said Daniel, "You see it was like this: there were — "

But just then a deep-toned bell out in the forest tolled twelve; and when the owl looked in the window the fire was out and every chair was vacant and not a soul was in the room, and the only noise was that of the winking of the owl's eyes and the breathing of the squirrel and the soft step of the rabbit as he found his way to the hole under the roots of the oak tree near the log cabin.

THE QUESTION BOX

1. What is a magic square? Where is it first found? How has it been used?

2. Can you arrange a magic square of nine figures in a different way from the one shown by Ching and Gupta?

3. If you take a number of two figures and reverse it, is the difference between the numbers always divisible by nine? Give five cases in which this is true.

4. Can you tell how to find out, without dividing, whether or not a number is exactly divisible by nine?

5. Find a number which when multiplied by 3 and the result added to 8 becomes 35.

6. Explain this old puzzle:

> Every lady in this land
> Has twenty nails upon each hand
> Five and twenty on hands and feet
> And this is true without deceit.

7. Write 78, using only the figure 7, but repeating it as often as you wish.

8. When the bell in the forest struck midnight, having struck the time every hour of the twenty-four, how many strokes had it made since the preceding midnight?

9. If there are 2 fathers and 2 sons in a room, and no one else is there, what is the smallest number of persons that can be in the room?

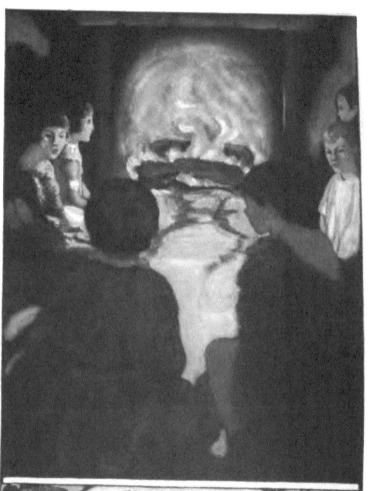

THE MEMORIES
GATHERED BEFORE THE LOG FIRE
IN THE FOREST

CHAPTER X

CURIOUS PROBLEMS BEFORE THE LOG FIRE

"Have you imagination still?" asked the Story-Teller, "or are you too proud to confess that you have any? Are you among those unfortunates who were barred from the log cabin when last there gathered the group of boys from many lands and many times? For if you have no imagination, or if you are afraid to confess that you have any, you should turn your back, for here again is the log cabin by the edge of the forest.

" The owl has been there, and the fire burns. The squirrel has looked in the window and seen the empty chairs. The rabbit has listened in vain for any footfalls. And yet, somehow, in some mysterious way, out from

the Somewhere have come our friends of old
— Ching and Chang and An-am and Lugal
and all the rest. Where a moment ago were
empty chairs, there are now chairs filled with
the boys of thousands of years ago, of yesterday, and of to-day, each with a pencil and a
pad of paper, and each with some curious
problem of the long ago. I suppose the
boys themselves were not there — just their
Memories; but this is the realm of Imagination, so let us not be like those stupid ones
who will not believe that Memories can talk."

"The problem that I have brought," said
Mohammed, " is a very old one that I learned
from an Arab more than a thousand years
ago. It is so easy that it is hard; but if you
will not try to make it hard, it is very easy.
It is easier to make it hard than it is to make
it easy, however, for most people find it quite
hard to make it easy."

"Well, if it is as hard to make it easy as it
is to make your statement easy, then it really
must be awfully hard," said Cuthbert.

"We don't want any easy ones," said Cuthbert, " so give us a good puzzle."

" There were two Arabs who sat down to eat," said Mohammed, " one with five loaves, and the other with three, all the loaves having the same value. Just as they were about to begin, a third Arab came along and proposed to eat with them, promising to pay eight cents for his part of the meal. If they ate equally and consumed all the bread, how should the eight cents be divided? Remember that one Arab furnished five loaves and the other furnished three loaves."

" While you are thinking of that," said Cuthbert, " here is another good one. A man had five pieces of chain, each having three links. He asked a blacksmith how much he would charge to make them into one piece of chain. The blacksmith replied that he charged two cents to cut a link and two cents to weld or fasten together a link. How much was the blacksmith's charge? "

The company disputed for some time, and could not agree upon the answer.

Finally Lugal said: " I have it! You see it is this way: all you need do is — "

" Don't tell," said the rest of the boys.

" I will give you a little problem," said

Johann, "but I warn you that there is a trick in it. How may you arrange the figures 1, 6, 8 so that the three-figure number that you make shall be exactly divisible by 9?"

"It can't be done," said Filippo, after a moment's thought.

"Yes, it can," said Johann, "but it is a trick, and you may think about it until to-morrow."

"I remember in my day," said Leonardo, "a very famous problem that I first heard from an Arab scholar. He told me that when chess was invented, the Persian king was filled with great joy and commanded that chessboards should be placed in all the temples of the kingdom.

"'Moreover,' he said to the inventor of the game, 'ask what you will.'

"Thereupon the inventor replied, 'Give me, O king, a single grain of wheat to place in the first square of the chessboard, two in the second, four in the third, and so on, doubling the number each time, until all the sixty-four squares are filled.'

"You will be surprised, I think, to know how many grains of wheat will be necessary."

" How many are there? " asked Ching.

" More than a hundred," said An-am.

" Rather! " said Leonardo; "for you have $1 + 2 + 4 + 8 + 16 + 32 + 64 + 128 + 256 +$, and so on, for the sixty-four squares, and since the next three numbers are 512, 1024, and 2048, you see that they are rapidly becoming very large. The total number of grains is enormous; it is 18,446,744,073,709,551,615, and this would make more wheat than there is to be found in all the world."

" I remember," said Cuthbert Tonstall, "a problem somewhat like that. According to this problem a man wanted a blacksmith to shoe his horse. The blacksmith said he would do so if he were paid one cent for the first nail, two cents for the second, four cents for the third, eight cents for the fourth, and so on, doubling the amount each time. There being twenty-four nails, how much did it cost to shoe the horse? The answer is —"

" Don't tell us," cried several of the boys. " We can work out such a simple problem as that for ourselves."

" Here is an interesting problem that I remember to have seen many years ago," said

141

Michael. "A girl was carrying a basket of eggs, and a man driving a horse hit the basket and broke all the eggs. Wishing to pay for the damage, he asked the girl how many eggs she had. The girl said she did not know, but she remembered that when she counted them by twos, there was one egg left over; when she counted them by threes, there was also one egg left over; when she counted them by fours, there was also one left over; but when she counted them by fives, there were no eggs left over."

" 'Well,' said the man, 'I can now tell you how many you had.'

" I wonder," continued Michael, " how many of you can tell the number of eggs? "

" I think," said Adriaen, " that there is more than one answer."

"Yes," replied Michael; "but the girl probably had not more than four or five dozen eggs in the basket, and there is only one answer less than these numbers."

" We can find the answer," said several of the company.

And so I leave it for you.

"When I was a boy," said Titus, "I remember to have heard a simple little problem that was

brought to Rome from Alexandria, in Egypt:
A mule and a horse were carrying some
bales of cloth. The mule said to the horse,
'If you give me one of your bales, I shall
carry as many as you.'

"'If you give me one of yours,' replied the
horse, 'I shall carry twice as many as you.'

" How many bales was each carrying? "

" Yes," said Leonardo, " I heard the same
one when I was a boy, and when I became
a man I put it in my arithmetic."

" The answer," said Titus, " is — "

" Oh, that is too easy; we can work it out,'
said Cuthbert, and this met with the approval
of the company, so I leave it for you.

" Although I was born in Florence," said
Filippo, "my parents took me once to Venice.
There I found that the clocks struck from 1 to
24 instead of striking from 1 to 12. I was much
interested to know how many strokes a clock
made in twenty-four hours, and so I added
the numbers from 1 to 24. But I afterwards
learned that there was a shorter way of finding the answer. Do you know this way? "

At this the company was silent for a
minute, when Leonardo remembered that he

had it in one of the books that he wrote when he grew up to be a man, and Cuthbert remembered that it was in his book, and Michael had it in his; so perhaps it is just as well to leave it for some of you to find out.

"It is getting late," said Robert Record, "and we have n't time for any more problems."

"Just a few more," cried the company.

"Well," said Robert, "who has a few short problems that will set us thinking?"

"I have one," said Caius.

"All right; go ahead," said Robert.

"I heard this from a Greek teacher who came to Rome when I was a boy," said Caius. "I was playing in the Forum one day when this Greek teacher came along and stopped where several of us were throwing a ball from one to another. He asked me how long it would take Achilles (a kĭlّēz) to overtake a turtle that had a mile the start. I told him it would depend on how fast Achilles ran.

"'Well,' said he, 'suppose that Achilles ran ten times as fast as the turtle and that he ran a mile in ten minutes.'

"'Then,' said I, 'it would take him about fifteen minutes.'

"'No,' said he, 'Achilles could never overtake the turtle.'

" I did not like to contradict him, but I said that I felt sure that I could catch up with a turtle in a very short time.

"'This is how it is,' he replied. 'When Achilles reaches the place where the turtle was, the turtle will be $\frac{1}{10}$ of a mile ahead, because the turtle runs $\frac{1}{10}$ as fast as Achilles.'

"'Yes,' said I.

"'And when Achilles reaches the place where the turtle then is, the turtle will be $\frac{1}{100}$ of a mile ahead.'

"'Yes,' I replied.

- "'And when Achilles reaches the place where the turtle then is, the turtle will be $\frac{1}{1000}$ of a mile ahead.'

"'Yes,' said I, 'but $\frac{1}{1000}$ of a mile is only about five feet.'

"'Yes, but don't you see that when Achilles reaches that point, the turtle will be $\frac{1}{10}$ of that distance ahead?'

"'Yes,' I replied.

"'Then,' said he, 'because Achilles is continually reaching some place where the turtle was, and the turtle is then always $\frac{1}{10}$ the last distance ahead, Achilles can never catch up with the turtle.'

"It seemed too much for any of us boys, but we gave up playing ball and began to think about the Greek's problem. That was nearly two thousand years ago, and I have n't yet been able to see how Achilles could ever catch up with that turtle. It seems to me that the turtle will always be a very little ahead of Achilles."

" I don't know how to help you," said Cuthbert, " but I will give you something else to think about. Can you tell me how to distribute ten pieces of sugar in three cups so that every cup shall contain an odd number of pieces ? "

" It can't be done," said Wu.

" That is because you don't know how," replied Cuthbert. " Try this: In a box there are six apples. Divide these equally among six boys in such a way as to leave one apple in the box, but do not cut any apple."

While some of the boys were thinking about Cuthbert's problem, Wu gave this one: "A man sold his farm for $5000, which is what it cost him, then bought it back for

$4500, and then sold it again for $5500. How much did he gain?"

"He gained $1500," said Adriaen.

"Wrong," replied Wu.

Can any of you tell how much he gained?

"I will give you a good puzzle," said Ching. "What is the number of two figures which multiplied by 8 becomes 20?"

"There is n't any such number," said Lugal.

"There must be some catch about it," said An-am.

"Yes, but it is a nice catch after all," answered Ching, "and I will leave it for all of you to think about."

"Did you know that six and six are eleven?" asked Titus.

"That is one of your old tricks with Roman numerals," said Cuthbert. "If you can show that, you can show that four and four are nine and that seven and seven are twelve."

"Of course I can," said Titus.

The rest of the boys thought that all this was too easy. What do you think?

"Here is a better one, then," said Titus. "Three brothers divided four apples among themselves so that one had no more than the others, and yet no apple was divided. Explain how this was possible."

" It can't be done," said Menes.

" Oh, yes, it can," said Titus.

" Well, then, there is some trick about it," said Jakob.

" Of course there is," answered Titus, " but it is a good trick and you can't see it."

" But each must have had an apple and a third," said Chang.

" No, because the apples could not have been divided equally."

" Well, I don't see it at all," said Chang, "and I want to think about it further."

The rest of the boys laughed, because no one could see how it could be done. Do you see how to do it?

" Here are two easy ones," said Leonardo, " but each is like one you have already had: How can you show that half of 18 is 10?"

" That takes me back to some of our Roman problems," said Titus.

" Hardly," answered Leonardo. " Here is the other one: What number, not composed of ones, is the same when turned wrong side up?"

" These are too easy," said the boys.

" If you wish a real bad catch, here is one," said Johann. " Take eleven marbles, take away five, add three, and the result is eight."

" That can't be possible," said Leonardo. " The result is nine."

' 'That depends on how you do it," answered Johann. " I told you it had a bad catch in it."

It must have been a bad one, because it puzzled the rest of the boys.

" I have an old English puzzle," said Cuthbert, "but I know you cannot guess it."

" There is no harm in trying," said Wu.

"Well," said Cuthbert, "show how to take 45 from 45 and have 45 left."

After the others had thought for several minutes, Cuthbert wrote this on a piece of paper and passed it around the room:

$$9 + 8 + 7 + 6 + 5 + 4 + 3 + 2 + 1 = 45$$
$$1 + 2 + 3 + 4 + 5 + 6 + 7 + 8 + 9 = 45$$
$$8 + 6 + 4 + 1 + 9 + 7 + 5 + 3 + 2 = 45$$

He then said: " If you subtract just as with whole numbers, you will find the difference as I have written it. That is, $11 - 9 = 2$, $11 - 8 = 3$, $12 - 7 = 5$, and so on."

"It seems to me," said Robert, "that these are good problems for us to sleep on. We have had an interesting evening, and have heard some curious problems, and now it is nearly twelve o'clock."

"It can't be," said Chang.

"It must be nearly so," said Adriaen.

"You must be wrong," said Wu. "It is twelve now, and — "

But before he could say another word, way out in the dark forest a bell began to toll the midnight hour; and where there was a company of boys about the great roaring fire, there was now a roomful of empty chairs; and where there were a half-dozen burning logs, there was now only a mass of ashes.

The owl looked into the window and blinked wisely. The squirrel scratched his head in a puzzled fashion. The rabbit seemed listening to his own heart beating. The forest was asleep, and the log cabin was silent except for a few lonesome puzzles which were left to cover themselves with blankets of leaves and lie down to sleep on the warm hearthstone in anticipation of other nights with the Memories.

THE QUESTION BOX

1. What is the answer to Mohammed's problem about the Arabs?

2. What is the answer to the problem about the chain?

3. What is the answer to the problem about the eggs?

4. How long would it take you to cut a 60-yard piece of cloth into 1-yard lengths, at 1 minute to each cut?

5. Show that half of 88 is twice as much as nothing and that half of 888 is three times as much.

6. If you walk halfway to the door and then walk half of the remaining distance, and then half of what is left, and so on continually, how long will it take you to get out of the room?

7. A man with $1 wanted $1.25. He pawned the $1 for 75 cents and then sold the pawn ticket for 50 cents. He then had his $1.25. Who lost on the transaction?

8. In a certain town three per cent of the inhabitants are one-legged and half of the others go barefoot. How many shoes are necessary?

PRONOUNCING VOCABULARY

Abacus, ăb'ȧ kŭs

Achilles, ȧ kĭl'ēz

Acropolis, ȧ crŏp'ȯ lĭs

Adriaen, äd'rē än

Ahmes, ä'mĕs

Alexandria, ăl'ĕg̅ zăn'drĭ ȧ

Alpha, ăl'fȧ

An-am, ä näm

Athens, ăth'ĕnz

Babylon, băb'ĭ lŏn

Babylonian, băb'ĭ lō'nĭ ăn

Bagdad, băg däd'

Bel, bĕl

Beta, bā'tȧ

Bruges, brōo'jĕz

Caius, kā'yŭs

Calandri, kä län'drē

Calculi, kăl'kŭ lē

Calculus, kăl'kŭ lŭs

Caliph, kā'lĭf

Chang, chäng

Cuneiform, kŭ nē'ĭ fôrm

Cuthbert, kŭth'bĕrt

Daniel, dăn'yĕl

Egypt, ē'jĭpt

Euphrates, ṷ frā'tēz

Filippo, fė̇ lēp'pō

Gerbert, zhĕr bâr'

Gupta, gōōp'tä

Harun-al-Rashid, hä rōōn'
    är rȧ shĕd'

Heron, hē'rŏn

Hippias, hĭp'ĭ ȧs

Hwangho, hwänghō'

Indus, ĭn'dŭs

Jakob, yä'kŏp

Johann, yō hän'

Korea, kȯ rē'ȧ

Leonardo, lä ȯ när'dō

Lugal, lōō'gäl

Menes, mē'nēz

Mesopotamia, mĕs'ȯ pȯ tā'mĭ ȧ

Michael, mī'kȧ ĕl

Mohammed, mȯ hăm'ĕd

Nile, nīl

Papyrus, pȧ pī'rŭs

Pergamon, pûr'gȧ mŏn

Pisa, pē'zä

152

Record, rĕk'ŏrd

Seki, sā kē

Shantung, shän'tŏŏng'

Soroban, sŏ'rō bän'

Stevin, stā văn'

Stifel, stē'fĕl

Suan pan, swän pän

Sylvester, sĭl vĕs'tēr

Tigris, tī'grĭs

Titus, tī'tŭs

Tonstall, tŭn'stăl

Van Roomen, văn rō'mĕn

Widman, vĭd'män

Wu, wōō

Yih King, yē kĭng

Yu, yōō

THE TEACHING OF ARITHMETIC

BY

DAVID EUGENE SMITH

PROFESSOR OF MATHEMATICS IN TEACHERS COLLEGE
COLUMBIA UNIVERSITY

THE TEACHING OF ARITHMETIC

CHAPTER I

THE HISTORY OF ARITHMETIC

Of all the sciences, of all the subjects generally taught in the common schools, arithmetic is by far the oldest. Long before man had found for himself an alphabet, long before he first made rude ideographs upon wood or stone, he counted, he kept his tallies upon notched sticks, and he computed in some simple way by his fingers or by pebbles on the ground. He did not always count by tens, as in our decimal system; indeed, this was a rather late device, and one suggested by his digits. At first he was quite content to count to two, and generations later to three, and then to four. Then he repeated his threes and had what we call a scale of three, and then, as time went on, he used a scale of four, and then a scale of five. In measurements he often used the scale of twelve, because he found that twelve is divisible by more factors than ten, and particularly by two and three and four; but by the time he was ready to write his numbers the convenience of finger reckoning had become so generally recognized that ten was practically the universal radix. Nevertheless, there remain in our language and customs numerous relics of the duodecimal (scale of twelve) idea, such as the number of inches in a foot, of ounces in a troy pound, and of pence in a shilling, all influenced by the Roman inclination to make much use of twelve in practical computation.

The writing of numbers has undergone even more change than the number names. Not only was there usually a notation for each written language in ancient times, but some languages had several sets of numerals, as is seen in the three standard systems of Egypt, the two of Greece, and the somewhat varied forms in use in Rome. The Roman supremacy gave the numerals of these people great influence in Europe, and they were practically in universal use in the West until the close of the Middle Ages. The Romans themselves had no definite standard for their numerals. Whereas we write IV for four, IX for nine, and XL for forty, they usually wrote IIII, VIIII, and XXXX. Occasionally they wrote IIXX for eighteen, and they would have written the year 1914 as MDCCCCXIIII rather than MCMXIV. Soon after books began to be printed a slight effort was made to use Roman numerals in fractions, as in the following facsimile from a German work of 1514:

I
IIII   Dieſſe figur iſt vñ bedeüt ain fiertel von ainez
gantzen/alſo mag man auch ain fünfftail/ayn
ſechſtail/ain ſybentail oder zwai ſechſtail 2c. vnd alle
ander brüch beſchreibeu/Als $\frac{I}{V}$ | $\frac{I}{VI}$ | $\frac{I}{VII}$ | $\frac{I}{VI}$ 2c.

VI
VIII   Diß ſein Sechs achtail/das ſein ſechstail der
acht ain gantz machen.

IX
XI   Diß Figur betzaigt ann newn ayilſſtail das ſeyn
IX·tail/der XI·ain gantz machen.

XX
XXXI   Diß Figur betzaichet/zwentzigk ainundrey⸗
ſigk tail /das ſein zwentzigk tail .der ains⸗
undreiſſigk ain gantz machen.

IIC
IIIIC.LX   Diß ſein zwaihundert tail/der Sierhun⸗
dert vnd ſechzigk ain gantz machen.

FROM KÖBEL'S ARITHMETIC OF 1514

158

The Romans, however, never wrote fractions like this, and much that has been quite recently taught in the schools about these numerals is entirely modern.

It may sometimes be wondered how the world was able to handle numbers in the days of Roman numerals. How, for example, did people add CLXVI and DXXIX, or multiply one of these numbers by another? The answer is that they used small disks on a ruled board, or pebbles that were moved on wires or in grooves. The Latin name for "pebble" was *calculus*, and from this we get our word "calculate." The following illustration shows the appearance of the medieval calculating board:

FROM THE TITLE-PAGE OF KÖBEL'S ARITHMETIC, 1514

Meantime there had arisen in the East, probably in India, although very likely subjected to influence from without, our present system of notation, and little by little this permeated the West. When it arose it was without a zero, and hence without such place value as we use to-day ; but probably about the seventh century the zero appeared, and the completed system found its way northward into Persia and Arabia, and thence in due time it was transmitted to the West.

Some of the earliest Hindu forms are shown in the following table : [1]

TABLE SHOWING THE PROGRESS OF NUMBER FORMS IN INDIA

After the zero was invented, the numerals appear in various manuscripts with forms like those on page 5.

All of this goes to show how long it took the world to settle upon the forms that we teach our children.

[1] This and similar tables are from Smith and Karpinski's "The Hindu-Arabic Numerals," Ginn and Company, Boston, 1911, to which reference is made for complete descriptions.

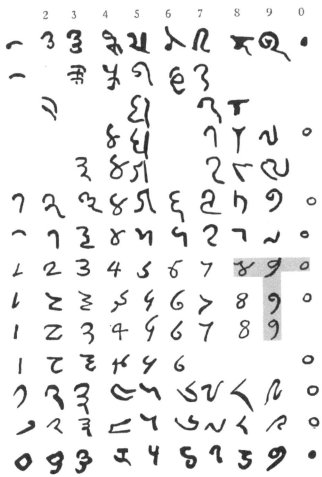

NUMERALS USED WITH PLACE VALUE

At first the subject of arithmetic was purely practical, the counting of arrows or sheep or men. For a long time this was all that number meant to the world, until the mystic age developed and philosophy began. Then numbers were differentiated, and odd and even were distinguished, and " There 's

161

luck in odd numbers" became a tenet of faith, while the even numbers became designated as earthly and feminine. The story is long and interesting, that of the development of this mysticism, with its special prominence of three and

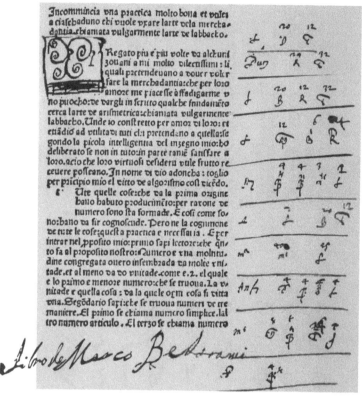

FIRST PAGE OF THE TREVISO ARITHMETIC, 1478

seven. Furthermore, the movement led to a study of the properties of numbers, roots, and series. Number games became connected with the abacus, and so the practical and the mysterious were more or less blended even at times when they are generally regarded as widely separated.

The first printed arithmetic appeared at Treviso, a city situated north of Venice, in 1478. It may add a little to the interest of the subject to see the facsimile of the first page of this very rare book as shown on page 6. The first three lines read as follows : " Here beginneth a practica, very good and useful to anyone who wishes to use the mercantile art commonly called the art of the abacus." " Practica " and " art of the abacus " were then common names for business arithmetic.

The methods of multiplying have changed greatly in modern times. To illustrate this fact, two cases of multiplication, each showing the product of 456,789 by 987,654, taken from an Italian manuscript of the fifteenth century, are shown on page 8.

Long division has changed very greatly, and it will probably be of interest to the reader to see a facsimile of the first printed page in which our modern form occurs. It is from Calandri's arithmetic of 1491, printed at Florence, and is shown on page 9.

The growth of topics of arithmetic is also an interesting subject for investigation. We say that there are four fundamental operations, although once there was only one, and at another time the world recognized as many as nine. We operate chiefly with decimal fractions, as in working with dollars and cents, although these fractions are scarcely three hundred years old. We are impatient that a child stumbles over common fractions, and yet, so difficult did the world find the subject that for thousands of years only the unit fraction was used. We wonder how the long division form of greatest common divisor ever had place in arithmetic, and yet it was a practical necessity in business until about 1600 A.D. We feel that " partnership involving time " could never have been practical, and yet until a couple of centuries ago it was

163

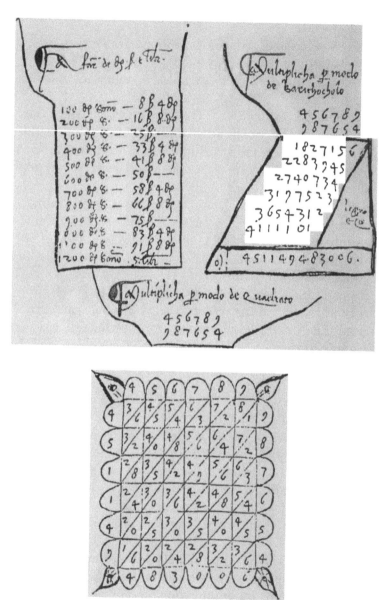

Parti 5349 > per 83

Uienne   5349> ——— 83
         00644 - $\frac{45}{83}$

534
498
———
365
33~
———
3>>
33~
———
45
       0 $\frac{45}{83}$

             | 83

Parti $\frac{3}{8}$ p 60   Parti 13> $\frac{1}{2}$ p 12

$\frac{3}{8}$ —— 60   13> $\frac{1}{2}$ —— 12

0 $\frac{3}{8}$ / $\frac{0}{60}$ 13> $\frac{1}{2}$ / 1$\frac{5}{2}$

0 $\frac{3}{480}$ Uienne 11 $\frac{11}{24}$

uienne $\frac{1}{160}$

Parti 60 p $\frac{3}{8}$ Parti $\frac{2}{7}$ p $\frac{2}{9}$

60 —— $\frac{3}{8}$ $\frac{2}{7}$ —— $\frac{2}{9}$

480 | 13   3$\frac{3}{5}$ / $\frac{3}{7}$ | 2

uienne 160   Uienne 0 $\frac{18}{35}$

FROM CALANDRI'S ARITHMETIC, 1491

decidedly so. And thus it is with many topics of arithmetic, — they have changed from century to century, and even in our own time from year to year. It is well for a teacher to know a little of this history of the subject taught, although space does not allow for any serious consideration of the topic in this work. In the bibliography some reference will be found to sources easily available, and the teacher who wishes to see arithmetic in progress, as opposed to arithmetic stagnant and filled with the obsolete, should become acquainted with one or more of these works upon the subject. The history of arithmetic is the best single stimulus to good method in teaching the subject.

Bibliography. Smith, The Teaching of Elementary Mathematics, New York, 1900; Smith, Rara Arithmetica, Boston, 1909; Smith and Karpinski, Hindu-Arabic Numerals, Boston, 1911; Ball, A Primer of the History of Mathematics, London, 1895, and A Short Account of the History of Mathematics, London, 4th edition, 1908; Fink, History of Mathematics, translated by Beman and Smith, Chicago, 1900; Cajori, History of Elementary Mathematics, New York, 1896, and History of Mathematics, New York, 1893; Jackson, The Educational Significance of Sixteenth Century Arithmetic, New York, 1906; Gow. A Short History of Greek Mathematics, Cambridge, 1884; Conant, The Number Concept, New York, 1896; Brooks, Philosophy of Arithmetic, revised edition, Philadelphia, 1902. There are numerous works in German on the history of mathematics and of mathematical teaching, and a considerable number of works in French and Italian.

CHAPTER II

THE REASONS FOR TEACHING ARITHMETIC

The ancients had less difficulty than we have in assigning a reason for teaching arithmetic, because they generally differentiated clearly between two phases of the subject. The Greeks, for example, called numerical calculation by the name *logistic*, and this subject was taught solely for practical purposes to those who were going into trade. A man might have been a very good philosopher or statesman or warrior without ever having learned to divide one long number by another. Such a piece of knowledge would probably have been looked upon as a bit of technical training, like our use of the slide rule or the arithmometer, two of the several modern machines by the use of which we can add, subtract, multiply, divide, raise to powers, and extract roots of numbers. On the other hand, the Greeks called their science of numbers *arithmetic*, a subject that had nothing whatever to do with addition, subtraction, multiplication, or division, and that excluded all applications to trade and industry. This subject was taught to the philosopher, and to the man of "liberal education," as we still call him. It considered questions like the factorability of numbers, powers and roots, and series — topics having little if any practical application in the common walks of life. Therefore when a Greek was asked why he taught logistic, his answer was definite : It is to make a business man able to compute sufficiently well for his trade. If asked why he taught arithmetic, as the term was then used, his answer was still fairly clear, although open to debate: I teach it because it makes a man's mind more philosophic.

THE TEACHING OF ARITHMETIC

In the present day we have a somewhat more difficult task when we attempt to answer this question. Arithmetic with us includes the ancient logistic, and we teach the subject to all classes of people : to one who will become a day laborer, belonging to a class that never in the history of the world studied such a subject until very recently ; to the tradesman, who never uses or cares to use the chapter on prime numbers; to the statesman, who will probably have little opportunity to employ logarithms in any work that may come to him ; to the clergyman, to whom the metric system will soon be merely a name ; and to the housewife, the farmer, and all those who travel the multifarious walks of our complex human life. For us to tell why we teach the American arithmetic to all these people is by no means so easy as it was for the Greek to answer his simple question.

In general, however, we may say that as we have combined the ancient logistic (calculation) and arithmetic (theory) in one subject, so we have combined the Greek purposes, and teach this branch because it is useful in a business way to every one, and also because it gives a kind of training that other subjects do not give.

As to the first reason there can be no question. When the great mass of men were slaves the business phase was not so important ; but now that every man is to a great extent his own master, receiving money and spending it, some knowledge of calculation is necessary for every American citizen. To elaborate upon this point is superfluous. There is, however, one principle that should guide us in the consideration of this phase of the question : *Whatever pretends to be practical in arithmetic should really be so.* We have no right to inject a mass of problems on antiquated investments, on obsolete forms of partnership, on forgotten methods of mercantile business, or on measures no longer in common use, and make the claim that these problems are practical. If we wish them for some other purpose, well and good ; but as practical problems they have no right to appear. To set up a false custom of the business world is as bad as to teach any other untruth ; it places arithmetic in particular, and education in general, in a false light before pupils and parents, and is unjustified by any reason that we can adduce. An obsolete business problem has just one reason for being, and this reason is that it has historical interest. We can secure the mental discipline as well by other means, and we have no right to handicap a child's mind with things that he will be forced to forget the minute he enters practical life.

Axiomatic as this statement may seem, however, it is by no means easy to limit the subject matter in arithmetic to the art of calculation and to problems that are representative only of the real business life of to-day. The custom of the school, the familiarity of the teacher with the traditional problem rather than with the demands of modern business, the genuine interest that children find in puzzle problems, the influence of the official curriculum — all militate against as rapid reform as might be desired. This condition of affairs is by no means limited to our own country; it is characteristic of the school everywhere and always. How it affects arithmetic in its details will be seen in the subsequent chapters.

There remains the side of mental discipline which I have elsewhere called, for want of another term and following various other writers, the culture side. What mental training does a child get from arithmetic that he does not get from biology, or Latin, or music? This is a question so difficult to answer that no one has yet satisfied the world in his reply, and no one is likely to do so. There have been elaborate articles written to show that the proper study of arithmetic has an ethical value, though exactly what there is in the subject to make us treat our neighbor better it is a little difficult to say. Others have said that arithmetic, through its very rhythm, has an æsthetic value, as is doubtless true ; but that this is generally realized, or that it serves to make us more appreciative of the beautiful, is hardly to be argued with any seriousness. Still others have felt that by coming in contact with exact and provable truth an individual sets for himself a higher standard in all other lines of work, and this again is probably the case, although the measure of its influence has never been satisfactorily ascertained. And to these reasons may be added many more, such as the training of a deductive science, although elementary arithmetic is to a large extent inductive ; the training in concentration, although the untangling of a Latin construction requires quite as close attention ; the exaltation of mind that comes from the study of numbers that may increase or decrease indefinitely, and others of like nature. And out of it all, what shall we say ? That arithmetic can offer no mental discipline that other subjects do not give ? No one really feels this, in spite of the fact that the exact nature of this discipline is hard to formulate. Every one is conscious that he got something out of the study, aside from training in calculation and business applications, that has made him stronger, and the few really scientific investigations that have been made as to the effect of mathematical study bear out this intuitive feeling.

Nevertheless, if we ask a class of recently trained teachers if there is any value in the study of arithmetic except the utilitarian one, an animated and general response greets us in the familiar words, "The doctrine of formal discipline has been exploded." These words have been repeated so often that they have lost whatever of meaning they may once have had, and they usually signify but little more than a Latin phrase would to a child. If one asks, What is the mental discipline that has been exploded? there comes no general reply, although a few may answer that "power acquired in one line cannot be transferred." And if we ask what this means, some of the more thoughtful of our hearers may say that the memorizing of rules in arithmetic does not help us to memorize the rules of grammar — if we do either of these things to-day.

Statements like these are interesting, but they mean little. The fact is, some one has set up a man of straw and, with the help of several thousand followers, is slaying him. No one claims any such mental discipline for arithmetic, nor does any one claim that rapidity in acquiring or reciting the multiplication table is going perceptibly to increase a child's rapidity in learning or reciting the names of the trunk lines that radiate from Chicago. No one believes that accuracy in multiplication is a power that will be so transferred as to make a child perceptibly more accurate in map drawing. It would be absurd to assert that a child who comes to like arithmetic would thereby like his mother the better, or like to go to bed or to get up any more ardently. All such "transfers of power" are of course ridiculous, and no one makes or ever has made any such claims for mental discipline on the part of arithmetic. And if any one is tempted to believe that this form of mental discipline has been exploded, the only true reply is that no one ever asserted it.

It has, however, been asserted that arithmetic strengthens the reasoning powers, and there seems to be no doubt that this assertion has been made in times past with unwarranted emphasis. Every one knows of cases where a person reasons well in arithmetic and not in other subjects. This is probably due to the fact that he has a greater interest in mathematics than in other branches of study, and hence gives less attention to the latter. At any rate, it is probable that the claim has been exaggerated, although the efforts of the psychologists to weigh the value of arithmetic, or of any other subject of study, have not progressed far enough to produce results that can be described as other than crude. It is impossible to weigh a child's mind before a certain subject has been studied, and again after it has been completed, and say that the subject has added or subtracted so much of mental power. We must, after all, fall back on our own experience, with such little help as experimental psychology can render.

Not to dismiss the mental-discipline side too summarily, however, and at the same time seeking to avoid the endless verbiage that usually characterizes the discussion, it is well to set forth more clearly some of the objects to be sought on the culture side of arithmetic. In the first place, we seek an absolute accuracy of operation that differs from the kind of accuracy we seek in science or linguistics or music. The fact that we have, in thousands of problems, sought a result so exact as to stand every test leads us to set a higher standard of accuracy in all lines than we could have set without it. This justifies the introduction of any part of theoretical arithmetic for which the pupil is mentally ready. It is one reason why cube root was formerly studied, when pupils were more mature than now, and in the same way it has justified progressions and a more elaborate treatment of primes than any business need would warrant. Here, then, is a reason for teaching arithmetic that is above and beyond the merely practical of the present moment.

A similar and related reason appears in the fact that mathematics in general, and arithmetic in particular, requires a helpful form of analysis that does not stand out so clearly in other studies. "I can prove this if I can prove that; I can prove that if I can prove a third thing; but I can prove that third thing; hence I see my way to proving the first." This is the analytic form that has come down to us from Plato. It appears more evidently in geometry, but is essentially the reasoning of arithmetic as well. " I can find the cost of $2\frac{1}{2}$ yd. if I can find the cost of 1 yd. ; but I know the cost of $6\frac{1}{4}$ yd., so I can find the cost of 1 yd. ; hence I can solve my problem," is the unworded line of the child's analysis. Such a training, unconsciously received and often unconsciously given, is valuable in every problem we meet, leading us to exclude the nonessential and hold with tenacity to a definite line of argument.

Furthermore, in mathematics in general, and in arithmetic in particular, we set down our results with a clearness and terseness of expression that is not found in other subjects. It is difficult to weigh the influence of a habit thus acquired. It may not show itself to-day or to-morrow, but when the need for it arises, possibly long after arithmetic as a study has been laid aside, it may again appear. The assertion that a statement is "mathematically exact" is not without meaning, and the habit acquired under some helpful, sympathetic, inspiring teacher, of setting forth the work in arithmetic neatly, clearly, and with no superfluous labor, is one of those mental acquisitions that may easily "carry over" into the ordinary work of practical life.

These three phases of the culture side of arithmetic, the side of mental discipline, will then suffice for our present purpose, which is to show that such a side exists : (1) the contact with absolute truth ; (2) the acquisition of helpful forms of analytic reasoning; (3) the acquisition of certain habits that "carry over" into related fields of work. With respect to all three it may be said that our psychologists are more sympathetic to-day than they were a few years ago. That these exhaust the list of values of arithmetic from the culture standpoint must not, however, be inferred.

ARITHMETIC

FOR

YOUNG CHILDREN

BEING

A SERIES OF EXERCISES EXEMPLIFYING THE MANNER
IN WHICH ARITHMETIC SHOULD BE TAUGHT
TO YOUNG CHILDREN

By HORACE GRANT

American Edition

EDITED BY WILLARD SMALL

REMARKS

ON

TEACHING ARITHMETIC;

AND ON

THE PARTICULAR DESIGN OF THIS TREATISE.

THE following little Treatise is intended for the instruction of children between the age of three or four, and six or seven ; but older children, whether they have or have not commenced Arithmetic, may perform many of the exercises with advantage, as nothing can compensate for the absence of such an accurate knowledge of the foundation of the science as exercises of this description are calculated to give.

To most persons, the earlier operations of Arithmetic appear sufficiently simple for the comprehension of an infant ; but those who have had the greatest experience in teaching, have found that abstract numbers are much less simple than they appear ; and that, even with children of the age of five or six,

some pains must be taken, and much repetition en-
dured, in laying clearly and firmly the foundation of
the Mathematics.   This pains and trouble will,
however, be amply repaid by the rapid progress of
the pupil afterwards, not only in Arithmetic, but in
every branch of mathematical science.

Arithmetic is commonly learned by rote, and is
never thoroughly learned; it is almost always an
unpleasant task both to teacher and pupil, and
conduces very little to the general improvement of
the mind.   An endeavor has, therefore, been made
to prepare this Treatise in such a manner that the
pupils shall be entertained in their progress, and
shall be led on to discover most things for themselves,
and to exert and improve their mental faculties.

This first stage, or horn-book of Arithmetic, consists almost entirely of mental Arithmetic.   For the
mass of mankind, written Arithmetic, like written
language, is of comparatively little use; but that
arithmetic of the head, which is never absent when
once firmly associated with every thing around, is of
incalculable use, even though it should stop short of
the larger numbers.   If a young person goes no further than to the extent of this little Treatise, he has
done much ; more, indeed, than many of those who
have, as it is phrased, gone through Arithmetic.   He
has thoroughly mastered the smaller numbers, which

are used a hundred times for once that larger numbers are required, and which are the pivots whereon the larger turn. He possesses an instrument, small indeed, and of limited power, but perfectly under his command, and of service to him every hour ; whereas the schoolboy arithmetician knows nothing of the instrument which he works blindly, and which he can only work under peculiar and favorable circumstances. Other instruments he must have to render the first available ; and, after all, the little he knows is apt to waste rapidly away.

A great defect of the existing elementary works on Arithmetic arises from the little variety they offer to the child, either in objects, thought, or language. Their authors are satisfied if they present a proposition, regarding number, under one point of view, when it is ten to one if the child can apprehend it thoroughly unless it be presented in many lights, and under many varieties of language. In fact, the whole of Arithmetic is too apt to be taught as a series of tables of abstract number, and the pupils ever after find it difficult to extricate themselves from the deep and narrow ruts into which they have been driven.

A systematic treatise on Arithmetic, also, is divided into strict rules ; and the pupil is required to exhaust the most difficult points of one rule before he is permitted to commence the simplest parts of the next. In this Treatise rules are not mentioned, because it is not necessary to mention them. The pupil discovers them for himself when he wants them. He goes through the various portions of the subject according to their difficulty, and to the light they throw upon each other; not according to their place in a scientific arrangement. He is, by this means, in a condition to multiply and to divide small numbers, and to perform simple calculations in fractions, long before he can attempt the addition of large numbers. And as each operation facilitates the rest, he soon can grapple powerfully with the smaller numbers. For him they really have a meaning; so far as they go, they are a distinct language, and a clear and powerful instrument of thought. And this knowledge is attained in a space of time that would have been occupied, under ordinary circumstances, in groping painfully, and perhaps fruitlessly, at the very threshold.

Although we should not forget that we ought to teach knowledge for the purpose of improving all our faculties, still we must remember that we should also teach it because it is wanted for use in the world; we must teach it in the way in which it will be wanted and used in the world, and also in conjunction with those things that will render it useful. We should not teach any subject so as to separate it from everything else, and render it practically useless, merely because the entire abstraction or separation of a science from all others happens to be best for some other purposes. A child, if sent to a foreign country, will learn the language in a few months. Instruct him, at home, by means of scientific works on grammar, by plans and books suited only to the learned or the initiated, and he shall learn less in as many years. The memory is refreshed, and the mind is to a certain extent instructed, by looking over an ordinary scientific work; but it is little of the real nature of a subject that can be learned by the beginner from this external labelling and ticketing. A science may be arranged and prepared for the instruction of youth; it may also be arranged in the most compact and logical form for the use of the philosopher: these arrangements may be equally scientific; but they must be materially different, because they have a very different purpose to serve.

Some reason has generally existed for the peculiar arrangement of this Treatise, though, at first sight, the work may present no signs of order. When a child sees four counters or two pebbles, he understands their number long before he has any clear notion of the words four and two, used alone. Counting with objects is, therefore, the first stage practicable. Children also remember and understand the numbers of those things with which they are very familiar, before they comprehend abstract numbers: questions respecting familiar absent objects are, therefore, the next in difficulty. And the most difficult questions of all are those connected with abstract numbers, that is to say, with the names of numbers without any reference to present or absent objects. But as children are in a condition to understand *easy* questions of the second and third sort before they can manage difficult exercises of the first kind, questions of all three sorts have been mingled together, according to their relative difficulty, so that they shall mutually assist each other, and give that variety to the subject which the infant mind urgently requires.

The Arabic numerals, or ordinary figures, have been most studiously kept out of sight until near the conclusion of the Treatise, because it has been found that, when they are introduced very early, they relieve the pupil from the necessity of examining numbers thoroughly. They present a bright and clear picture to the eye, compared with which all other impressions and notions connected with number are slow of acquirement and dim; and thus their superficial clearness overpowers the more solid properties of their brethren. When kept in proper subordination, and allowed only their fair share of attention, they become most valuable assistants.

The Exercises have been confined almost entirely to numbers under thirteen, because it has not been thought advisable to run the risk of confusing the pupil with the larger numbers until he is thoroughly conversant with smaller ones of which the larger are compounded. The larger numbers also demand the immediate introduction of Numeration and Notation: these are the most important and difficult rules in Arithmetic; and it is chiefly owing to imperfect knowledge of them that the succeeding rules are found so difficult, and require so much time to get through, even in the mechanical and repulsive mode at present pursued.

No arithmetical tables of any kind, nor tables of moneys, weights and measures, should be learned by the child during the first stage : they would be of no use at this period, and would be very apt to disgust him with Arithmetic. In lieu of tables, a few of the most useful weights and measures should be shown to the pupil ; and such manual, as well as arithmetical exercises, should be performed with them, as are indicated in various parts of this Treatise. With these the child would be much delighted ; an agreeable variety of calculation would be attained ; he would never forget what he had seen and handled ;

and would take an interest in all future calculations about weights and measures.

The above remarks will explain, in some degree, the cause of the repetitions, and of the apparently trifling and homely nature of many of the questions, and also of the language in which they are couched. The state of mind of the child frequently prevents us from using the most correct and elegant phraseology and illustration. Variety of expression and copiousness of illustration, however, must be provided ; and it will soon be found that they who restrict themselves to the most correct and scientific language are unintelligible to children. Great variety of language must studiously be used, or we shall not prevent the pupil from falling into many serious errors, which are certain to result from the invariable use of a single form of words. Before a child can understand the peculiar language of a science, he must understand something of the science itself. Besides, the general ignorance of children necessarily precludes forms of expression and modes of illustration which might be employed with advantage in teaching adults.

Although the teacher may find a new method of instruction somewhat awkward at first, a little practice will convince him of the pleasantness and efficacy of a rational procedure. He will soon find that much is to be learned by teaching others, provided he does not teach by rote ; and he will be ready to ascribe some instances of failure to his inexperience rather than to the dulness of the pupil.

When the teacher is acquainted with this plan, which is very simple, he will find little difficulty in modifying it, and providing additional exercises, so that it may be rendered exactly suitable to the children he has to instruct. Questions that are suitable for a child of four or five may be too simple for a child of nine or ten years of age. A country child and a town child will each require a different modification of the Exercises. A considerable variety has accordingly been provided; and the teacher may omit or delay, or alter any that are not found to be appropriate.

As Arithmetic only regards one quality of objects, namely, Number, an exclusive attention to it (or indeed to any other single study) is liable to contract the mind. Number should, therefore, form one of several simultaneous studies, and its study should occasionally be suspended altogether.

This Treatise is but the beginning of the subject; though, it is hoped, a rational beginning. With more experience it might have been made better; and it is now only offered as an introduction to the systematic study of Number, until a better work shall supersede it.

REMARKS ON TEACHING ARITHMETIC.

The second stage of Arithmetic may consist of Arithmetic taught upon the common plan; and it will be found that by previously going over this first stage, many of the ordinary difficulties of the science will be removed or lessened, and the time usually expended upon it greatly diminished.

A second stage is however projected, as a continuation of the present Treatise. It will commence with Numeration, and will include the most useful rules of Arithmetic applied to large numbers and fractions. It will be treated upon a plan differing considerably from that ordinarily adopted, and calculated (or at least intended) to make the science of Number agreeable, intelligible, and rational, — to make it practical in the highest degree, and yet to treat it as a science itself, and as an introduction to other sciences. In the first stage the pupil is taught to think and speak in numbers; in the second stage he will continue his former practice, and will unite with it the art of writing numbers; for there is no reason why we should violate, in Arithmetic, those laws of nature which hold good in general life, and which prescribe that we should think before we speak, and that we should both think and speak before we are in a fit condition to learn to write.

THE TEACHING OF
GEOMETRY

DAVID EUGENE SMITH

CHAPTER II

WHY GEOMETRY IS STUDIED

With geometry, as with other subjects, it is easier to set forth what are not the reasons for studying it than to proceed positively and enumerate the advantages. Although such a negative course is not satisfying to the mind as a finality, it possesses definite advantages in the beginning of such a discussion as this. Whenever false prophets arise, and with an attitude of pained superiority proclaim unworthy aims in human life, it is well to show the fallacy of their position before proceeding to a constructive philosophy. Taking for a moment this negative course, let us inquire as to what are not the reasons for studying geometry, or, to be more emphatic, as to what are not the worthy reasons.

In view of a periodic activity in favor of the utilities of geometry, it is well to understand, in the first place, that geometry is not studied, and never has been studied, because of its positive utility in commercial life or even in the workshop. In America we commonly allow at least a year to plane geometry and a half year to solid geometry; but all of the facts that a skilled mechanic or an engineer would ever need could be taught in a few lessons. All the rest is either obvious or is commercially and technically useless. We prove, for example, that the angles opposite the equal sides of a triangle are equal, a fact that is probably quite as obvious as the postulate that but one line can be drawn through a given point parallel to a given line. We then prove, sometimes by the unsatisfactory process of *reductio ad absurdum*, the converse of this proposition, — a fact that is as obvious as most other facts that come to our consciousness, at least after the preceding proposition has been proved. And these two theorems are perfectly fair types of upwards of one hundred sixty or seventy propositions comprising Euclid's books on plane geometry. They are generally not useful in daily life, and they were never intended to be so. There is an oft-repeated but not well-authenticated story of Euclid that illustrates the feeling of the founders of geometry as well as of its most worthy teachers. A Greek writer, Stobæus, relates the story in these words :

> Some one who had begun to read geometry with Euclid, when he had learned the first theorem, asked, " But what shall I get by learning these things? " Euclid called his slave and said, " Give him three obols, since he must make gain out of what he learns."

Whether true or not, the story expresses the sentiment that runs through Euclid's work, and not improbably we have here a bit of real biography, — practically all of the personal Euclid that has come down to us from the world's first great textbook maker. It is well that we read the story occasionally, and also such words as the following, recently uttered[1] by Sir Conan Doyle, — words bearing the same lesson, although upon a different theme :

> In the present utilitarian age one frequently hears the question asked, " What is the use of it all? " as if every noble deed was not its own justification. As if every action which makes for

[1] In an address in London, June 15, 1909, at a dinner to Sir Ernest Shackelton.

self-denial, for hardihood, and for endurance was not in itself a most precious lesson to mankind. That people can be found to ask such a question shows how far materialism has gone, and how needful it is that we insist upon the value of all that is nobler and higher in life.

An American statesman and jurist, speaking upon a similar occasion,[1] gave utterance to the same sentiments in these words:

When the time comes that knowledge will not be sought for its own sake, and men will not press forward simply in a desire of achievement, without hope of gain, to extend the limits of human knowledge and information, then, indeed, will the race enter upon its decadence.

There have not been wanting, however, in every age, those whose zeal is in inverse proportion to their experience, who were possessed with the idea that it is the duty of the schools to make geometry practical. We have them to-day, and the world had them yesterday, and the future shall see them as active as ever.

These people do good to the world, and their labors should always be welcome, for out of the myriad of suggestions that they make a few have value, and these are helpful both to the mathematician and the artisan. Not infrequently they have contributed material that serves to make geometry somewhat more interesting, but it must be confessed that most of their work is merely the threshing of old straw, like the work of those who follow the will-o'-the-wisp of the circle squarers. The medieval astrologers wished to make geometry more practical, and so they carried to a considerable length the study of the star polygon, a figure that they could use in their profession. The cathedral builders, as their

[1] Governor Hughes, now Justice Hughes, of New York, at the Peary testimonial on February 8, 1910, at New York City.

art progressed, found that architectural drawings were more exact if made with a single opening of the compasses, and it is probable that their influence led to the development of this phase of geometry in the Middle Ages as a practical application of the science. Later, and about the beginning of the sixteenth century, the revival of art, and particularly the great development of painting, led to the practical application of geometry to the study of perspective and of those curves [1] that occur most frequently in the graphic arts. The sixteenth and seventeenth centuries witnessed the publication of a large number of treatises on practical geometry, usually relating to the measuring of distances and partly answering the purposes of our present trigonometry. Such were the well-known treatises of Belli (1569), Cataneo (1567), and Bartoli (1589).[2]

The period of two centuries from about 1600 to about 1800 was quite as much given to experiments in the creation of a practical geometry as is the present time, and it was no doubt as much by way of protest against this false idea of the subject as a desire to improve upon Euclid that led the great French mathematician, Legendre, to publish his geometry in 1794, — a work that soon replaced Euclid in the schools of America.

It thus appears that the effort to make geometry practical is by no means new. Euclid knew of it, the Middle Ages contributed to it, that period vaguely styled the Renaissance joined in the movement, and the first three centuries of printing contributed a large literature to the

---

[1] The first work upon this subject, and indeed the first printed treatise on curves in general, was written by the famous artist of Nürnberg, Albrecht Dürer.

[2] Several of these writers are mentioned in Chapter IV.

subject. Out of all this effort some genuine good remains, but relatively not very much.[1] And so it will be with the present movement; it will serve its greatest purpose in making teachers think and read, and in adding to their interest and enthusiasm and to the interest of their pupils; but it will not greatly change geometry, because no serious person ever believed that geometry was taught chiefly for practical purposes, or was made more interesting or valuable through such a pretense. Changes in sequence, in definitions, and in proofs will come little by little; but that there will be any such radical change in these matters in the immediate future, as some writers have anticipated, is not probable.[2]

A recent writer of much acumen[3] has summed up this thought in these words:

Not one tenth of the graduates of our high schools ever enter professions in which their algebra and geometry are applied to concrete realities; not one day in three hundred sixty-five is a high-school graduate called upon to "apply," as it is called, an algebraic or a geometrical proposition. . . . Why, then, do we teach these subjects, if this alone is the sense of the word "practical"! . . . To me the solution of this paradox consists in boldly confronting the dilemma, and in saying that our conception of the practical utility of those studies must be readjusted, and that we have frankly to face the truth that the "practical" ends we seek are in a sense *ideal* practical ends, yet such as have, after all, an eminently utilitarian value in the intellectual sphere.

[1] If any reader chances upon George Birkbeck's English translation of Charles Dupin's "Mathematics Practically Applied," Halifax, 1854, he will find that Dupin gave more good applications of geometry than all of our American advocates of practical geometry combined.

[2] See, for example, Henrici's "Congruent Figures," London, 1879, and the review of Borel's "Elements of Mathematics," by Professor Sisam in the *Bulletin of the American Mathematical Society*, July, 1910, a matter discussed later in this work.

[3] T. J. McCormack, "Why do we study Mathematics: a Philosophical and Historical Retrospect," p. 9, Cedar Rapids, Iowa, 1910.

He quotes from C. S. Jackson, a progressive contemporary teacher of mechanics in England, who speaks of pupils confusing millimeters and centimeters in some simple computation, and who adds:

> There is the enemy! The real enemy we have to fight against, whatever we teach, is carelessness, inaccuracy, forgetfulness, and slovenliness. That battle has been fought and won with diverse weapons. It has, for instance, been fought with Latin grammar before now, and won. I say that because we must be very careful to guard against the notion that there is any one panacea for this sort of thing. It borders on quackery to say that elementary physics will cure everything.

And of course the same thing may be said for mathematics. Nevertheless it is doubtful if we have any other subject that does so much to bring to the front this danger of carelessness, of slovenly reasoning, of inaccuracy, and of forgetfulness as this science of geometry, which has been so polished and perfected as the centuries have gone on.

There have been those who did not proclaim the utilitarian value of geometry, but who fell into as serious an error, namely, the advocating of geometry as a means of training the memory. In times not so very far past, and to some extent to-day, the memorizing of proofs has been justified on this ground. This error has, however, been fully exposed by our modern psychologists. They have shown that the person who memorizes the propositions of Euclid by number is no more capable of memorizing other facts than he was before, and that the learning of proofs verbatim is of no assistance whatever in retaining matter that is helpful in other lines of work. Geometry, therefore, as a training of the memory is of no more value than any other subject in the curriculum.

If geometry is not studied chiefly because it is practical, or because it trains the memory, what reasons can be adduced for its presence in the courses of study of every civilized country? Is it not, after all, a mere fetish, and are not those virulent writers correct who see nothing good in the subject save only its utilities?[1] Of this type one of the most entertaining is William J. Locke,[2] whose words upon the subject are well worth reading:

> ... I earned my living at school slavery, teaching to children the most useless, the most disastrous, the most soul-cramping branch of knowledge wherewith pedagogues in their insensate folly have crippled the minds and blasted the lives of thousands of their fellow creatures — elementary mathematics. There is no more reason for any human being on God's earth to be acquainted with the binomial theorem or the solution of triangles, unless he is a professional scientist, — when he can begin to specialize in mathematics at the same age as the lawyer begins to specialize in law or the surgeon in anatomy, — than for him to be expert in Choctaw, the Cabala, or the Book of Mormon. I look back with feelings of shame and degradation to the days when, for a crust of bread, I prostituted my intelligence to wasting the precious hours of impressionable childhood, which could have been filled with so many beautiful and meaningful things, over this utterly futile and inhuman subject. It trains the mind, — it teaches boys to think, they say. It does n't. In reality it is a cut-and-dried subject, easy to fit into a school curriculum. Its sacrosanctity saves educationalists an enormous amount of trouble, and its chief use is to enable mindless young men from the universities to make a dishonest living by teaching it to others, who in their turn may teach it to a future generation.

To be fair we must face just such attacks, and we must recognize that they set forth the feelings of many

---

[1] Of the fair and candid arguments against the culture value of mathematics, one of the best of the recent ones is that by G. F. Swain, in the *Atti del IV Congresso Internazionale dei Matematici*, Rome, 1909, Vol. III, p. 361. The literature of this school is quite extensive, but Perry's "England's Neglect of Science," London, 1900, and "Discussion on the Teaching of Mathematics," London, 1901, are typical.

[2] In his novel, "The Morals of Marcus Ordeyne."

honest people. One is tempted to inquire if Mr. Locke could have written in such an incisive style if he had not, as was the case, graduated with honors in mathematics at one of the great universities. But he might reply that if his mind had not been warped by mathematics, he would have written more temperately, so the honors in the argument would be even. Much more to the point is the fact that Mr. Locke taught mathematics in the schools of England, and that these schools do not seem to the rest of the world to furnish a good type of the teaching of elementary mathematics. No country goes to England for its model in this particular branch of education, although the work is rapidly changing there, and Mr. Locke pictures a local condition in teaching rather than a general condition in mathematics. Few visitors to the schools of England would care to teach mathematics as they see it taught there, in spite of their recognition of the thoroughness of the work and the earnestness of many of the teachers. It is also of interest to note that the greatest protests against formal mathematics have come from England, as witness the utterances of such men as Sir William Hamilton and Professors Perry, Minchin, Henrici, and Alfred Lodge. It may therefore be questioned whether these scholars are not unconsciously protesting against the English methods and curriculum rather than against the subject itself. When Professor Minchin says that he had been through the six books of Euclid without really understanding an angle, it is Euclid's text and his own teacher that are at fault, and not geometry.

Before considering directly the question as to why geometry should be taught, let us turn for a moment to the other subjects in the secondary curriculum. Why, for example, do we study literature ? "It does not lower the price of bread," as Malherbe remarked in speaking of the commentary of Bachet on the great work of Diophantus. Is it for the purpose of making authors ? Not one person out of ten thousand who study literature ever writes for publication. And why do we allow pupils to waste their time in physical education ? It uses valuable hours, it wastes money, and it is dangerous to life and limb. Would it not be better to set pupils at sawing wood ? And why do we study music ? To give pleasure by our performances ? How many who attempt to play the piano or to sing give much pleasure to any but themselves, and possibly their parents ? The study of grammar does not make an accurate writer, nor the study of rhetoric an orator, nor the study of meter a poet, nor the study of pedagogy a teacher. The study of geography in the school does not make travel particularly easier, nor does the study of biology tend to populate the earth. So we might pass in review the various subjects that we study and ought to study, and in no case would we find utility the moving cause, and in every case would we find it difficult to state the one great reason for the pursuit of the subject in question, — and so it is with geometry.

What positive reasons can now be adduced for the study of a subject that occupies upwards of a year in the school course, and that is, perhaps unwisely, required of all pupils ? Probably the primary reason, if we do not attempt to deceive ourselves, is pleasure. We study music because music gives us pleasure, not necessarily our own music, but good music, whether ours, or, as is more probable, that of others. We study literature because we derive pleasure from books ; the better the book the more subtle and lasting the pleasure. We study art because we receive pleasure from the great works of the masters, and probably we appreciate them the more because we have dabbled a little in pigments or in clay. We do not expect to be composers, or poets, or sculptors, but we wish to appreciate music and letters and the fine arts, and to derive pleasure from them and to be uplifted by them. At any rate, these are the nobler reasons for their study.

So it is with geometry. We study it because we derive pleasure from contact with a great and an ancient body of learning that has occupied the attention of master minds during the thousands of years in which it has been perfected, and we are uplifted by it. To deny that our pupils derive this pleasure from the study is to confess ourselves poor teachers, for most pupils do have positive enjoyment in the pursuit of geometry, in spite of the tradition that leads them to proclaim a general dislike for all study. This enjoyment is partly that of the game, — the playing of a game that can always be won, but that cannot be won too easily. It is partly that of the æsthetic, the pleasure of symmetry of form, the delight of fitting things together. But probably it lies chiefly in the mental uplift that geometry brings, the contact with absolute truth, and the approach that one makes to the Infinite. We are not quite sure of any one thing in biology ; our knowledge of geology is relatively very slight, and the economic laws of society are uncertain to every one except some individual who attempts to set them forth ; but before the world was fashioned the square on the hypotenuse was equal to the sum of the squares on the other two sides of a right triangle, and it will be so after this world is dead ; and the inhabitant of

Mars, if he exists, probably knows its truth as we know it. The uplift of this contact with absolute truth, with truth eternal, gives pleasure to humanity to a greater or less degree, depending upon the mental equipment of the particular individual; but it probably gives an appreciable amount of pleasure to every student of geometry who has a teacher worthy of the name. First, then, and foremost as a reason for studying geometry has always stood, and will always stand, the pleasure and the mental uplift that comes from contact with such a great body of human learning, and particularly with the exact truth that it contains. The teacher who is imbued with this feeling is on the road to success, whatever method of presentation he may use; the one who is not imbued with it is on the road to failure, however logical his presentation or however large his supply of practical applications.

Subordinate to these reasons for studying geometry are many others, exactly as with all other subjects of the curriculum. Geometry, for example, offers the best developed application of logic that we have, or are likely to have, in the school course. This does not mean that it always exemplifies perfect logic, for it does not; but to the pupil who is not ready for logic, per se, it offers an example of close reasoning such as his other subjects do not offer. We may say, and possibly with truth, that one who studies geometry will not reason more clearly on a financial proposition than one who does not; but in spite of the results of the very meager experiments of the psychologists, it is probable that the man who has had some drill in syllogisms, and who has learned to select the essentials and to neglect the nonessentials in reaching his conclusions, has acquired habits in reasoning that will help him in every line of work. As part of this equipment there is also a terseness of statement and a clearness in arrangement of points in an argument that has been the subject of comment by many writers.

Upon this same topic an English writer, in one of the sanest of recent monographs upon the subject,[1] has expressed his views in the following words:

The statement that a given individual has received a sound geometrical training implies that he has segregated from the whole of his sense impressions a certain set of these impressions, that he has then eliminated from their consideration all irrelevant impressions (in other words, acquired a subjective command of these impressions), that he has developed on the basis of these impressions an ordered and continuous system of logical deduction, and finally that he is capable of expressing the nature of these impressions and his deductions therefrom in terms simple and free from ambiguity. Now the slightest consideration will convince any one not already conversant with the idea, that the same sequence of mental processes underlies the whole career of any individual in any walk of life if only he is not concerned entirely with manual labor; consequently a full training in the performance of such sequences must be regarded as forming an essential part of any education worthy of the name. Moreover, the full appreciation of such processes has a higher value than is contained in the mental training involved, great though this be, for it induces an appreciation of intellectual unity and beauty which plays for the mind that part which the appreciation of schemes of shape and color plays for the artistic faculties; or, again, that part which the appreciation of a body of religious doctrine plays for the ethical aspirations. Now geometry is not the sole possible basis for inculcating this appreciation. Logic is an alternative for adults, provided that the individual is possessed of sufficient wide, though rough, experience on which to base his reasoning. Geometry is, however, highly desirable in that the objective bases are so simple and precise that they can be grasped at an early age, that the amount of training for the imagination is very large, that the deductive processes are not beyond the scope of

[1] G. W. L. Carson, "The Functions of Geometry as a Subject of Education," p. 3, Tonbridge, 1910.

ordinary boys, and finally that it affords a better basis for exercise in the art of simple and exact expression than any other possible subject of a school course.

Are these results really secured by teachers, however, or are they merely imagined by the pedagogue as a justification for his existence? Do teachers have any such appreciation of geometry as has been suggested, and even if they have it, do they impart it to their pupils? In reply it may be said, probably with perfect safety, that teachers of geometry appreciate their subject and lead their pupils to appreciate it to quite as great a degree as obtains in any other branch of education. What teacher appreciates fully the beauties of " In Memoriam," or of " Hamlet," or of " Paradise Lost," and what one inspires his pupils with all the nobility of these world classics? What teacher sees in biology all the grandeur of the evolution of the race, or imparts to his pupils the noble lessons of life that the study of this subject should suggest? What teacher of Latin brings his pupils to read the ancient letters with full appreciation of the dignity of style and the nobility of thought that they contain? And what teacher of French succeeds in bringing a pupil to carry on a conversation, to read a French magazine, to see the history imbedded in the words that are used, to realize the charm and power of the language, or to appreciate to the full a single classic? In other words, none of us fully appreciates his subject, and none of us can hope to bring his pupils to the ideal attitude toward any part of it. But it is probable that the teacher of geometry succeeds relatively better than the teacher of other subjects, because the science has reached a relatively higher state of perfection. The body of truth in geometry has been more clearly marked out, it has been more successfully fitted together, its lesson is more patent, and the experience of centuries has brought it into a shape that is more usable in the school. While, therefore, we have all kinds of teaching in all kinds of subjects, the very nature of the case leads to the belief that the class in geometry receives quite as much from the teacher and the subject as the class in any other branch in the school curriculum.

But is this not mere conjecture? What are the results of scientific investigation of the teaching of geometry? Unfortunately there is little hope from the results of such an inquiry, either here or in other fields. We cannot first weigh a pupil in an intellectual or moral balance, then feed him geometry, and then weigh him again, and then set back his clock of time and begin all over again with the same individual. There is no " before taking " and " after taking " of a subject that extends over a year or two of a pupil's life. We can weigh utilities roughly, we can estimate the pleasure of a subject relatively, but we cannot say that geometry is worth so many dollars, and history so many, and so on through the curriculum. The best we can do is to ask ourselves what the various subjects, with teachers of fairly equal merit, have done for us, and to inquire what has been the experience of other persons. Such an investigation results in showing that, with few exceptions, people who have studied geometry received as much of pleasure, of inspiration, of satisfaction, of what they call training from geometry as from any other subject of study, — given teachers of equal merit, — and that they would not willingly give up the something which geometry brought to them. If this were not the feeling, and if humanity believed that geometry is what Mr. Locke's words would seem to indicate, it would long ago have banished it from the schools, since upon this ground rather than upon the ground of utility the subject has always stood.

These seem to be the great reasons for the study of geometry, and to search for others would tend to weaken the argument. At first sight they may not seem to justify the expenditure of time that geometry demands, and they may seem unduly to neglect the argument that geometry is a stepping-stone to higher mathematics. Each of these points, however, has been neglected purposely. A pupil has a number of school years at his disposal; to what shall they be devoted? To literature? What claim has letters that is such as to justify the exclusion of geometry? To music, or natural science, or language? These are all valuable, and all should be studied by one seeking a liberal education; but for the same reason geometry should have its place. What subject, in fine, can supply exactly what geometry does? And if none, then how can the pupil's time be better expended than in the study of this science?[1] As to the second point, that a claim should be set forth that geometry is a *sine qua non* to higher mathematics, this belief is considerably exaggerated because there are relatively few who proceed from geometry to a higher branch of mathematics. This argument would justify its status as an elective rather than as a required subject.

Let us then stand upon the ground already marked out, holding that the pleasure, the culture, the mental poise, the habits of exact reasoning that geometry brings,

[1] It may well be, however, that the growing curriculum may justify some reduction in the time formerly assigned to geometry, and any reasonable proposition of this nature should be fairly met by teachers of mathematics.

and the general experience of mankind upon the subject are sufficient to justify us in demanding for it a reasonable amount of time in the framing of a curriculum. Let us be fair in our appreciation of all other branches, but let us urge that every student may have an opportunity to know of real geometry, say for a single year, thereafter pursuing it or not, according as we succeed in making its value apparent, or fail in our attempt to present worthily an ancient and noble science to the mind confided to our instruction.

The shortsightedness of a narrow education, of an education that teaches only machines to a prospective mechanic, and agriculture to a prospective farmer, and cooking and dressmaking to the girl, and that would exclude all mathematics that is not utilitarian in the narrow sense, cannot endure.

The community has found out that such schemes may be well fitted to give the children a good time in school, but lead them to a bad time afterward. Life is hard work, and if they have never learned in school to give their concentrated attention to that which does not appeal to them and which does not interest them immediately, they have missed the most valuable lesson of their school years. The little practical information they could have learned at any time; the energy of attention and concentration can no longer be learned if the early years are wasted. However narrow and commercial the standpoint which is chosen may be, it can always be found that it is the general education which pays best, and the more the period of cultural work can be expanded the more efficient will be the services of the school for the practical services of the nation.[1]

Of course no one should construe these remarks as opposing in the slightest degree the laudable efforts that are constantly being put forth to make geometry more

[1] Professor Münsterberg, in the *Metropolitan Magazine* for July, 1910.

interesting and to vitalize it by establishing as strong motives as possible for its study. Let the home, the workshop, physics, art, play, — all contribute their quota of motive to geometry as to all mathematics and all other branches. But let us never forget that geometry has a *raison d'être* beyond all this, and that these applications are sought primarily for the sake of geometry, and that geometry is not taught primarily for the sake of these applications.

When we consider how often geometry is attacked by those who profess to be its friends, and how teachers who have been trained in mathematics occasionally seem to make of the subject little besides a mongrel course in drawing and measuring, all the time insisting that they are progressive while the champions of real geometry are reactionary, it is well to read some of the opinions of the masters. The following quotations may be given occasionally in geometry classes as showing the esteem in which the subject has been held in various ages, and at any rate they should serve to inspire the teacher to greater love for his subject.

The enemies of geometry, those who know it only imperfectly, look upon the theoretical problems, which constitute the most difficult part of the subject, as mental games which consume time and energy that might better be employed in other ways. Such a belief is false, and it would block the progress of science if it were credible. But aside from the fact that the speculative problems, which at first sight seem barren, can often be applied to useful purposes, they always stand as among the best means to develop and to express all the forces of the human intelligence. — Abbé Bossut.

The sailor whom an exact observation of longitude saves from shipwreck owes his life to a theory developed two thousand years ago by men who had in mind merely the speculations of abstract geometry. — Condorcet.

THE TEACHING OF GEOMETRY

If mathematical heights are hard to climb, the fundamental principles lie at every threshold, and this fact allows them to be comprehended by that common sense which Descartes declared was "apportioned equally among all men." — COLLET.

It may seem strange that geometry is unable to define the terms which it uses most frequently, since it defines neither movement, nor number, nor space, — the three things with which it is chiefly concerned. But we shall not be surprised if we stop to consider that this admirable science concerns only the most simple things, and the very quality that renders these things worthy of study renders them incapable of being defined. Thus the very lack of definition is rather an evidence of perfection than a defect, since it comes not from the obscurity of the terms, but from the fact that they are so very well known. — PASCAL.

God eternally geometrizes. — PLATO.

God is a circle of which the center is everywhere and the circumference nowhere. — RABELAIS.

Without mathematics no one can fathom the depths of philosophy. Without philosophy no one can fathom the depths of mathematics. Without the two no one can fathom the depths of anything. — BORDAS-DEMOULIN.

We may look upon geometry as a practical logic, for the truths which it studies, being the most simple and most clearly understood of all truths, are on this account the most susceptible of ready application in reasoning. — D'ALEMBERT.

The advance and the perfecting of mathematics are closely joined to the prosperity of the nation. — NAPOLEON.

Hold nothing as certain save what can be demonstrated. — NEWTON.

To measure is to know. — KEPLER.

The method of making no mistake is sought by every one. The logicians profess to show the way, but the geometers alone ever reach it, and aside from their science there is no genuine demonstration. — PASCAL.

The taste for exactness, the impossibility of contenting one's self with vague notions or of leaning upon mere hypotheses, the necessity for perceiving clearly the connection between certain propositions and the object in view, — these are the most precious fruits of the study of mathematics. — LACROIX.

WHY GEOMETRY IS STUDIED

Bibliography. Smith, The Teaching of Elementary Mathematics, p. 234, New York, 1900 ; Henrici, Presidential Address before the British Association, *Nature*, Vol. XXVIII, p. 497 ; Hill, Educational Value of Mathematics, *Educational Review*, Vol. IX, p. 349 ; Young, The Teaching of Mathematics, p. 9, New York, 1907. The closing quotations are from Rebière, Mathématiques et Mathématiciens, Paris, 1893.

CHAPTER III

A BRIEF HISTORY OF GEOMETRY

The geometry of very ancient peoples was largely the mensuration of simple areas and solids, such as is taught to children in elementary arithmetic to-day. They early learned how to find the area of a rectangle, and in the oldest mathematical records that have come down to us there is some discussion of the area of triangles and the volume of solids.

The earliest documents that we have relating to geometry come to us from Babylon and Egypt. Those from Babylon are written on small clay tablets, some of them about the size of the hand, these tablets afterwards having been baked in the sun. They show that the Babylonians of that period knew something of land measures, and perhaps had advanced far enough to compute the area of a trapezoid. For the mensuration of the circle they later used, as did the early Hebrews, the value $\pi = 3$. A tablet in the British Museum shows that they also used such geometric forms as triangles and circular segments in astrology or as talismans.

The Egyptians must have had a fair knowledge of practical geometry long before the date of any mathematical treatise that has come down to us, for the building of the pyramids, between 3000 and 2400 B.C., required the application of several geometric principles. Some knowledge of surveying must also have been necessary to carry out the extensive plans for irrigation that were executed under Amenemhat III, about 2200 B.C.

The first definite knowledge that we have of Egyptian mathematics comes to us from a manuscript copied on papyrus, a kind of paper used about the Mediterranean in early times. This copy was made by one Aah-mesu (The Moon-born), commonly called Ahmes, who probably flourished about 1700 B.C. The original from which he copied, written about 2300 B.C., has been lost, but the papyrus of Ahmes, written nearly four thousand years ago, is still preserved, and is now in the British Museum. In this manuscript, which is devoted chiefly to fractions and to a crude algebra, is found some work on mensuration. Among the curious rules are the incorrect ones that the area of an isosceles triangle equals half the product of the base and one of the equal sides; and that the area of a trapezoid having bases b, b', and the nonparallel sides each equal to a, is $\frac{1}{2} a (b + b')$. One noteworthy advance appears, however. Ahmes gives a rule for finding the area of a circle, substantially as follows: Multiply the square on the radius by $(\frac{16}{9})^2$, which is equivalent to taking for π the value 3.1605. This papyrus also contains some treatment of the mensuration of solids, particularly with reference to the capacity of granaries. There is also some slight mention of similar figures, and an extensive treatment of unit fractions, — fractions that were quite universal among the ancients. In the line of algebra it contains a brief treatment of the equation of the first degree with one unknown, and of progressions.[1]

---

[1] It was published in German translation by A. Eisenlohr, " Ein mathematisches Handbuch der alten Aegypter," Leipzig, 1877, and in facsimile by the British Museum, under the title, " The Rhind Papyrus," in 1898.

THE TEACHING OF GEOMETRY

Herodotus tells us that Sesostris, king of Egypt,[1] divided the land among his people and marked out the boundaries after the overflow of the Nile, so that surveying must have been well known in his day. Indeed, the *harpedonaptæ*, or rope stretchers, acquired their name because they stretched cords, in which were knots, so as to make the right triangle 3, 4, 5, when they wished to erect a perpendicular. This is a plan occasionally used by surveyors to-day, and it shows that the practical application of the Pythagorean Theorem was known long before Pythagoras gave what seems to have been the first general proof of the proposition.

From Egypt, and possibly from Babylon, geometry passed to the shores of Asia Minor and Greece. The scientific study of the subject begins with Thales, one of the Seven Wise Men of the Grecian civilization. Born at Miletus, not far from Smyrna and Ephesus, about 640 B.C., he died at Athens in 548 B.C. He spent his early manhood as a merchant, accumulating the wealth that enabled him to spend his later years in study. He visited Egypt, and is said to have learned such elements of geometry as were known there. He founded a school of mathematics and philosophy at Miletus, known from the country as the Ionic School. How elementary the knowledge of geometry then was may be understood from the fact that tradition attributes only about four propositions to Thales, — (1) that vertical angles are equal, (2) that equal angles lie opposite the equal sides of an isosceles triangle, (3) that a triangle is determined by two angles and the included side, (4) that a diameter bisects the circle, and possibly the propositions about the

[1] Generally known as Rameses II. He reigned in Egypt about 1350 B.C.

angle-sum of a triangle for special cases, and the angle inscribed in a semicircle.[1]

The greatest pupil of Thales, and one of the most remarkable men of antiquity, was Pythagoras. Born probably on the island of Samos, just off the coast of Asia Minor, about the year 580 B.C., Pythagoras set forth as a young man to travel. He went to Miletus and studied under Thales, probably spent several years in Egypt, very likely went to Babylon, and possibly went even to India, since tradition asserts this and the nature of his work in mathematics suggests it. In later life he went to a Greek colony in southern Italy, and at Crotona, in the southeastern part of the peninsula, he founded a school and established a secret society to propagate his doctrines. In geometry he is said to have been the first to demonstrate the proposition that the square on the hypotenuse is equal to the sum of the squares upon the other two sides of a right triangle. The proposition was known in India and Egypt before his time, at any rate for special cases, but he seems to have been the first to prove it. To him or to his school seems also to have been due the construction of the regular pentagon and of the five regular polyhedrons. The construction of the regular pentagon requires the dividing of a line into extreme and mean ratio, and this problem is commonly assigned to the Pythagoreans, although it played an important part in Plato's school. Pythagoras is also said to have known that six equilateral triangles, three

---

[1] Two excellent works on Thales and his successors, and indeed the best in English, are the following: G. J. Allman, "Greek Geometry from Thales to Euclid," Dublin, 1889 ; J. Gow, "A History of Greek Mathematics," Cambridge, 1884. On all mathematical subjects the best general history is that of M. Cantor, "Geschichte der Mathematik," 4 vols, Leipzig, 1880–1908.

regular hexagons, or four squares, can be placed about a point so as just to fill the 360°, but that no other regular polygons can be so placed. To his school is also due the proof for the general case that the sum of the angles of a triangle equals two right angles, the first knowledge

of the size of each angle of a regular polygon, and the construction of at least one star-polygon, the star-pentagon, which became the badge of his fraternity. The brotherhood founded by Pythagoras proved so offensive to the government that it was dispersed before the death of the master. Pythagoras fled to Megapontum, a seaport lying to the north of Crotona, and there he died about 501 B.C.[1]

FANCIFUL PORTRAIT OF PYTHAGORAS
Calandri's Arithmetic, 1491

For two centuries after Pythagoras geometry passed through a period of discovery of propositions. The state

---

[1] Another good work on Greek geometry, with considerable material on Pythagoras, is by C. A. Bretschneider, "Die Geometrie und die Geometer vor Eukleides," Leipzig, 1870.

of the science may be seen from the fact that Œnopides of Chios, who flourished about 465 B.C., and who had studied in Egypt, was celebrated because he showed how to let fall a perpendicular to a line, and how to make an angle equal to a given angle. A few years later, about 440 B.C., Hippocrates of Chios wrote the first Greek textbook on mathematics. He knew that the areas of circles are proportional to the squares on their radii, but was ignorant of the fact that equal central angles or equal inscribed angles intercept equal arcs.

Antiphon and Bryson, two Greek scholars, flourished about 430 B.C. The former attempted to find the area of a circle by doubling the number of sides of a regular inscribed polygon, and the latter by doing the same for both inscribed and circumscribed polygons. They thus approximately exhausted the area between the polygon and the circle, and hence this method is known as the method of exhaustions.

About 420 B.C. Hippias of Elis invented a certain curve called the quadratrix, by means of which he could square the circle and trisect any angle. This curve cannot be constructed by the unmarked straightedge and the compasses, and when we say that it is impossible to square the circle or to trisect any angle, we mean that it is impossible by the help of these two instruments alone.

During this period the great philosophic school of Plato (429–348 B.C.) flourished at Athens, and to this school is due the first systematic attempt to create exact definitions, axioms, and postulates, and to distinguish between elementary and higher geometry. It was at this time that elementary geometry became limited to the use of the compasses and the unmarked straightedge, which took from this domain the possibility of constructing a square equivalent to a given circle ("squaring the circle"), of trisecting any given angle, and of constructing a cube that should have twice the volume of a given cube ("duplicating the cube"), these being the three famous problems of antiquity. Plato and his school interested themselves with the so-called Pythagorean numbers, that is, with numbers that would represent the three sides of a right triangle and hence fulfill the condition that $a^2 + b^2 = c^2$. Pythagoras had already given a rule that would be expressed in modern form, as $\frac{1}{4}(m^2+1)^2 = m^2 + \frac{1}{4}(m^2-1)^2$. The school of Plato found that $[(\frac{1}{2}m)^2+1]^2 = m^2 + [(\frac{1}{2}m)^2-1]^2$. By giving various values to m, different Pythagorean numbers may be found. Plato's nephew, Speusippus (about 350 B.C.), wrote upon this subject. Such numbers were known, however, both in India and in Egypt, long before this time.

One of Plato's pupils was Philippus of Mende, in Egypt, who flourished about 380 B.C. It is said that he discovered the proposition relating to the exterior angle of a triangle. His interest, however, was chiefly in astronomy.

Another of Plato's pupils was Eudoxus of Cnidus (408–355 B.C.). He elaborated the theory of proportion, placing it upon a thoroughly scientific foundation. It is probable that Book V of Euclid, which is devoted to proportion, is essentially the work of Eudoxus. By means of the method of exhaustions of Antiphon and Bryson he proved that the pyramid is one third of a prism, and the cone is one third of a cylinder, each of the same base and the same altitude. He wrote the first textbook known on solid geometry.

The subject of conic sections starts with another pupil of Plato's, Menæchmus, who lived about 350 B.C. He cut the three forms of conics (the ellipse, parabola, and hyperbola) out of three different forms of cone, — the acute-angled, right-angled, and obtuse-angled, — not noticing that he could have obtained all three from any form of right circular cone. It is interesting to see the far-reaching influence of Plato. While primarily interested in philosophy, he laid the first scientific foundations for a system of mathematics, and his pupils were the leaders in this science in the generation following his greatest activity.

The great successor of Plato at Athens was Aristotle, the teacher of Alexander the Great. He also was more interested in philosophy than in mathematics, but in natural rather than mental philosophy. With him comes the first application of mathematics to physics in the hands of a great man, and with noteworthy results. He seems to have been the first to represent an unknown quantity by letters. He set forth the theory of the parallelogram of forces, using only rectangular components, however. To one of his pupils, Eudemus of Rhodes, we are indebted for a history of ancient geometry, some fragments of which have come down to us.

The first great textbook on geometry, and the greatest one that has ever appeared, was written by Euclid, who taught mathematics in the great university at Alexandria, Egypt, about 300 B.C. Alexandria was then practically a Greek city, having been named in honor of Alexander the Great, and being ruled by the Greeks.

In his work Euclid placed all of the leading propositions of plane geometry then known, and arranged them in a logical order. Most geometries of any importance written since his time have been based upon Euclid, improving the sequence, symbols, and wording as occasion demanded. He also wrote upon other branches of mathematics besides elementary geometry, including a work on optics. He was not a great creator of mathematics, but was rather a compiler of the work of others, an office quite as difficult to fill and quite as honorable.

Euclid did not give much solid geometry because not much was known then. It was to Archimedes (287–212 B.C.), a famous mathematician of Syracuse, on the island of Sicily, that some of the most important propositions of solid geometry are due, particularly those relating to the sphere and cylinder. He also showed how to find the approximate value of π by a method similar to the one we teach to-day, proving that the real value lay between $3\frac{1}{7}$ and $3\frac{10}{71}$. The story goes that the sphere and cylinder were engraved upon his tomb, and Cicero, visiting Syracuse many years after his death, found the tomb by looking for these symbols. Archimedes was the greatest mathematical physicist of ancient times.

The Greeks contributed little more to elementary geometry, although Apollonius of Perga, who taught at Alexandria between 250 and 200 B.C., wrote extensively on conic sections, and Hypsicles of Alexandria, about 190 B.C., wrote on regular polyhedrons. Hypsicles was the first Greek writer who is known to have used sexagesimal fractions, — the degrees, minutes, and seconds of our angle measure. Zenodorus (180 B.C.) wrote on isoperimetric figures, and his contemporary, Nicomedes of Gerasa, invented a curve known as the conchoid, by means of which he could trisect any angle. Another contemporary, Diocles, invented the cissoid, or ivy-shaped curve, by means of which he solved the famous problem of duplicating the cube, that is, constructing a cube that should have twice the volume of a given cube.

The greatest of the Greek astronomers, Hipparchus (180–125 B.C.), lived about this period, and with him begins spherical trigonometry as a definite science. A kind of plane trigonometry had been known to the ancient Egyptians. The Greeks usually employed the chord of an angle instead of the half chord (sine), the latter having been preferred by the later Arab writers.

The most celebrated of the later Greek physicists was Heron of Alexandria, formerly supposed to have lived about 100 B.C., but now assigned to the first century A.D. His contribution to geometry was the formula for the area of a triangle in terms of its sides a, b, and c, with s standing for the semiperimeter $\frac{1}{2}(a + b + c)$. The formula is $\sqrt{s(s - a)(s - b)(s - c)}$.

Probably nearly contemporary with Heron was Menelaus of Alexandria, who wrote a spherical trigonometry. He gave an interesting proposition relating to plane and spherical triangles, their sides being cut by a transversal. For the plane triangle ABC, the sides a, b, and c being cut respectively in X, Y, and Z, the theorem asserts substantially that

$$\frac{AZ}{BZ} \cdot \frac{BX}{CX} \cdot \frac{CY}{AY} = 1.$$

The most popular writer on astronomy among the Greeks was Ptolemy (Claudius Ptolemaeus, 87–165 A.D.), who lived at Alexandria. He wrote a work entitled " Megale Syntaxis " (The Great Collection), which his followers designated as *Megistos* (greatest), on which account the Arab translators gave it the name "Almagest " (*al* meaning "the"). He advanced the science of trigonometry, but did not contribute to geometry.

At the close of the third century Pappus of Alexandria (295 A.D.) wrote on geometry, and one of his theorems, a generalized form of the Pythagorean proposition, is mentioned in Chapter XVI of this work. Only two other Greek writers on geometry need be mentioned. Theon of Alexandria (370 A.D.), the father of the Hypatia who is the heroine of Charles Kingsley's well-known novel, wrote a commentary on Euclid to which we are indebted for some historical information. Proclus (410–485 A.D.) also wrote a commentary on Euclid, and much of our information concerning the first Book of Euclid is due to him.

The East did little for geometry, although contributing considerably to algebra. The first great Hindu writer was Aryabhatta, who was born in 476 A.D. He gave the very close approximation for π, expressed in modern notation as 3.1416. He also gave rules for finding the volume of the pyramid and sphere, but they were incorrect, showing that the Greek mathematics had not yet reached the Ganges. Another Hindu writer, Brahmagupta (born in 598 A.D.), wrote an encyclopedia of mathematics. He gave a rule for finding Pythagorean numbers, expressed in modern symbols as follows:

$$\frac{1}{4}\left(\frac{p^2}{q}+q\right)^2=\frac{1}{4}\left(\frac{p^2}{q}-q\right)^2+p^2.$$

He also generalized Heron's formula by asserting that the area of an inscribed quadrilateral of sides a, b, c, d, and semiperimeter s, is $\sqrt{(s-a)(s-b)(s-c)(s-d)}$.

The Arabs, about the time of the "Arabian Nights Tales" (800 A.D.), did much for mathematics, translating the Greek authors into their language and also bringing learning from India. Indeed, it is to them that modern Europe owed its first knowledge of Euclid. They contributed nothing of importance to elementary geometry, however.

The greatest of the Arab writers was Mohammed ibn Musa al-Khowarazmi (820 A.D.). He lived at Bagdad and Damascus. Although chiefly interested in astronomy, he wrote the first book bearing the name "algebra" ("Al-jabr wa'l-muqābalah," Restoration and Equation), composed an arithmetic using the Hindu numerals,[1] and paid much attention to geometry and trigonometry.

Euclid was translated from the Arabic into Latin in the twelfth century, Greek manuscripts not being then at hand, or being neglected because of ignorance of the language. The leading translators were Athelhard of Bath (1120), an English monk; Gherard of Cremona (1160), an Italian monk; and Johannes Campanus (1250), chaplain to Pope Urban IV.

The greatest European mathematician of the Middle Ages was Leonardo of Pisa[2] (ca. 1170–1250). He was very influential in making the Hindu-Arabic numerals known in Europe, wrote extensively on algebra, and was the author of one book on geometry. He contributed nothing to the elementary theory, however. The first edition of Euclid was printed in Latin in 1482, the first one in English appearing in 1570.

Our symbols are modern, + and − first appearing in a German work in 1489; = in Recorde's "Whetstone of Witte" in 1557; > and < in the works of Harriot (1560–1621); and × in a publication by Oughtred (1574–1660).

[1] Smith and Karpinski, "The Hindu-Arabic Numerals," Boston, 1911.
[2] For a sketch of his life see Smith and Karpinski, loc. cit.

THE TEACHING OF GEOMETRY

The most noteworthy advance in geometry in modern times was made by the great French philosopher Descartes, who published a small work entitled "La Géométrie" in 1637. From this springs the modern analytic geometry, a subject that has revolutionized the methods of all mathematics. Most of the subsequent discoveries in mathematics have been in higher branches. To the great Swiss mathematician Euler (1707-1783) is due, however, one proposition that has found its way into elementary geometry, the one showing the relation between the number of edges, vertices, and faces of a polyhedron.

There has of late arisen a modern elementary geometry devoted chiefly to special points and lines relating to the triangle and the circle, and many interesting propositions have been discovered. The subject is so extensive that it cannot find any place in our crowded curriculum, and must necessarily be left to the specialist.[1] Some idea of the nature of the work may be obtained from a mention of a few propositions:

The medians of a triangle are concurrent in the centroid, or center of gravity of the triangle.

The bisectors of the various interior and exterior angles of a triangle are concurrent by threes in the incenter or in one of the three excenters of the triangle.

The common chord of two intersecting circles is a special case of their radical axis, and tangents to the circles from any point on the radical axis are equal.

---

[1] Those who care for a brief description of this phase of the subject may consult J. Casey, "A Sequel to Euclid," Dublin, fifth edition, 1888; W. J. M'Clelland, "A Treatise on the Geometry of the Circle," New York, 1891; M. Simon, "Über die Entwicklung der Elementar-Geometrie im XIX. Jahrhundert," Leipzig, 1906.

If O is the orthocenter of the triangle ABC, and X, Y, Z are the feet of the perpendiculars from A, B, C respectively, and P, Q, R are the mid-points of a, b, c respectively, and L, M, N are the mid-points of OA, OB, OC respectively; then the points L, M, N; P, Q, R; X, Y, Z all lie on a circle, the "nine points circle."

In the teaching of geometry it adds a human interest to the subject to mention occasionally some of the historical facts connected with it. For this reason this brief sketch will be supplemented by many notes upon the various important propositions as they occur in the several books described in the later chapters of this work.

CHAPTER IV

DEVELOPMENT OF THE TEACHING OF GEOMETRY

We know little of the teaching of geometry in very ancient times, but we can infer its nature from the teaching that is still seen in the native schools of the East. Here a man, learned in any science, will have a group of voluntary students sitting about him, and to them he will expound the truth. Such schools may still be seen in India, Persia, and China, the master sitting on a mat placed on the ground or on the floor of a veranda, and the pupils reading aloud or listening to his words of exposition.

In Egypt geometry seems to have been in early times mere mensuration, confined largely to the priestly caste. It was taught to novices who gave promise of success in this subject, and not to others, the idea of general culture, of training in logic, of the cultivation of exact expression, and of coming in contact with truth being wholly wanting.

In Greece it was taught in the schools of philosophy, often as a general preparation for philosophic study. Thus Thales introduced it into his Ionic school, Pythagoras made it very prominent in his great school at Crotona in southern Italy (Magna Græcia), and Plato placed above the door of his *Academia* the words, " Let no one ignorant of geometry enter here," — a kind of entrance examination for his school of philosophy. In these gatherings of students it is probable that geometry was taught in much the way already mentioned for the schools of the East, a small group of students being instructed by a master. Printing was unknown, papyrus was dear, parchment was only in process of invention. Paper such as we know had not yet appeared, so that instruction was largely oral, and geometric figures were drawn by a pointed stick on a board covered with fine sand, or on a tablet of wax.

But with these crude materials there went an abundance of time, so that a number of great results were accomplished in spite of the difficulties attending the study of the subject. It is said that Hippocrates of Chios (*ca.* 440 B.C.) wrote the first elementary textbook on mathematics and invented the method of geometric reduction, the replacing of a proposition to be proved by another which, when proved, allows the first one to be demonstrated. A little later Eudoxus of Cnidus (*ca.* 375 B.C.), a pupil of Plato's, used the *reductio ad absurdum*, and Plato is said to have invented the method of proof by analysis, an elaboration of the plan used by Hippocrates. Thus these early philosophers taught their pupils not facts alone, but methods of proof, giving them power as well as knowledge. Furthermore, they taught them how to discuss their problems, investigating the conditions under which they are capable of solution. This feature of the work they called the *diorismus*, and it seems to have started with Leon, a follower of Plato.

Between the time of Plato (*ca.* 400 B.C.) and Euclid (*ca.* 300 B.C.) several attempts were made to arrange the accumulated material of elementary geometry in a textbook. Plato had laid the foundations for the science, in the form of axioms, postulates, and definitions, and he had limited the instruments to the straightedge and the compasses. Aristotle (*ca.* 350 B.C.) had paid special attention to the history of the subject, thus finding out what had already been accomplished, and had also made much of the applications of geometry. The world was therefore ready for a good teacher who should gather the material and arrange it scientifically. After several attempts to find the man for such a task, he was discovered in Euclid, and to his work the next chapter is devoted.

After Euclid, Archimedes (*ca.* 250 B.C.) made his great contributions. He was not a teacher like his illustrious predecessor, but he was a great discoverer. He has left us, however, a statement of his methods of investigation which is helpful to those who teach. These methods were largely experimental, even extending to the weighing of geometric forms to discover certain relations, the proof being given later. Here was born, perhaps, what has been called the laboratory method of the present.

Of the other Greek teachers we have but little information as to methods of imparting instruction. It is not until the Middle Ages that there is much known in this line. Whatever of geometry was taught seems to have been imparted by word of mouth in the way of expounding Euclid, and this was done in the ancient fashion.

The early Church leaders usually paid no attention to geometry, but as time progressed the *quadrivium*, or four sciences of arithmetic, music, geometry, and astronomy, came to rank with the *trivium* (grammar, rhetoric, dialectics), the two making up the "seven liberal arts." All that there was of geometry in the first thousand years of Christianity, however, at least in the great majority of Church schools, was summed up in a few definitions and rules of mensuration. Gerbert, who became Pope Sylvester II in 999 A.D., gave a new impetus to geometry by discovering a manuscript of the old Roman surveyors and a copy of the geometry of Boethius, who paraphrased Euclid about 500 A.D. He thereupon wrote a brief geometry, and his elevation to the papal chair tended to bring the study of mathematics again into prominence.

Geometry now began to have some place in the Church schools, naturally the only schools of high rank in the Middle Ages. The study of the subject, however, seems to have been merely a matter of memorizing. Geometry received another impetus in the book written by Leonardo of Pisa in 1220, the "Practica Geometriae." Euclid was also translated into Latin about this time (strangely enough, as already stated, from the Arabic instead of the Greek), and thus the treasury of elementary geometry was opened to scholars in Europe. From now on, until the invention of printing (ca. 1450), numerous writers on geometry appear, but, so far as we know, the method of instruction remained much as it had always been. The universities began to appear about the thirteenth century, and Sacrobosco, a well-known medieval mathematician, taught mathematics about 1250 in the University of Paris. In 1336 this university decreed that mathematics should be required for a degree. In the thirteenth century Oxford required six books of Euclid for one who was to teach, but this amount of work seems to have been merely nominal, for in 1450 only two books were actually read. The universities of Prague (founded in 1350) and Vienna (statutes of 1389) required most of plane geometry for the teacher's license, although Vienna demanded but one book for the bachelor's degree. So, in general, the universities of the thirteenth, fourteenth, and fifteenth centuries required less for the degree of master of arts than we now require from a pupil in our American high schools. On the other hand, the university students were younger than now, and were really doing only high-school work.

The invention of printing made possible the study of geometry in a new fashion. It now became possible for any one to study from a book, whereas before this time instruction was chiefly by word of mouth, consisting of an explanation of Euclid. The first Euclid was printed in 1482, at Venice, and new editions and variations of this text came out frequently in the next century. Practical geometries became very popular, and the reaction against the idea of mental discipline threatened to abolish the old style of text. It was argued that geometry was uninteresting, that it was not sufficient in itself, that boys needed to see the practical uses of the subject, that only those propositions that were capable of application should be retained, that there must be a fusion between the demands of culture and the demands of business, and that every man who stood for mathematical ideals represented an obsolete type. Such writers as Finæus (1556), Bartoli (1589), Belli (1569), and Cataneo (1567), in the sixteenth century, and Capra (1673), Gargiolli (1655), and many others in the seventeenth century, either directly or inferentially, took this attitude towards the subject, — exactly the attitude that is being taken at the present time by a number of teachers in the United States. As is always the case, to such an extreme did this movement lead that there was a reaction that brought the Euclid type of book again to the front, and it has maintained its prominence even to the present.

The study of geometry in the high schools is relatively recent. The Gymnasium (classical school preparatory to the university) at Nürnberg, founded in 1526, and the Cathedral school at Württemberg (as shown by the curriculum of 1556) seem to have had no geometry before 1600, although the Gymnasium at Strassburg included some of this branch of mathematics in 1578, and an elective course in geometry was offered at Zwickau, in Saxony, in 1521. In the seventeenth century geometry is found in a considerable number of secondary schools, as at Coburg (1605), Kurfalz (1615, elective), Erfurt (1643), Gotha (1605), Giessen (1605), and numerous other places in Germany, although it appeared but rarely in the secondary schools of France before the eighteenth century. In Germany the Realschulen — schools with more science and less classics than are found in the Gymnasium — came into being in the eighteenth century, and considerable effort was made to construct a course in geometry that should be more practical than that of the modified Euclid. At the opening of the nineteenth century the Prussian schools were reorganized, and from that time on geometry has had a firm position in the secondary schools of all Germany. In the eighteenth century some excellent textbooks on geometry appeared in France, among the best being that of Legendre (1794), which influenced in such a marked degree the geometries of America. Soon after the opening of the nineteenth century the *lycées* of France became strong institutions, and geometry, chiefly based on Legendre, was well taught in the mathematical divisions. A worthy rival of Legendre's geometry was the work of Lacroix, who called attention continually to the analogy between the theorems of plane and solid geometry, and even went so far as to suggest treating the related propositions together in certain cases.

In England the preparatory schools, such as Rugby, Harrow, and Eton, did not commonly teach geometry until quite recently, leaving this work for the universities. In Christ's Hospital, London, however, geometry was taught as early as 1681, from a work written by several teachers of prominence. The highest class at Harrow studied "Euclid and vulgar fractions" one period a week in 1829, but geometry was not seriously studied before 1837. In the Edinburgh Academy as early as 1835, and in Rugby by 1839, plane geometry was completed.

Not until 1844 did Harvard require any plane geometry for entrance. In 1855 Yale required only two books of Euclid. It was therefore from 1850 to 1875 that plane geometry took a definite place in the American high school. Solid geometry has not been generally required for entrance to any eastern college, although in the West this is not the case. The East teaches plane geometry more thoroughly, but allows a pupil to enter college or to go into business with no solid geometry. Given a year to the subject, it is possible to do little more than cover plane geometry; with a year and a half the solid geometry ought easily to be covered also.

Bibliography. Stamper, A History of the Teaching of Elementary Geometry, New York, 1909, with a very full bibliography of the subject; Cajori, The Teaching of Mathematics in the United States, Washington, 1890; Cantor, Geschichte der Mathematik, Vol. IV, p. 321, Leipzig, 1908; Schotten, Inhalt und Methode des planimetrischen Unterrichts, Leipzig, 1890.

CHAPTER V

EUCLID

It is fitting that a chapter in a book upon the teaching of this subject should be devoted to the life and labors of the greatest of all textbook writers, Euclid, — a man whose name has been, for more than two thousand years, a synonym for elementary plane geometry wherever the subject has been studied. And yet when an effort is made to pick up the scattered fragments of his biography, we are surprised to find how little is known of one whose fame is so universal. Although more editions of his work have been printed than of any other book save the Bible,[1] we do not know when he was born, or in what city, or even in what country, nor do we know his race, his parentage, or the time of his death. We should not feel that we knew much of the life of a man who lived when the Magna Charta was wrested from King John, if our first and only source of information was a paragraph in the works of some historian of to-day; and yet this is about the situation in respect to Euclid. Proclus of Alexandria, philosopher, teacher, and mathematician, lived from 410 to 485 A.D., and wrote a commentary on the works of Euclid. In his writings, which seem to set forth in amplified form his lectures to the students in the Neoplatonist School

---

[1] Riccardi, Saggio di una bibliografia Euclidea, Part I, p. 3, Bologna, 1887. Riccardi lists well towards two thousand editions.

of Alexandria, Proclus makes this statement, and of Euclid's life we have little else:

Not much younger than these[1] is Euclid, who put together the "Elements," collecting many of the theorems of Eudoxus, perfecting many of those of Theætetus, and also demonstrating with perfect certainty what his predecessors had but insufficiently proved. He flourished in the time of the first Ptolemy, for Archimedes, who closely followed this ruler,[2] speaks of Euclid. Furthermore it is related that Ptolemy one time demanded of him if there was in geometry no shorter way than that of the "Elements," to whom he replied that there was no royal road to geometry.[3] He was therefore younger than the pupils of Plato, but older than Eratosthenes and Archimedes; for the latter were contemporary with one another, as Eratosthenes somewhere says.[4]

Thus we have in a few lines, from one who lived perhaps seven or eight hundred years after Euclid, nearly all that is known of the most famous teacher of geometry that ever lived. Nevertheless, even this little tells us about when he flourished, for Hermotimus and Philippus were pupils of Plato, who died in 347 B.C., whereas Archimedes was born about 287 B.C. and was writing about 250 B.C. Furthermore, since Ptolemy I reigned from 306 to 283 B.C., Euclid must have been teaching about 300 B.C., and this is the date that is generally assigned to him.

Euclid probably studied at Athens, for until he himself assisted in transferring the center of mathematical

---

[1] Hermotimus of Colophon and Philippus of Mende.

[2] Literally, "Who closely followed the first," i.e. the first Ptolemy.

[3] Menæchmus is said to have replied to a similar question of Alexander the Great: "O King, through the country there are royal roads and roads for common citizens, but in geometry there is one road for all."

[4] This is also shown in a letter from Archimedes to Eratosthenes, recently discovered by Heiberg.

culture to Alexandria, it had long been in the Grecian capital, indeed since the time of Pythagoras. Moreover, numerous attempts had been made at Athens to do exactly what Euclid succeeded in doing, — to construct a logical sequence of propositions; in other words, to write a textbook on plane geometry. It was at Athens, therefore, that he could best have received the inspiration to compose his "Elements." [1] After finishing his education at Athens it is quite probable that he, like other savants of the period, was called to Alexandria by Ptolemy Soter, the king, to assist in establishing the great school which made that city the center of the world's learning for several centuries. In this school he taught, and here he wrote the "Elements" and numerous other works, perhaps ten in all.

Although the Greek writers who may have known something of the life of Euclid have little to say of him, the Arab writers, who could have known nothing save from Greek sources, have allowed their imaginations the usual latitude in speaking of him and of his labors. Thus Al-Qiftī, who wrote in the thirteenth century, has this to say in his biographical treatise "Ta'rīkh al-Ḥukamā":

Euclid, son of Naucrates, grandson of Zenarchus, called the author of geometry, a Greek by nationality, domiciled at Damascus, born at Tyre, most learned in the science of geometry, published a most excellent and most useful work entitled "The Foundation or Elements of Geometry," a subject in which no more general treatise existed before among the Greeks; nay, there was no one even of later date who did not walk in his footsteps and frankly profess his doctrine.

[1] On this phase of the subject, and indeed upon Euclid and his propositions and works in general, consult T. L. Heath, "The Thirteen Books of Euclid's Elements," 3 vols., Cambridge, 1908, a masterly treatise of which frequent use has been made in preparing this work.

This is rather a specimen of the Arab tendency to manufacture history than a serious contribution to the biography of Euclid, of whose personal history we have only the information given by Proclus.

EUCLID
From an old print

Euclid's works at once took high rank, and they are mentioned by various classical authors. Cicero knew of them, and Capella (*ca.* 470 A.D.), Cassiodorius (*ca.* 515 A.D.), and Boethius (*ca.* 480–524 A.D.) were all more

232

or less familiar with the " Elements." With the advance
of the Dark Ages, however, learning was held in less and
less esteem, so that Euclid was finally forgotten, and
manuscripts of his works were either destroyed or buried
in some remote cloister. The Arabs, however, whose
civilization assumed prominence from about 750 A.D. to
about 1500, translated the most important treatises of
the Greeks, and Euclid's " Elements " among the rest.
One of these Arabic editions an English monk of the
twelfth century, one Athelhard (Æthelhard) of Bath,
found and translated into Latin (*ca.* 1120 A.D.). A little
later Gherard of Cremona (1114–1187) made a new
translation from the Arabic, differing in essential fea-
tures from that of Athelhard, and about 1260 Johannes
Campanus made still a third translation, also from
Arabic into Latin.[1] There is reason to believe that
Athelhard, Campanus, and Gherard may all have had
access to an earlier Latin translation, since all are quite
alike in some particulars while diverging noticeably in
others. Indeed, there is an old English verse that relates:

> The clerk Euclide on this wyse hit fonde
> Thys craft of gemetry yn Egypte londe . . .
> Thys craft com into England, as y yow say,
> Yn tyme of good Kyng Adelstone's day.

If this be true, Euclid was known in England as early
as 924–940 A.D.

Without going into particulars further, it suffices to
say that the modern knowledge of Euclid came first
through the Arabic into the Latin, and the first printed

---

[1] A contemporary copy of this translation is now in the library of
George A. Plimpton, Esq., of New York. See the author's " Rara
Arithmetica," p. 433, Boston, 1909.

edition of the "Elements" (Venice, 1482) was the
Campanus translation. Greek manuscripts now began
to appear, and at the present time several are known.
There is a manuscript of the ninth century in the Bod-
leian library at Oxford, one of the tenth century in the
Vatican, another of the tenth century in Florence, one
of the eleventh century at Bologna, and two of the
twelfth century at Paris. There are also fragments containing bits of Euclid in Greek, and going back as far as
the second and third century A.D. The first modern
translation from the Greek into the Latin was made by
Zamberti (or Zamberto),[1] and was printed at Venice in
1513. The first translation into English was made by Sir
Henry Billingsley and was printed in 1570, sixteen
years before he became Lord Mayor of London.

Proclus, in his commentary upon Euclid's work,
remarks :

> In the whole of geometry there are certain leading theorems,
> bearing to those which follow the relation of a principle, all-per-
> vading, and furnishing proofs of many properties. Such theorems
> are called by the name of *elements*, and their function may be
> compared to that of the letters of the alphabet in relation to
> language, letters being indeed called by the same name in Greek
> [στοιχεῖα, stoicheia].[2]

This characterizes the work of Euclid, a collection of
the basic propositions of geometry, and chiefly of plane
geometry, arranged in logical sequence, the proof of
each depending upon some preceding proposition, definition, or assumption (axiom or postulate). The number

---

[1] A beautiful vellum manuscript of this translation is in the
library of George A. Plimpton, Esq., of New York. See the author's
"Rara Arithmetica," p. 481, Boston, 1909.

[2] Heath, loc. cit., Vol. I, p. 114.

of the propositions of plane geometry included in the "Elements" is not entirely certain, owing to some disagreement in the manuscripts, but it was between one hundred sixty and one hundred seventy-five. It is possible to reduce this number by about thirty or forty, because Euclid included a certain amount of geometric algebra; but beyond this we cannot safely go in the way of elimination, since from the very nature of the "Elements" these propositions are basic. The efforts at revising Euclid have been generally confined, therefore, to rearranging his material, to rendering more modern his phraseology, and to making a book that is more usable with beginners if not more logical in its presentation of the subject. While there has been an improvement upon Euclid in the art of bookmaking, and in minor matters of phraseology and sequence, the educational gain has not been commensurate with the effort put forth. With a little modification of Euclid's semi-algebraic Book II and of his treatment of proportion, with some scattering of the definitions and the inclusion of well-graded exercises at proper places, and with attention to the modern science of bookmaking, the "Elements" would answer quite as well for a textbook today as most of our modern substitutes, and much better than some of them. It would, moreover, have the advantage of being a classic,— somewhat the same advantage that comes from reading Homer in the original instead of from Pope's metrical translation. This is not a plea for a return to the Euclid text, but for a recognition of the excellence of Euclid's work.

The distinctive feature of Euclid's "Elements," compared with the modern American textbook, is perhaps this: Euclid begins a book with what seems to him the easiest proposition, be it theorem or problem; upon this he builds another; upon these a third, and so on, concerning himself but little with the classification of propositions. Furthermore, he arranges his propositions so as to construct his figures before using them. We, on the other hand, make some little attempt to classify our propositions within each book, and we make no attempt to construct our figures before using them, or at least to prove that the constructions are correct. Indeed, we go so far as to study the properties of figures that we cannot construct, as when we ask for the size of the angle of a regular heptagon. Thus Euclid begins Book I by a problem, to construct an equilateral triangle on a given line. His object is to follow this by problems on drawing a straight line equal to a given straight line, and cutting off from the greater of two straight lines a line equal to the less. He now introduces a theorem, which might equally well have been his first proposition, namely, the case of the congruence of two triangles, having given two sides and the included angle. By means of his third and fourth propositions he is now able to prove the *pons asinorum*, that the angles at the base of an isosceles triangle are equal. We, on the other hand, seek to group our propositions where this can conveniently be done, putting the congruent propositions together, those about inequalities by themselves, and the propositions about parallels in one set. The results of the two arrangements are not radically different, and the effect of either upon the pupil's mind does not seem particularly better than that of the other. Teachers who have used both plans quite commonly feel that, apart from Books II and V, Euclid is nearly as easily understood as our modern texts, if presented in as satisfactory dress.

The topics treated and the number of propositions in the plane geometry of the " Elements " are as follows :

Book I. Rectilinear figures 48
Book II. Geometric algebra 14
Book III. Circles 37
Book IV. Problems about circles 16
Book V. Proportion 25
Book VI. Applications of proportion 33
                                              ———
                                              173

Of these we now omit Euclid's Book II, because we have an algebraic symbolism that was unknown in his time, although he would not have used it in geometry even had it been known. Thus his first proposition in Book II is as follows :

If there be two straight lines, and one of them be cut into any number of segments whatever, the rectangle contained by the two straight lines is equal to the rectangles contained by the uncut straight line and each of the segments.

This amounts to saying that if $x = p + q + r + \cdots$, then $ax = ap + aq + ar + \cdots$. We also materially simplify Euclid's Book V. He, for example, proves that " If four magnitudes be proportional, they will also be proportional alternately." This he proves generally for any kind of magnitude, while we merely prove it for numbers having a common measure. We say that we may substitute for the older form of proportion, namely,

$$a : b = c : d,$$

the fractional form $\quad\quad \dfrac{a}{b} = \dfrac{c}{d}.$

From this we have $\quad\quad ad = bc.$

Whence $\quad\quad\quad\quad \dfrac{a}{c} = \dfrac{b}{d}.$

In this work we assume that we may multiply equals by b and d. But suppose b and d are cubes, of which, indeed, we do not even know the approximate numerical measure; what shall we do? To Euclid the multiplication by a cube or a polygon or a sphere would have been entirely meaningless, as it always is from the standpoint of pure geometry. Hence it is that our treatment of proportion has no serious standing in geometry as compared with Euclid's, and our only justification for it lies in the fact that it is easier. Euclid's treatment is much more rigorous than ours, but it is adapted to the comprehension of only advanced students, while ours is merely a confession, and it should be a frank confession, of the weakness of our pupils, and possibly, at times, of ourselves.

If we should take Euclid's Books II and V for granted, or as sufficiently evident from our study of algebra, we should have remaining only one hundred thirty-four propositions, most of which may be designated as basal propositions of plane geometry. Revise Euclid as we will, we shall not be able to eliminate any large number of his fundamental truths, while we might do much worse than to adopt these one hundred thirty-four propositions *in toto* as the bases, and indeed as the definition, of elementary plane geometry.

Bibliography. Heath, The Thirteen Books of Euclid's Elements, 3 vols., Cambridge, 1908; Frankland, The First Book of Euclid, Cambridge, 1906; Smith, Dictionary of Greek and Roman Biography, article Eukleides; Simon, Euclid und die sechs planimetrischen Bücher, Leipzig, 1901; Gow, History of Greek Mathematics, Cambridge, 1884, and any of the standard histories of mathematics. Both Heath and Simon give extensive bibliographies. The latest standard Greek and Latin texts are Heiberg's, published by Teubner of Leipzig.

THE TEACHING

OF

ELEMENTARY MATHEMATICS

BY

DAVID EUGENE SMITH

PROFESSOR OF MATHEMATICS IN TEACHERS' COLLEGE, COLUMBIA
UNIVERSITY, NEW YORK.

CHAPTER VI

THE GROWTH OF ALGEBRA

Egyptian algebra — Reserving for the following chapter the question of the definition of algebra, we may say that the science is by no means a new one. Or rather, to be more precise, the idea of the equation is not new, for this is only a part of the rather undefined discipline which we call algebra. In the oldest of extant deciphered mathematical manuscripts, the Ahmes papyrus to which reference has already been made, the simple equation appears. It is true that neither symbols nor terms familiar in our day are used, but in the so-called *hau* computation the linear equation with one unknown quantity is solved. Symbols for addition, subtraction, equality, and the unknown quantity are used. The following is an example of the simpler problems which Ahmes gives, his twenty-fourth: "*Hau* (literally *heap*), its seventh, its whole, it makes 19," which put in modern symbols means $\frac{x}{7} + x = 19$. Somewhat more difficult problems are also given, like the following (his thirty-first): "*Hau*, its $\frac{2}{3}$, its $\frac{1}{2}$, its $\frac{1}{7}$, its whole, it makes 33,"

$$i.e., \tfrac{2}{3}x + \tfrac{1}{2}x + \tfrac{1}{7}x + x = 33.$$

L

It must be said, however, that Ahmes had no notion of solving the equation by any of our present algebraic methods. His was rather a "rule of false position," as it was called in mediæval times, — guessing at an answer, finding the error, and then modifying the guess accordingly.[1] Ahmes also gives some work in arithmetical series and one example in geometric.

Greek algebra — Algebra made no further progress, so far as now known, among the Egyptians. But in the declining generations of Greece, long after the "golden age" had passed, it assumed some importance. As already stated, the Greek mind had a leaning toward form, and so it worked out a wonderful system of geometry and warped its other mathematics accordingly. The fact that the sum of the first n odd numbers is n^2, for example, was discovered or proved by a geometric figure; square root was extracted with reference to a geometric diagram; figurate numbers tell by their name that geometry entered into their study.

So we find in Euclid's "Elements of Geometry" (B.C., c. 300) formulae for $(a + b)^2$ and other simple algebraic relations worked out and proved by geometric figures. Hence Euclid and his followers knew

[1] Besides Eisenlohr's translation already mentioned, see Cantor, I, p. 38. A short sketch is given in Gow's History of Greek Mathematics, p. 18.

from the figure that to "complete the square," the geometric square, of $x^2 + 2\,ax$, it is necessary to add a^2. He also solved, geometrically, quadratic equations of the form $ax - x^2 = b$, $ax + x^2 = b$, and simultaneous equations of the form $x \pm y = a$, $xy = b$.[1]

With the older Greek view of mathematics, however, it was impossible for algebra to make much headway. Recognizing the linear, quadratic, and cubic functions of a variable, because these could be represented by lines, squares, and cubes, the Greeks of Euclid's time refused to consider the fourth power of a variable because the fourth dimension was beyond their empirical space.

Algebra had, however, made a beginning before Euclid's time. Thymaridas of Paros, whose personal history is quite unknown, had already solved some simple equations, and had been the first to use the expressions *given* or *defined* (ὡρισμένοι), and *unknown* or *undefined* (ἀόριστοι),[2] and it seems not improbable that the quadratic equation was somewhat familiar before the Alexandrian school was founded.[3] Aristotle, too, had employed letters to indicate unknown quantities in the statement of a problem, although not in an equation.[4]

---

[1] Heath, T. L., Diophantos of Alexandria, Cambridge, 1885, p. 140.

[2] Cantor, I, p. 148 ; Gow, p. 97, 107.

[3] Cantor, I, p. 301 ; but see Heath's Diophantos, p. 139.

[4] Gow, p. 105.

The most notable advance before the Christian era was made by Heron of Alexandria, about 100 B.C. Breaking away from the pure geometry of his predecessors, and not hesitating to speak of the fourth power of lines, he solved the quadratic equation[1] and even ran up against imaginary roots.[2] This was the turning-point of Greek mathematics, the downfall of their pure geometry, the rise of a new discipline.

But it is to Diophantus that we owe the first serious attempt to work out this new science. An Alexandrian, living in the fourth century, probably in the first half, he wrote a work, Ἀριθμητικά, almost entirely devoted to algebra.[3] This work is the first one known to have been written upon algebra alone (or chiefly). Diophantus uses only one unknown quantity, ὁ ἀριθμός or ὁ ἀόριστος ἀριθμός, symbolizing it by ς′ or ς⁰′.[4] The square he calls δύναμις, *power* (its symbol δ͡), the cube κύβος (κ͡), and he also gives names to the fourth, fifth, and sixth powers. He has symbols for equality and for subtraction, and the modern expression $x^3 - 5x^2 + 8x - 1$ he would write

---

[1] Cantor, I, p. 377; Gow, p. 106.

[2] Cantor, I, p. 374; Beman, W. W., vice-presidential address, Section A, American Assoc. Adv. Sci., 1897.

[3] Heath, T. L., Diophantos of Alexandria, Cambridge, 1885; Gow, p. 100; Hankel and Cantor, of course, on all such names. De Morgan has a good article on Diophantus in Smith's Dict. of Gk. and Rom. Biog., a work containing several valuable biographies of mathematicians.
[4] For discussion of the symbol, see Heath, p. 56–60.

in the form $\kappa^{\upsilon}\bar{\alpha}\varsigma^{o\iota}\bar{\eta}\eta\delta^{\upsilon}\bar{\epsilon}\mu^{o}\bar{\alpha},$[1] a form not particularly more difficult than our own. The nature of his solutions will be understood from the following example, modern symbols being here used: "Find two numbers whose sum is 20 and the difference of whose squares is 80.

Put for the numbers $x + 10$, $10 - x$.

Squaring, we have $x^2 + 20x + 100$, $x^2 + 100 - 20x$.

The difference,　　　$40x = 80$.

Dividing,　　　　　　$x = 2$.

Result, greater is 12, less is 8."[2] This does not differ from our own present plan, although being less troubled by negative numbers we would probably say:

$$(20 - x)^2 - x^2 = 80.$$
$$\therefore 400 - 40x = 80.$$
$$\therefore 320 = 40x.$$
$$\therefore 8 = x, \text{ and } 20 - x = 12.$$

It thus appears that Diophantus understood the simple equation fairly well. The quadratic, however, he solved merely by rule. Thus he says, "$84x^2 - 7x = 7$, therefore $x = \frac{1}{3}$," giving but one of the two roots. Of the negative quantity he apparently knew nothing, and his work was limited, with the exception of a single easy cubic, to equations of the first two degrees. His favorite subject was indeterminate

[1] Heath, p. 72.　　　　　　[2] Ib., p. 76.

equations of the second degree, and on this account indeterminate equations in general are often designated as Diophantine. One of the most remarkable facts connected with the work of Diophantus is that, although most other algebraists down to about 1700 A.D., used geometric figures more or less, he nowhere appeals to them.[1] Summing up the work of the Greeks in this field, we may say that they could solve simple and quadratic equations, could represent geometrically the positive roots of the latter, and could handle indeterminate equations of the first and second degrees.

Oriental algebra — It was long after the time of Diophantus, and in a country well removed from Greece, and among a race greatly differing from the Hellenic people, that algebra took its next noteworthy step forward. It is true that Aryabhatta, a Hindu mathematician (b. 476), made some contributions to the subject not long after Diophantus wrote, but he did not carry the subject materially farther than the Greeks,[2] and it was not until about 800 A.D. that the next real advance was made.

When under the Calif Al-Mansur (the Victorious, c. 712 – 775) it was decided to build a new capital for

---

[1] Gow, p. 114 n.; Hankel, p. 162.

[2] Cantor, I, p. 575; Hankel, p. 172; Matthiessen, L., Grundzüge der antiken und modernen Algebra der litteralen Gleichungen, 2. Ausg., Leipzig, 1896, p. 967.

the Mohammedan rulers, the site of an ancient city dating back to Nebuchadnezzar's time, on the banks of the Tigris, was chosen. To this new city of Bagdad were called scholars from all over the civilized world, Christians from the West, Buddhists from the East, and such Mohammedans as might, in those early days of that religion, be available. With this enlightened educational policy, a policy opposed to in-breeding and to sectarianism, Bagdad soon grew to be the centre of the civilization of that period. Under Harun-al-Raschid (Aaron the Just, calif from 786 to 809) the califate reached the summit of its power, extending from the Indus to the Pillars of Hercules. His son Al-Mamun (786 – 833), whom Sismondi calls "the father of letters and the Augustus of Bagdad," brought Arab learning to its height. It was during his reign, in the first quarter of the ninth century, that there came from Kharezm (Khwarazm), a province of Central Asia, a mathematician known from his birthplace as Al-Khowarazmi.[1] He wrote the first general work of any importance on algebra, that of Diophantus being largely confined to a single class of equations, and to the science he gave its present name. He designated it *Ilm al-jabr wa'l mu-qabalah*, that is, "the science of redintegration and equation," a title which appeared in the thirteenth century Latin as *ludus algebræ almucgrabalæque*, in six-

[1] Abu Ja'far Mohammed ben Musa al-Khowarazmi, Abu Ja'far Mohammed son of Moses from Kharezm. Cantor, I, p. 670.

teenth century English as *algicbar and almachabel*, and in modern English as *algebra*.[1] So important were also his writings on arithmetic, that just as "Euclid" is in England a synonym for elementary geometry, so *algoritmi* (from *al-Khowarazmi*) was for a long time a synonym for the science of numbers, a word which has survived in our *algorism* (algorithm).

Al-Khowarazmi discussed the solution of simple and quadratic equations in a scientific manner, distinguishing six different classes, much as our old-style writers on arithmetic distinguished the various "cases" of percentage. His classes were, in modern notation, $ax^2 = bx$, $ax^2 = c$, $bx = c$, $x^2 + bx = c$, $x^2 + c = bx$, $x^2 = bx + c$,[2] showing how primitive was the science which could not grasp the general type $ax^2 + bx + c = 0$. His method of stating and solving a problem may be seen in the following:[3] "Roots and squares are equal to numbers; for instance, one square and ten roots of the same amount to thirty-nine;[4] that is to say, what must be the square which, when increased by ten of its own roots, amounts to thirty-nine? The solution is this: you halve the number of the roots, which in the present instance yields five. This you multiply by itself; the product is twenty-five. Add

---

[1] See also Heath, p. 149.   [2] Cantor, I, p. 676.

[3] From The Algebra of Mohammed-ben-Musa, edited and translated by Frederic Rosen, London, 1831.

[4] *I.e.*, $x^2 + 10x = 39$.

this to thirty-nine; the sum is sixty-four. Now take the root[1] of this, which is eight, and subtract from it half the number of the root, which is five; the remainder is three. This is the root of the square for which you sought."[2] The solution merely sets forth without explanation the rule expressed in our familiar formula for the solution of $x^2 + px + q = 0$, i.e., $x = -\dfrac{p}{2} \pm \tfrac{1}{2} \sqrt{p^2 - 4q}$, except that only one root is given. He however recognizes the existence of two roots where both are real and positive, as in the equation $x^2 + 21 = 10x$.[3] In practice he commonly uses but one root.

Sixteenth century algebra — Algebra made little advance, save in the way of the solution of a few special cubics, from the time of Mohammed ben Musa to the sixteenth century, seven hundred years. Its course had run from Egypt to Greece, and from Greece (and Grecian Alexandria) to Persia. It now transfers itself from Persia to Italy and works slowly northward.

In a famous work printed in Nürnberg in 1545, the "Ars magna,"[4] Cardan gives a complete solution of a cubic equation; that is, he solves an equation of the

---

[1] *I.e.*, the square root.

[2] The successive steps are as follows: $\tfrac{1}{2}$ of $10 = 5$; $5 \cdot 5 = 25$; $25 + 39 = 64$; $\sqrt{64} = 8$; $8 - 5 = 3$.

[3] Rosen, p. 11.

[4] Hieronymi Cardani, præstantissimi mathematici, philosophi, ac medici, Artis Magnæ, sive de regvlis algebraicis, Lib. unus.

form $x^3 + px = q$, to which all other cubics can be reduced. He mentions, however, his indebtedness to earlier writers, though not as generously as seems to have been their due.[1]

This is not the place to consider the relative claims of Cardan, Tartaglia (Tartalea), Ferro (Ferreus), and Fiori (Florido). Cardan seems to have obtained Tartaglia's solution of the cubic under pledge of secrecy and then to have published it. But however this was, by the middle of the sixteenth century the cubic equation was solved, and Ludovico Ferrari at about the same time solved the quartic.

Algebra had now reached such a point that mathematicians were able to solve, in one way or another, general equations of the first four degrees. Thereafter the chief improvements were (1) in symbolism, (2) in understanding the number system of algebra, (3) in finding approximate roots of higher numerical equations, (4) in simplifying the methods of attacking equations, and (5) in the study of algebraic forms. For the purposes of elementary algebra we need at this time to speak only of the first three.

---

[1] Scipio Ferreus Bononiensis iam annis ab hinc triginta ferme capitulum hoc inuenit, tradidit uero Anthonio Mariæ Florido Veneto, qui cũ in certamen cũ Nicolao Tartalea Brixellense aliquando uenisset, occasionem dedit, ut Nicolaus inuenerit, & ipse, qui cum nobis rogantibus tradidisset, *suppressa demonstratione*, freti hoc auxilio, demonstrationem quæsiuimus, eamque in modos, quod difficillimum fuit, redactam sic subiecimus. Fol. 29, v.

Growth of symbolism — Algebra, as is readily seen, is very dependent upon its symbolism. Its history has been divided into three periods, of rhetorical, of syncopated, and of symbolic algebra. The rhetorical algebra is that in which the equation is written out in words, as in the example given on p. 152 from Al-Khowarazmi; the syncopated, that in which the words are abbreviated, as in most of the example given on p. 149 from Diophantus; the symbolic, that in which an arbitrary shorthand is used, as in our common algebra of to-day.

The growth of symbolism has been slow. From the radical sign of Chuquet (1484), R^4. 10, through various other forms, as $\sqrt{\frac{3}{3}}$ 10, to our common symbol, $\sqrt[4]{10}$ and to the more refined $10^{\frac{1}{4}}$, which is only slowly becoming appreciated in elementary schools, is a tedious and a wandering path. So from Cardan's

cubus p 6. rebus æqualis 20, for $x^3 + 6x = 20$,

through Vieta's

$1C - 8Q + 16N$ æqu. 40, for $x^3 - 8x^2 + 16x = 40$,

and Descartes's

$$x^2 \infty ax - bb, \text{ for } x^2 = ax - b^2,$$

and Hudde's

$$x^3 \infty qx.r, \text{ for } x^3 = qx + r, [1]$$

---

[1] Beman and Smith's translation of Fink's History of Mathematics, p. 108.

has likewise been a long and tiresome journey. Such simple symbols as the $\times$ for multiplication,[1] and the still simpler dot used by Descartes, the $=$ for equality,[2] the x^{-n} for $\frac{1}{x^n}$,[3] these all had a long struggle for recognition. Even now the symbol $\div$ has only a limited acceptance in the mathematical world, and there are three widely used forms for the decimal point.[4] Thus symbolism has been a subject of slow growth, and we are still in the period of unrest.

We may, however, assign to the Frenchman Vieta[5] the honor of being the founder of symbolic algebra in large measure as we recognize it to-day. His first book on algebra, " In artem analyticam isagoge," appeared in 1591.[6] Laisant thus summarizes his contribution : " He it is who should be looked upon as the founder of algebra as we conceive it to-day. The powerful impulse which he gave consisted in this, that while unknown quantities had already been represented by letters to facilitate writing, it was he who applied the same method to known quantities as well. From that day, when the search for values gave way to the search for the operations to be performed, the idea of the mathematical

---

[1] First used by Oughtred in 1631.

[2] Recorde, 1556. [3] Wallis.

[4] $2\frac{1}{2}$ is usually written 2.5 in America, 2·5 in England, 2,5 on the Continent.

[5] François Viète, 1540–1603.

[6] Cantor, II, p. 577; for a general summary of his work, see p. 595.

function enters into the science, and this is the source of its subsequent progress." [1]

Number systems — The difficulty of understanding the number systems of algebra has been, perhaps, the greatest obstacle to its progress. The primitive, natural number is the positive integer. So long as the world met only problems which may be represented by the modern form $ax + b = c$, where $c > b$ and $c - b$ is a multiple of a, as in $3x + 2 = 11$, these numbers sufficed. But when problems appeared which involve the form of equation $ax = b$ where b is not a multiple of a, as in $3x = 1$, or 2, or 5, then other kinds of number are necessary, the unit fraction, the general proper fraction, and the improper fraction or mixed number. We have seen (Chap. III) how the world had to struggle for many centuries before it came to understand numbers of this kind. It was only by an appeal to graphic methods (the representation of numbers by lines) that the fraction came to be understood. When, further, problems requiring the solution of an equation like $x^n = a$, a not being an nth power, as in $x^2 = 2$, still a new kind of number was necessary, the real and irrational number, a form which the Greeks interpreted geometrically for square and cube roots.

The next step led to equations like $x + a = b$, with $a > b$, as in $x + 5 = 2$, a form which for many centuries baffled mathematicians because they could not bring

[1] La Mathématique, p. 55.

themselves to take the step into the domain of negative numbers. It was not until the genius of Descartes (1637) more completely grasped the idea of the one-to-one correspondence between algebra and geometry, that the negative number was taken out of the domain of *numeræ fictæ*[1] and made entirely real. One more step was, however, necessary for the solution of equations of the form $x^n + a = 0$. What to do with an equation like $x^2 + 4 = 0$ was still an unanswered question. To say that $x = \sqrt{-4}$, or $2\sqrt{-1}$, or $\pm 2\sqrt{-1}$, avails nothing unless we know the meaning of the symbol "$\sqrt{-1}$." It was not until the close of the eighteenth century that any considerable progress was made in the interpretation of the symbol $a + b\sqrt{-1}$. In 1797 Caspar Wessel, a Norwegian, suggested the modern interpretation, and published a memoir upon complex numbers in the proceedings of the Royal Academy of Sciences and Letters of Denmark for 1797.[2] Not, however, until Gauss published his great memoir on the subject (1832) was the theory of the graphic representation of

[1] Cardan, Ars magna, 1545, Fol. 3, v.

[2] This has recently been republished in French translation, under the title Essai sur la réprésentation analytique de la direction, Copenhague, 1897, with a historical preface by H. Valentiner. For a valuable summary of the history, see the vice-presidential address of Professor Beman, Section A of the American Assoc. Adv. Sci., 1897. A brief summary is also given in the author's History of Modern Mathematics, in Merriman and Woodward's Higher Mathematics, New York, 1896.

the complex number generally known to the mathematical world. Elementary text-book writers still seem indisposed to give the subject place, although its presentation is as simple as that of negative numbers.[1]

For the purposes of elementary teaching only a single other historical question demands consideration, the approximate solution of numerical equations, and even this is rather one of arithmetic than of algebra. Algebra has proved that there is no way of solving the general equation of degree higher than four; that is, that by the common operations of algebra we can solve the equation

$$ax^4 + bx^3 + cx^2 + dx + e = 0,$$

but that we cannot solve the equation

$$ax^5 + bx^4 + cx^3 + dx^2 + ex + f = 0.[2]$$

We can, however, approximate the real roots of any numerical algebraic equation, and this suffices for practical work. That is, we can find that one root of the equation

$$x^5 + 12x^4 + 59x^3 + 150x^2 + 210x - 207 = 0$$

is $\quad\quad\quad\quad\quad 0.638605803 +,$

but we have no formula for solving such equations by algebraic operations as we have for solving

$$x^2 + px + q = 0.$$

---

[1] For an elementary treatment, see Beman and Smith's Algebra, Boston, 1900.

[2] For historical résumé, see the author's History of Modern Mathematics already cited, p. 519.

The simple method now generally used for this approximation is due to an Englishman, W. G. Horner, who published it in 1819, and it now appears in elementary works in English as "Horner's method." Foreign writers have, however, been singularly slow in recognizing its value.

CHAPTER VII

ALGEBRA, — WHAT AND WHY TAUGHT

Algebra defined — In Chapter VI the growth of algebra was considered in a general way, assuming that its nature was fairly well known. Nor is it without good reason that this order was taken, for the definition of the subject is best understood when considered historically. But before proceeding to discuss the teaching of the subject it is necessary to examine more carefully into its nature.

It is manifestly impossible to draw a definite line between the various related sciences, as between botany and zoölogy, between physics and astronomy, between algebra and arithmetic, and so on. The child who meets the expression $2 \times (?) = 8$, in the first grade, has touched the elements of algebra. The student of algebra who is called upon to simplify

$$(2 + \sqrt{3})/(2 - \sqrt{3})$$

is facing merely a problem of arithmetic. In fact, a considerable number of topics which are properly parts of algebra, as the treatment of proportion, found lodgment in arithmetic before its sister science became generally known; while much of arithmetic, like the theory of irrational (including complex) numbers, has found place in algebra simply because it was not much needed in practical arithmetic.[1]

Recognizing this laxness of distinction between the two sciences, Comte[2] proposed to define algebra " as having for its object the resolution of equations; taking this expression in its full logical meaning, which signifies the transformation of implicit functions into equivalent explicit ones.[3] In the same way arithmetic may be defined as destined to the determination of the values of functions. Henceforth, therefore, we will briefly say that *Algebra is the Calculus of Functions*, and *Arithmetic the Calculus of Values*." [4]

Of course this must not be taken as a definition universally accepted. As a prominent writer upon "methodology" says: " It is very difficult to give a

---

[1] Teachers who care to examine one of the best elementary works upon arithmetic in the strict sense of the term, should read Tannery, Jules, Leçons d'Arithmétique théorique et pratique, Paris, 1894.

[2] The Philosophy of Mathematics, translated from the Cours de Philosophie positive, by W. M. Gillespie, New York, 1851, p. 55.

[3] *I.e.*, in $x^2 + px + q = 0$ we have an implicit function of x equated to zero ; this equation may be so transformed as to give the explicit function

$$x = -\frac{p}{2} \pm \tfrac{1}{2}\sqrt{p^2 - 4\,q},$$

and this transformation belongs to the domain of algebra.

[4] Laisant begins his chapter L'Algèbre (La Mathématique, p. 46) by reference to this definition, and makes it the foundation of his discussion of the science.

good definition of algebra. We say that it is merely a generalized or universal arithmetic, or rather that 'it is the science of calculating magnitudes considered generally' (D'Alembert). But as Poinsot has well observed, this is to consider it under a point of view altogether too limited, for algebra has two distinct parts. The first part may be called universal arithmetic. . . . The other part rests on the theory of combinations and arrangement. . . . We may give the following definition. . . . Algebra has for its object the generalizing of the solutions of problems relating to the computation of magnitudes, and of studying the composition and transformations of formulae to which this generalization leads."[1] The best of recent English and French elementary algebras make no attempt at defining the subject.[2]

The function — Taking Comte's definition as a point of departure, it is evident that one of the first steps in the scientific teaching of algebra is the fixing of the idea of *function*. How necessary this is, apart from all question of definition, is realized by all advanced teachers. "I found," says Professor Chrystal, "when I first tried to teach university students coördinate geometry, that I had to go back and

[1] Dauge, Félix, Cours de Méthodologie Mathématique, 2. éd., Gand et Paris, 1896, p. 103.
[2] Chrystal, G., 2 vols. 2 ed., Edinburgh, 1889. Bourlet, C., Leçons d'Algèbre élémentaire, Paris, 1896.

teach them algebra over again. The fundamental idea of an integral function of a certain degree, having a certain form and so many coefficients, was to them as much an unknown quantity as the proverbial x."[1]

Happily this is not only pedagogically one of the first steps, but practically it is a very easy one because of the abundance of familiar illustrations. "Two general circumstances strike the mind; one, that all that we see is subjected to continual transformation, and the other that these changes are mutually interdependent."[2] Among the best elementary illustrations are those involving time; a stone falls, and the distance varies as the time, and *vice versa;* we call the distance a function of the time, and the time a function of the distance. We take a railway journey; the distance again varies as the time, and again time and distance are functions of each other. Similarly, the interest on a note is a function of the time, and also of the rate and the principal.

This notion of function is not necessarily foreign to the common way of presenting algebra, except that here the idea is emphasized and the name is made prominent. Teachers always give to beginners problems of this nature: Evaluate $x^2 + 2x + 1$ for $x = 2$, 3, etc., which is nothing else than finding the

---

[1] Presidential address, 1885.   [2] Laisant, p. 46.

value of a function for various values of the variable. Similarly, to find the value of $a^3 + 3\,a^2b + 3\,ab^2 + b^3$ for $a = 1$, $b = 2$, is merely to evaluate a certain function of a and b, or, as the mathematician would say, $f(a,\,b)$, for special values of the variables. It is thus seen that the emphasizing of the nature of the function and the introduction of the name and the symbol are not at all difficult for beginners, and they constitute a natural point of departure. The introduction to algebra should therefore include the giving of values to the quantities which enter into a function, and thus the evaluation of the function itself.

Having now defined algebra as the study of certain functions,[1] which includes as a large portion the solution of equations, the question arises as to its value in the curriculum.

Why studied — Why should one study this theory of certain simple functions, or seek to solve the quadratic equation, or concern himself with the highest common factor of two functions? It is the same question which meets all branches of learning, — *cui bono?* Why should we study theology, biology, geology — God, life, earth? What doth it profit to know music, to appreciate Pheidias, to stand before the façade at Rheims, or to wonder

---

[1] *Certain* functions, for functions are classified into algebraic and transcendental, and with the latter elementary algebra concerns itself but little. *E.g.*, algebra solves the algebraic equation $x^a = b$, but with the transcendental equation $a^x = b$ it does not directly concern itself.

at the magic of Titian's coloring? As Malesherbes remarked on Bachet's commentary on Diophantus, "It won't lessen the price of bread;"[1] or as D'Alembert retorts from the mathematical side, *à propos* of the Iphigénie of Racine, "What does this prove?"

Professor Hudson has made answer: "To pursue an intellectual study because it 'pays' indicates a sordid spirit, of the same nature as that of Simon, who wanted to purchase with money the power of an apostle. The real reason for learning, as it is for teaching algebra, is, that it is a part of Truth, the knowledge of which is its own reward.

"Such an answer is rarely satisfactory to the questioner. He or she considers it too vague and too wide, as it may be used to justify the teaching and the learning of any and every branch of truth; and so, indeed, it does. A true education should seek to give a knowledge of every branch of truth, slight perhaps, but sound as far as it goes, and sufficient to enable the possessor to sympathize in some degree with those whose privilege it is to acquire, for themselves at least, and it may be for the world at large, a fuller and deeper knowledge. A person who is wholly ignorant of any great subject of knowledge is like one who is born without a limb, and is thereby cut off from many of the pleasures and interests of life.

---

[1] "Le commentaire de Bachet sur Diophante ne fera pas diminuer le prix du pain."

"I maintain, therefore, that algebra is not to be taught on account of its utility, not to be learnt on account of any benefit which may be supposed to be got from it; but because it is a part of mathematical truth, and no one ought to be wholly alien from that important department of human knowledge."[1]

The sentiments expressed by Professor Hudson will meet the approval of all true teachers. Algebra is taught but slightly for its utilities to the average citizen. Useful it is, and that to a great degree, in all subsequent mathematical work; but for the merchant, the lawyer, the mechanic, it is of slight practical value.

Training in logic — But Professor Hudson states, in the above extract, only a part of the reason for teaching the subject — that we need to know of it as a branch of human knowledge. This might permit, and sometimes seems to give rise to, very poor teaching. We need it also as an exercise in logic, and this gives character to the teacher's work, raising it from the tedious, barren, mechanical humdrum of rule-imparting to the plane of true education. Professor Hudson expresses this idea later in his paper when he says, "Rules are always mischievous so long as they are necessary: it is only when they are superfluous that they are useful."

Thus to be able to extract the fourth root of $x^4 + 4x^3 + 6x^2 + 4x + 1$ is a matter of very little moment. The

[1] Hudson, W. H. H., On the Teaching of Elementary Algebra, paper before the Educational Society (London), Nov. 29, 1886.

pupil cannot use the result, nor will he be liable to use the process in his subsequent work in algebra. But that he should have power to grasp the logic involved in extracting this root is very important, for it is this very mental power, with its attendant habit of concentration, with its antagonism to wool-gathering, that we should seek to foster. To have a rule for finding the highest common factor of three functions is likewise a matter of little importance, since the rule will soon fade from the memory, and in case of necessity a text-book can easily be found to supply it; but to follow the logic of the process, to keep the mind intent upon the operation while performing it, herein lies much of the value of the subject, — here is to be sought its chief *raison d'être*.

Hence the teacher who fails to emphasize the idea of algebraic function fails to reach the pith of the science. The one who seeks merely the answers to a set of unreal problems, usually so manufactured as to give rational results alone, instead of seeking to give that power which is the chief reason for algebra's being, will fail of success. It is of little value in itself that the necessary and sufficient condition for $x^3 - x = 0$ is that $x = 0$, $x = 1$, $x = -1$; but it is of great value to see *why* this is such condition.

Practical value — Although for most people algebra is valuable only for the culture which it brings, at the same time it has never failed to appeal to the common sense of practical men as valuable for other reasons. All subsequent mathematics, the theory of astronomy, of physics, and of mechanics, the fashioning of guns, the computations of ship building, of bridge building, and of engineering in general, these rest upon the operations of elementary algebra. Napoleon, who was not a man to overrate the impractical, thus gave a statesman's estimate of the science of which algebra is a corner-stone: "The advancement, the perfecting of mathematics, are bound up with the prosperity of the State."[1]

Ethical value — There are those who make great claims for algebra, as for other mathematical disciplines, as a means of cultivating the love for truth, thus giving to the subject a high ethical value. Far be it from teachers of the science to gainsay all this, or to antagonize those who follow Herbart in bending all education to bear upon the moral building-up of the child. But we do well not to be extreme in our claims for mathematics. Cauchy, one of the greatest of the French mathematicians of the nineteenth century, has left us some advice along this line: "There are other truths than the truths of algebra, other realities than those of sensible objects. Let us cultivate with zeal the mathematical sciences, without seeking to extend them beyond their own limits; and let us not imagine that we can attack history by formulae, or employ the theorems of

[1] L'avancement, le perfectionnement des mathématiques sont liés à la prospérité de l'État.

algebra and the integral calculus in the study of ethics." For illustration, one has but to read Herbart's Psychology to see how absurd the extremes to which even a great thinker can carry the applications of mathematics.

Of course algebra has its ethical value, as has every subject whose aim is the search for truth. But the direct application of the study to the life we live is very slight. When we find ourselves making great claims of this kind for algebra, it is well to recall the words of Mme. de Staël, paying her respects to those who, in her day, were especially clamorous to mathematicize all life: "Nothing is less applicable to life than mathematical reasoning. A proposition in mathematics is decidedly false or true; everywhere else the true is mixed in with the false."

When studied — Having framed a tentative definition of algebra, and having considered the reason for studying the science, we are led to the question as to the place of algebra in the curriculum.

At the present time, in America, it is generally taken up in the ninth school year, after arithmetic and before demonstrative geometry. Since most teachers are tied to a particular local school system, as to matters of curriculum, the question is not to them a very practical one. But as a problem of education it has such interest as to deserve attention.

Quoting again from Professor Hudson: "The beginnings of all the great divisions of knowledge should find their place in a perfect curriculum of education; at first something of everything, in order later to learn everything of something. But it is needless to say all subjects cannot be taught at once, all cannot be learnt at once; there is an order to be observed, a certain sequence is necessary, and it may well be that one sequence is more beneficial than another. My opinion is that, of this ladder of learning, Algebra should form one of the lowest rungs; and I find that in the *Nineteenth Century* for October, 1886, the Bishop of Carlisle, Dr. Harvey Goodwin, quotes Comte, the Positivist Philosopher, with approval, to the same effect.

"The reason is this: Algebra is a certain science, it proceeds from unimpeachable axioms, and its conclusions are logically developed from them; it has its own special difficulties, but they are not those of weighing in the balance conflicting probable evidence which requires the stronger powers of a maturer mind. It is possible for the student to plant each step firmly before proceeding to the next, nothing is left hazy or in doubt; thus it strengthens the mind and enables it better to master studies of a different nature that are presented to it later. Mathematics give power, vigor, strength, to the mind; this is commonly given as the reason for studying them. I give it as the reason for studying Algebra early, that is to say, for beginning to study it early; it is not necessary, it is not even possible, to finish the study of Algebra before commencing another. On the other hand, it is not necessary to be always teaching Algebra; what we have to do, as elementary teachers, is to guide our pupils to learn enough to leave the door open for further progress; we take them over the threshold, but not into the innermost sanctuary.

"The age at which the study of Algebra should begin differs in each individual case. . . . It must be rare that a child younger than nine years of age is fit to begin; and although the subject, like most others, may be taken up at any age, there is no superior limit; my own opinion is, that it would be seldom advisable to defer the commencement to later than twelve years."

This opinion has been quoted not for indorsement, but rather as that of a teacher and a mathematician of such prominence as to command respect. The idea is quite at variance with the American custom of beginning at about the age of fourteen or fifteen, or even later, and it raises a serious question as to the wisdom of our course. Indeed, not only is the question of age involved, but also that of general sequence. Are we wise in teaching arithmetic for eight years, dropping it and taking up algebra, dropping that and taking up geometry, with possibly a brief review of all three later, at the close of the high school course?

Fully recognizing the folly of a dogmatic statement of what is the best course, and hence desiring to avoid any such statement, the author does not hesitate to express his personal conviction that the present plan is not a wisely considered one. He feels that with elementary arithmetic should go, as already set forth in Chapter V, the simple equation,[1] and also metrical geometry with the models in hand; that algebra and arithmetic should run side by side during the eighth and ninth years, and that demonstrative geometry should run side by side with the latter part of algebra. One of the best of recent series of text-books, Holzmüller's,[2] follows this general plan, and the arrangement has abundant justification in most of the Continental programmes. It is so scientifically sound that it must soon find larger acceptance in English and American schools.

Arrangement of text-books — As related to the subject just discussed, a word is in place concerning the arrangement of our text-books. It is probable that we shall long continue our present general plan of having a book on arithmetic, another on algebra, and still another on geometry, thus creating a mechanical barrier between these sciences. We shall also, doubt-

---

[1] There is a good article upon this by Oberlehrer Dr. M. Schuster, Die Gleichung in der Schule, in Hoffmann's Zeitschrift, XXIX. Jahrg. (1898), p. 81.

[2] Leipzig, B. G. Teubner.

less, combine in each book the theory and the exer-cises for practice, because this is the English and American custom, giving in our algebras a few pages of theory followed by a large number of exercises. The Continental plan, however, inclines decidedly toward the separation of the book of exercises from the book on the theory, thus allowing frequent changes of the former. It is doubtful, however, if the plan will find any favor in America, its advan-tages being outweighed by certain undesirable fea-tures.[1] There is, perhaps, more chance for the adoption of the plan of incorporating the necessary arithmetic, algebra, and geometry for two or three grades into a single book, a plan followed by Holzmüller with much success.

[1] An interesting set of statistics with respect to German text-books is given by J. W. A. Young in Hoffmann's Zeitschrift, XXIX. Jahrg. (1898), p. 410, under the title, Zur mathematischen Lehrbücherfrage.

W. W. SAWYER

MATHEMATICIAN'S
DELIGHT

PART I

THE APPROACH TO MATHEMATICS

CHAPTER 1

THE DREAD OF MATHEMATICS

'The greatest evil is fear.'
Epicurean Philosophy

THE main object of this book is to dispel the fear of mathematics. Many people regard mathematicians as a race apart, possessed of almost supernatural powers. While this is very flattering for successful mathematicians, it is very bad for those who, for one reason or another, are attempting to learn the subject.

Very many students feel that they will never be able to understand mathematics, but that they may learn enough to fool examiners into thinking they do. They are like a messenger who has to repeat a sentence in a language of which he is ignorant – full of anxiety to get the message delivered before memory fails, capable of making the most absurd mistakes in consequence.

It is clear that such study is a waste of time. Mathematical thinking is a tool. There is no point in acquiring it unless you mean to use it. It would be far better to spend time in physical exercise, which would at least promote health of body.

Further, it is extremely bad for human beings to acquire the habit of cowardice in any field. The ideal of mental health is to be ready to face any problem which life may bring – not to rush hastily, with averted eyes, past places where difficulties are found.

Why should such fear of mathematics be felt? Does it lie in the nature of the subject itself? Are great mathematicians essentially different from other people? Or does the fault lie mainly in the methods by which it is taught?

Quite certainly the cause does *not* lie in the nature of the subject itself. The most convincing proof of this is the fact that people in their everyday occupations – when they are making something – do, as a matter of fact, reason along lines *which are essentially the*

273

same as those used in mathematics: but they are unconscious of this fact, and would be appalled if anyone suggested that they should take a course in mathematics. Illustrations of this will be given later.

The fear of mathematics is a tradition handed down from days when the majority of teachers knew little about human nature, and nothing at all about the nature of mathematics itself. What they did teach was an imitation.

Imitation Subjects

Nearly every subject has a shadow, or imitation. It would, I suppose, be quite possible to teach a deaf and dumb child to play the piano. When it played a wrong note, it would see the frown of its teacher, and try again. But it would obviously have no idea of what it was doing, or why anyone should devote hours to such an extraordinary exercise. It would have learnt an imitation of music. And it would fear the piano exactly as most students fear what is supposed to be mathematics.

What is true of music is also true of other subjects. One can learn imitation history – kings and dates, but not the slightest idea of the motives behind it all; imitation literature – stacks of notes of Shakespeare's phrases, and a complete destruction of the power to enjoy Shakespeare. Two students of law once provided a good illustration: one learnt by heart long lists of clauses; the other imagined himself to be a farmer, with wife and children, and he related everything to this farm. If he had to draw up a will, he would say, 'I must not forget to provide for Minnie's education, and something will have to be arranged about that mortgage.' One moved in a world of half-meaningless words; the other lived in the world of real things.

The danger of parrot-learning is illustrated by the famous howler, 'The abdomen contains the stomach and the bowels, which are A, E, I, O and U.' What image was in the mind of the child who wrote this? Large metal letters in the intestines? Or no image at all? Probably it had heard so many incomprehensible statements from the teacher, that the bowels being A, E, I, O and

274

U seemed no more mysterious than other things heard in school.

A large proportion of examination papers contain mathematical errors which are at least as absurd as this howler, and the reason is the same – words which convey no picture, the lack of realistic thinking.

Parrot-learning always involves this danger. The deaf child at the piano, whatever discord it may produce, remains unaware of it. Real education makes howlers impossible, but this is the least of its advantages. Much more important is the saving of unnecessary strain, the achievement of security and confidence in mind. It is far easier to learn the real subject properly, than to learn the imitation badly. And the real subject is interesting. So long as a subject seems dull, you can be sure that you are approaching it from the wrong angle. All discoveries, all great achievements, have been made by men who delighted in their work. And these men were normal, they were no freaks or high-brows. Edison felt compelled to make scientific experiments in just the same way that other boys feel compelled to mess about with motor bicycles or to make wireless sets. It is easy to see this in the case of great scientists, great engineers, great explorers. But it is equally true of all other subjects.

To master anything – from football to relativity – requires effort. But it does *not* require *unpleasant* effort, drudgery. The main task of any teacher is to make a subject interesting. If a child left school at ten, knowing nothing of detailed information, but knowing the pleasure that comes from agreeable music, from reading, from making things, from finding things out, it would be better off than a man who left university at twenty-two, full of facts but without any desire to inquire further into such dry domains. Right at the beginning of any course there should be painted a vivid picture of the benefits that can be expected from mastering the subject, and at every step there should be some appeal to curiosity or to interest which will make that step worth while.

Bad teaching is almost entirely responsible for the dislike which is shown in such words as 'high-brow'. Children want to know things, they want to do things. Teachers do not have to put life into them: the life is there, waiting for an outlet. All that is needed is to preserve and to direct its flow.

Too often, unfortunately, teaching seems to proceed on the philosophy that adults have to do dull jobs, and that children should get used to dull work as quickly as possible. The result is an entirely justified hatred and contempt for all kinds of learning and intellectual life.

Many members of the teaching profession are already in revolt against the tradition of dull education. Some excellent teaching has been heard over the wireless. The same ideas, the same methods are being developed independently in all parts of the country. No claim for originality is therefore made in respect of this book. It is no more than an individual expression of a feeling shared by thousands.

In the following chapters I shall try to show what mathematics is about, how mathematicians think, when mathematics can be of some use. In such a short space it is impossible to go into details. If you want to master any special department of mathematics, you will certainly need text-books. But most text-books contain vast masses of information, the object of which is not always obvious. It would be useless to burden your memory with all this purposeless information. It would be like having a hammer so heavy that you could not lift it. Mathematics is like a chest of tools: before studying the tools in detail, a good workman should know the object of each, when it is used, how it is used, what it is used for.

CHAPTER 2

GEOMETRY – THE SCIENCE OF FURNITURE AND WALLS

'*So the Doctor buckled to his task again with renewed energy; to Euclid, Latin, grammar and fractions. Sam's good memory enabled him to make light of the grammar, and the fractions too were no*

*great difficulty, but the Euclid was an awful trial. He could not
make out what it was all about. He got on very well until he came
nearly to the end of the first book and then getting among the
parallelogram 'props' as we used to call them (may their fathers'
graves be defiled!) he stuck dead. For a whole evening did he pore
patiently over one of them till* AB, *setting to* CD, *crossed hands,
pousetted and whirled round ' in Sahara waltz' through his throbbing
head. Bed-time, but no rest! Who could sleep with that long-bodied
ill-tempered looking parallelogram* AH *standing on the bedclothes,
and crying out in tones loud enough to waken the house, that it
never had been, nor ever would be equal to the fat jolly square* CK?'

Henry Kingsley, *Geoffrey Hamlyn.*

In the previous chapter it was mentioned that people, in their
everyday life, used the same methods of reasoning as mathematicians, but that they did not realize this.

For instance, many people who would be paralysed if you said
to them, 'Kindly explain to me the geometrical construction for
a rectangle' would have no difficulty at all if you said, 'Please
tell me a good way to make a table.' A 'rectangle' means the
shape below –

and no one could make much of a table unless he understood
well what this shape was. Suppose for instance you had a table
like this

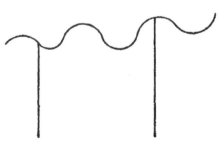

277

All the plates and tea-pots and milk-jugs would slide down into the hollows, or fall over, and altogether it would be very inconvenient. People who make tables are unanimous that the tops ought to be *straight*, not curved. Even if the top is straight, it may not be level; the table may look like this ⟋⟍. And when the top is right, the legs may still look queer, such as ⟋ ⟋ or ⟋⟍. In such cases the weight of the table-top would tend to break the joints. To avoid this, legs are usually made upright, and the table stands on the floor like this ⊓⊓.

Anyone who understands what a table should look like understands what a rectangle is. You will find a lot about rectangles in books on geometry, because this shape is so important in practical life – though the older geometry books give no hint of this reason *why* we study rectangles.

Another craft which uses rectangles is bricklaying. An ordinary brick has a rectangle on top, below, at the ends and sides. Why? It is easy to guess. The bricks have to be laid level, if they are not to slide. (Even in making walls from rough stone, such as the Yorkshire dry walls, one tries to build with level layers.) So that the bricks must fit in between two level lines. But it would still be possible to have fancy shapes for the ends –

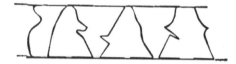

But this looks more like a jig-saw puzzle than a wall: the poor bricklayer would spend half his life looking for a brick that would fit. We want all the bricks to have the same shape. This can be done in several ways – ⫽⫽⫽⫽⫽ or ⦅⦅⦅⦅⦅. These would make ragged ends to the wall, and if two walls met there would be open spaces to fill. By having the ordinary shape of brick, all these complications are avoided.

No one will have any difficulty in following such an argument. Why, then, do people dislike geometry? Partly because it is a mystery to them: they do not realize (and are not told) how close it lies to everyday life. Secondly, because mathematics is supposed to be *perfect*. There is nothing in the geometry book about shapes being 'nearly triangles' or 'almost rectangles', while it is quite common for a door or table to be just a little out of true. This perfection puts people off. You can have several tries at making a table, and each attempt may be an improvement on the last. You learn as you go along. By insisting on 'mathematical exactness', it is easy to close this great road of advance, Trial and Error. If you remember how close geometry is to carpentry, you will not fall into this mistake. If you have a problem which puzzles you, the first thing to do is to try a few experiments: when you have found a method that seems to work, you may be able to find a logical, 'exact', 'perfect' justification for your method: you may be able to prove that it is right. But this perfection comes at the *end*: experiment comes at the beginning.

The first mathematicians, then, were practical men, carpenters and builders. This fact has left its mark on the very words used in the subject. What is a 'straight line'? If you look up 'straight' in the dictionary, you will find that it comes from the Old English word for 'stretched', while 'line' is the same word as 'linen', or 'linen thread'. A straight line, then, is a stretched linen thread – as anyone who is digging potatoes or laying bricks knows.

Euclid puts it rather differently. He says a straight line is the shortest distance between two points. But how do you find the shortest distance? If you take a tape-measure from one point to the other, and then pull one end as hard as you can, so that as little as possible of the tape-measure is left between the two points, you will have found the shortest path from one to the other. And the tape-measure will be 'stretched' in exactly the same way as the builder's or gardener's 'line'.

If you are told to define something, ask yourself, 'How would I make such a thing in practice?'

For instance, you might be asked to define a 'right angle'. A 'right angle' (in case the expression is new to you) means the figure formed when two lines meet as in a capital L, thus: |__ . You will find a right angle at every corner of this sheet of paper. On the other hand,/__ and __/ are not right angles.

How would you make a right angle? Suppose you want to tear

a sheet of note-paper into two neat halves: what do you do? You fold it over, and tear along the crease, which you know stands at the 'right' angle to the edge. If you fold it very carelessly, you do not get the 'right' angle, but something like ___/___ : too much paper is left on one side, too little on the other. We now see the special feature of a right angle – both sides of the crease *look the same*. If we had blots of ink on one side of the crease, we should get 'reflections' of these on the other when we unfolded the paper. The crease acts like a mirror. And the reflection of the edge of the paper – if we have the right angle – lies along the edge on the other side of the crease.

You can try this with a ruler or walking-stick. There is a position in which a stick can be held so that its reflection seems to be a continuation of the stick: you can look along the stick and its reflection, exactly as if you were squinting down the barrel of a rifle. The stick is then 'at right angles' to the mirror.

But suppose you are laying out a football field, and want to get a right angle. You cannot fold the touch-line over on to itself and notice where the crease comes! But this idea of a mirror shows a way of getting round the difficulty.

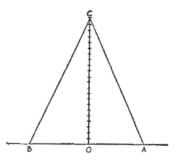

Suppose O is the point on the touch-line where you want to draw a line at right angles to the touch-line, OA. We know that a mirror, OC, in the correct position, would reflect the point A so that it appeared at B, also on the touch-line. If we folded the paper over the line OC, A would come on top of B. The line OA would just cover OB, and the line AC would just cover BC, after such folding.

But this suggests a way of finding the line OC. If we start at O, and measure OA, OB the same distance on opposite sides of O, we have A and its reflection, B. Since BC is the reflection of AC, both must be the same length. Take a rope of any convenient length, fasten one end to A, and walk round, scraping the other end of the rope in the ground. All the points on this 'scrape' will be a rope's length from A. Untie the rope from A, and fix it to B instead, and make another, similar scrape in the ground. Where the two scrapes cross, we have a point which is the same distance from B as it is from A. This will do for C. We drive a peg in

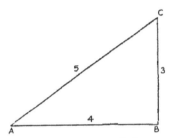

here, stretch a line from C to O, and whitewash along it.

You can easily see how the above method, suitable for football fields, can be translated into a method for drawing right angles on paper with ruler and compass.

But there is another, very remarkable, way, which is actually used for marking out football fields.

If you take three rods of lengths 3, 4, and 5 yards, and fit them together as shown in the figure, you will find that the angle at B turns out to be a right angle. No one could have guessed that this would be so. It seems to have been discovered about five thousand years ago, more or less by accident. It is not known who discovered it, but the discoverer was almost certainly someone engaged in the building trade – a workman or an architect. This way of making a right angle was used as part of the builder's craft: people did not ask why it was so, any more than a housewife asks why you use baking-powder. It was just known that you got good results if you used this method, and the Egyptians used it to make temples and pyramids with great success.

It is not known how far learned Egyptians bothered their heads trying to find an explanation of this fact, but certainly Greek travellers, who visited Egypt, found it a very intriguing and mysterious thing. Egyptian workmen saw nothing remarkable in it: if the Greeks asked them about it, they probably answered, 'Lor' bless you, it's always been done that way. How else would you do it?'

So the Greeks would go away still wondering, 'Why?' Why

3, 4, and 5? Why not 7, 8, and 9? Anyhow, what does happen if you try 7, 8, and 9? Or any other three numbers?

It would therefore be quite natural to start with fairly small numbers, and try making triangles, such as (1, 1, 1), (1, 1, 2), (1, 1, 3), (1, 2, 2), (2, 2, 2), etc. The Greeks had no Meccano – with Meccano it is easy to make such triangles quickly. How do they look?

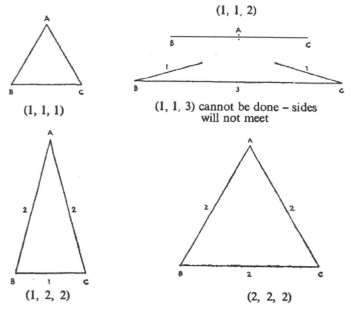

(1, 1, 2)

(1, 1, 1)

(1, 1, 3) cannot be done – sides will not meet

(1, 2, 2)

(2, 2, 2)

As soon as you start experimenting in this way, you begin to discover things. You sometimes find that it is impossible to make the triangle at all; e.g., (1, 1, 3), (1, 1, 4) and so on: in fact whenever one side (e. g., 3) is bigger than the other two sides (1 and 1) put together.

You may notice that doubling the sides of a triangle does not alter its shape: (2, 2, 2) looks much like (1, 1, 1).

Again the triangle (1, 2, 2) has a pleasing balanced appearance: if you turned it over, so that B and C changed places, it would still look just the same.

The more you experimented with drawing or making triangles, the more things you would notice about them. Not all these discoveries would be really new. For instance, we saw above that, in any triangle, AB plus AC must be bigger than BC. But this is not new. We know that the straight line BC is the shortest way from B to C, so naturally it is longer if we go from B to C via A, a distance equal to the sum of AB and AC. So that this particular result *could* have been found by reasoning: it follows from the fact that the straight line gives the shortest path between two points.

So that we can do two things in our study of the shapes of things. (i) We can discover a large number of facts. (ii) We can arrange them in a system, showing what follows from what.

Actually, these two things were done by the Greeks, and by 300 B.C. Euclid had written his famous book on geometry, putting all the facts known into the form of a system. In this book you will find why (3, 4, 5) gives a right-angled triangle; and it is shown that other triangles, such as (5, 12, 13) or (24, 25, 7) or (33, 56, 65), do the same.

But all this took time. The Great Pyramid was built in 3900 B.C., by rules based on practical experience: Euclid's system did not appear until *3,600 years later*. It is quite unfair to expect children to start studying geometry in the form that Euclid gave it. One cannot leap 3,600 years of human effort so lightly! The best way to learn geometry is to follow the road which the human race originally followed: *Do* things, *make* things, *notice* things, *arrange* things, and only then – *reason* about things.

Above all, do not try to hurry. Mathematics, as you can see, does not advance rapidly. The important thing is to be sure that you know what you are talking about: to have a clear picture in your mind. Keep turning things over in your mind until you have a vivid realization of each idea. Once you have learnt how to think in clear pictures, you will advance quickly, without strain. But it is fatal to advance and to leave the enemy – confused thought – in your rear. Rather than this, start again at the multiplication tables!

SOME EXPERIMENTS CONNECTED WITH GEOMETRY

1. A boy has a strip of wood, AC, which is 4 feet long. He wishes to join a second strip to it, as in the figure, so that a string, ABCD, passed round the outside, will form a rectangle.

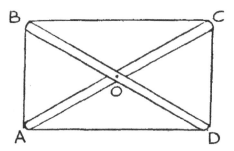

How long must he make the strip BD? At what point (O) must he nail the two strips together? Does it matter at what angle he places the two strips?

2. A flat piece of ground is to be covered with tiles. All the tiles must be the same shape and size, but it does not matter if there is a jagged edge on the outside border. Design as many different ways of doing this as you can. One example is shown in the drawing below.

3. A street lamp is 12 feet above the ground. A child, 3 feet in height, amuses itself by walking in such a way that the shadow of its head moves along lines chalked on the ground. How will it

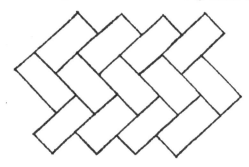

walk if the chalked line is (i) straight, (ii) a circle, (iii) a square? What is the rule connecting the size and shape of the child's track with those of the chalked line? (*Note* – Do not quarrel with any-

one about the answer to this, until you have actually made an experiment. A convenient form of experiment is to take an indoor lamp instead of the street lamp, and a pencil to represent the child. The pencil will record its own track as it moves.)

4. What difference would it make to the last question if the light came from the sun instead of from a lamp?

5. A man 6 feet tall stands at a distance of 10 feet from a lamp-post. The lamp is 12 feet above the ground. How long will the man's shadow be?

6. A hiker can see two church spires. One is straight in front of him. The other is directly to the left of him. He has a map on which the two churches are marked, but he has not the least idea of the direction in which he is facing, whether it is North or South, or any other point of the compass. What can he tell about where he is on the map? (Suggested method. Drive two

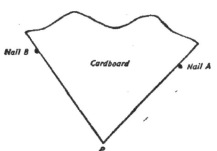

nails into a flat piece of wood. Let these represent the churches. Take a piece of cardboard, one corner of which is a right angle, and fit this between the nails, as in the figure. Then P is a possible position for the hiker. For if he is

285

looking in the direction PA, B will be directly on his left. Mark the position P on the wood. Slide the cardboard, and mark other possible positions in the same way. These marks all lie on a certain curve. What is the curve?)

7. In a miniature rifle-range, 25 yards long, it is desired to construct a moving target, to represent a lorry, 20 feet long and 15 feet high, half-a-mile away, moving at 20 miles an hour. The marksman is supposed to be in such a position that he sees one side of the lorry. How large should the model be, and how quickly should it move across the screen?

8. A spider wishes to crawl from one corner of a brick, A, to the opposite corner, B, by the shortest possible way. Which path should it take? The spider of course crawls over the surface of the brick – it cannot burrow through the brick.

(Material required – a number of bricks, having different shapes, and a piece of string to stretch from A to B. It is useful to make the bricks out of cardboard, by folding. After the

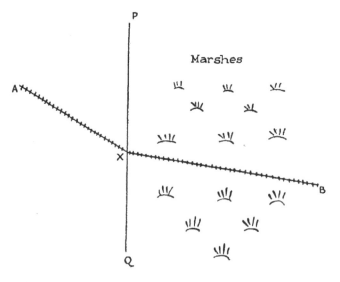

A to X, £10,000 a mile.   X to B, £20,000 a mile.
Find the best position for X.

286

shortest path has been found and marked on the cardboard, the cardboard can again be flattened out, and the form the path then takes should be noted.)

9. Get a globe of the world. Stretch a thread between two places. Make a note of the places over which the thread passes. Mark these places on a map of the world in an atlas (Mercator's projection). Notice how different the curve joining them is from a straight line drawn on the map. This fact is important for sailors, and airmen flying long distances ('Great Circle Navigation').

10. A railway is to be built joining two towns, A and B. The ground to the right of the line PQ is marshy, and as a result it

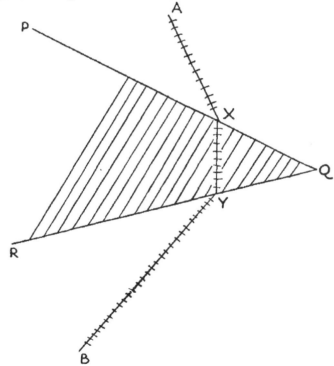

A to X £10,000 a mile. X to Y, £20,000 a mile. Y to B, £10,000 a mile. Find the best positions for X and Y.

costs twice as much to build one mile of railway here as it costs to build one mile on the ground to the left of PQ. Draw a number of possible routes for the railway from A to B, work out the costs of construction, and find, as nearly as you can, the route which makes the construction as cheap as possible. (See Fig., p. 20.)

(*Note* – You are *not* expected to answer this question purely by calculating. Draw a plan for yourself, put the towns A and B wherever you like, measure the lengths of any lines you want, assume that one mile of railway on the left of PQ costs £10,000. In real life, we want to get the answer by hook or by crook – by calculation, or by experiment, or by a mixture of the two. Never mind what Euclid said in 300 B.C.)

11. This question is similar to the last, except that the shape of the obstacle is different. A railway has to be built between A and B, but a wedge of difficult ground, PQR, lies between them. Find the best route for the railway. (This type of problem does occur in practice, when hilly country lies between towns. In this case, the extra expense would be due to the need to excavate cuttings.) (See Fig., p. 21.)

CHAPTER 3

THE NATURE OF REASONING

'*From my observations of men and boys I am inclined to think that my way of study is the common way, the natural way, and that the schoolmasters destroy it and replace it by something that conduces to mere learning.*' John Perry, 1901.

BERNARD SHAW once made an unkind remark to the effect that people who knew how to do anything went and did it; while those who did not know how to do anything were obliged to earn a living by teaching.

Actually, teaching is far harder than doing. You will find a hundred men who are brilliant footballers for every one that can teach you how to play the game well. You will find hundreds of clever children and hundreds of dull children, but you rarely find a child who was dull to begin with but became clever through the help of a teacher. But that is the test of a teacher. Most teachers who are honest with themselves are forced to admit that, in the main, the class would make the same progress if the teacher were not there at all, the clever remaining clever and the dull remaining dull.

Are there in fact two races of men, those who are born to succeed and those who are born to fail? Have the 'great men' some special way of thinking which ordinary people lack, and cannot understand?

There are, of course, certain differences between the bodies and brains which children inherit from their parents. There are cases of mental deficiency, where important glands fail to do their job, and the children have to be kept in special homes. It may be that glands, or other factors, set a natural limit to the powers of each one of us, and that it is foolish to strive for skill beyond this limit. This may be so. It is certain that not one person in a thousand makes full use of the glands and the brains actually possessed, or comes anywhere near the natural limit of intelligence. We certainly cannot explain it by glands if a person is bright and resourceful outside the classroom, and dull in everything connected with school. The reason must be sought elsewhere.

It is extremely interesting to inquire just what it is that the 'great man' or the successful performer does, that others fail to do. Just what qualities are necessary in order to play a game well, to be a painter, a musician, an engineer, a farmer or a mathematician? Can these qualities be developed by suitable exercises? Is it possible for an ordinary person, with determination, to acquire these qualities? When teachers are in a position to answer these questions, when everybody reaches the limit of his powers, the time will have come to talk about inherited differences in intelligence. But that will be a few centuries hence.

At present there are books which do really teach. It is better to spend hours searching a big library for such a book, rather than to read hundreds of books by second-rate authors. It is very unlikely that you or I possess any really original ideas. People seem to belong to certain types. If you feel strongly on any subject, the chances are that you will find some other individual has been concerned with exactly the same question, and you will find your own views worked out in his or her writings. You can then start to study the subject where that earlier worker left off.

One can often get help in teaching or learning a subject by reading books written on other subjects. In a library I came across a book, *Swimming for All*, by R. C. Venner (G. Bell & Sons, 1933). This book follows a method which could probably be applied to most other subjects. First the author explains the principles of swimming. He explains the difference between the movements which are needed in the water and those which we instinctively make as a result of living on dry land. Then he gives a series of experiments and exercises, by which one can convince oneself of the truth of his remarks, so that one not merely knows these facts, but comes to *feel* their truth and to do the right thing instinctively.

Writers on tennis make a remark which may serve as a parable. They say that you should not begin by trying to strike the ball into the court, but that you should begin by hitting it hard, and with a good style. Gradually you will find that the ball begins to land in the court. If you start by worrying about where the ball goes, you will always be a feeble player. Much the same holds in mathematics. The important thing is to learn how to strike out for yourself. Any mistakes you make can be corrected later. If you start by trying to be perfect, you will get nowhere. The road to perfection is by way of making mistakes.

This rather reminds me of a book on drawing, which I read several years ago. Unfortunately I did not make a note of the author's name.* He tried to teach drawing in such a way that his readers would be able to sit on the top of an omnibus and to record on paper the fleeting expressions of people's faces. According to him, you should use odd scraps of paper, and never alter a drawing. Throw it away if it goes wrong, and begin again. Do not bother if things are the right shape or not. Jot down

*Probably *Drawing for Children* by Vernon Blake. One remark quoted, however, is from L. Doust, *How to Sketch from Life*.

290

what you actually see, especially shadows. Do not draw lines unless you actually see them standing out. Regard your first drawings merely as sketches, noting what you actually see. Gradually you will find that the shapes of your drawings become more true to life, but even your earlier drawings, which have the wrong proportions, will suggest something solid and real. He gave very rough sketches to illustrate this fact. I know nothing about drawing, but if I wanted to learn, I should certainly learn this way.

In all subjects, it seems, there is a way of approach which is both interesting and encouraging. The 'great men' are often those who felt a strong interest in a subject and by accident, by experiment or through the influence of good teachers, hit on the correct approach. It is *ignorance of the way in which a subject is tackled* that causes geniuses to be regarded as a race apart. The more one studies the methods of the great, the more commonplace do these methods appear.

Very often anecdotes give us a false impression. There is a story about Newton and an apple: Newton saw an apple fall, and wondered *why* it fell – so we are told. It is extremely unlikely that Newton did anything of the sort. To this day we do not know *why* an apple falls. It is more likely that Newton thought rather as follows. What would happen if an apple were dropped from a very great height? Presumably it would still fall, however high, however far away from the earth it was taken. If not, there would be some height at which you suddenly found that the apple did not fall. This is possible, but not very likely. It seems probable, then, that, even if you went as far as the moon or the sun, you would still feel the pull of the earth, though perhaps not so strongly as you do here. Perhaps it is this pull which keeps the moon close to the earth, and keeps the earth circling round the sun? That at any rate was the conclusion to which the apple led Newton – that every piece of matter in the universe exerts a pull on every other piece, however far away it may be. No one denies the greatness of Newton. Equally, no one can say that there was anything superhuman about the type of argument he used.

Reasoning in Mathematics

Mathematics teaches us how to solve puzzles. Everyone knows that it is easy to do a puzzle if someone has told you the answer. That is simply a test of memory. You can claim to be a mathematician if, and only if, you feel that you will be able to solve a puzzle that neither you, nor anyone else, has studied before. That is the test of reasoning.

What exactly is this power of reasoning? Is it something separate from the other powers of our minds? Is it something fixed, or something that can be trained and encouraged? How do we come to possess such a power?

Mathematical reasoning does at first sight seem to be in a class by itself. It seems to find a place neither in the experimental sciences, nor in the creative arts.

Some subjects are clearly the result of experiment, or of experience. Chemistry deals with what happens when metals are dropped into liquids, or when the contents of one pot are mixed with those of another. Mechanics deals with the motion of solid objects. History records the actions of men. The study of languages deals with the words used by nations in different parts of the world. It is easy to see how the information contained in a book on chemistry, mechanics, history or French is obtained.

On the other hand there are the subjects (beloved by some people on which everybody disagrees. These are the subjects which do not depend on evidence at all – what you like, what you think ought to be done, the kind of person you admire, the political party you vote for: these are things for which you yourself take responsibility, they show what sort of person you are. You may be ready to fight to secure the type of world you think best: indeed, you should be. But you do not change your basic ideas of what is desirable as the result of argument and evidence. I suppose microbes have a vision of a world made safe for small-pox. We cannot *prove* that the world was not made for the benefit of microbes. All we can do is to use plenty of disinfectant.

Mathematics seems a peculiar subject. It is not a matter of taste. In it, more than in any other science, there is an answer which is right and an answer which is wrong. But, on the other hand, it does not seem to deal with anything definite. A great and important part of mathematics, for instance, deals with the square root of minus one – something which no one has ever seen or felt or tasted. Yet there is no sort of doubt about its properties.

In ancient times philosophers found it hard to explain man's powers of reasoning, and were led to more or less fantastic explanations. One such theory was that we lived in another world before we were born, and in that world were acquainted with the laws of arithmetic and geometry (how far the syllabus went I do not know). The object of education, in this world, was simply to awaken in us the memory of this knowledge.

One should not sneer at this ancient theory. It at least makes clear that education consists in co-operating with what is already inside a child's mind. A good teacher will nearly always be able to make his points simply by asking a class questions, by making the class realize clearly what they already know 'at the back of their minds'.

The clue which we possess today, which the old philosophers could hardly have guessed, comes from biology. It is now generally accepted that life has been on the earth for millions of years, and that we are born with instincts tested and tried in an age-long struggle for survival. On top of these instincts we have a training, given to us especially in the first five years of life, and based on traditions, some of which go back to the experience of thousands of years ago. By the time we are five years old we are, so to speak, a highly manufactured article, and it is generally after this age that we become aware of our ability to argue things out for ourselves.

If therefore we find in ourselves a strong desire to do a certain thing, or to believe a certain thing, it is at least possible that this desire exists in man, because it has enabled him to survive, because it has proved its worth in generations of struggle with the actual world. Those animals, those races survive, which *do* the correct thing. We should therefore expect human brains, human minds to be made on the whole in such a way as to produce *correct action* in any situation. We should *not* expect them to be made in such a way as to produce perfect, logical thought. In fact we often do find people doing the right thing for the wrong reason. A certain place is a centre of infection: savages know nothing of the causes of disease: they say that it is unlucky to go there, it is the abode of an evil spirit.

It was shown in Chapter 2 that geometry did, as a matter of fact, pass through the stage in which workmen *did* the right thing, but had no theory to explain why. Both geometry and arithmetic are closely connected with everyday life – geometry with building, arithmetic with money payment. If you give a tram-conductor threepence for two twopenny tickets, he is not prepared to believe that twice two being four is purely a university fad. He regards it as a fact, well established by the experience of everyday life.

It is now beginning to seem that mathematics is, like chemistry, something that we learn through experience of the real world. Some people will object strongly to this. They will say, 'I can imagine zinc being dropped into sulphuric acid and nothing happening. But can you imagine twice two being five?'

I certainly cannot imagine twice two being five. If a man claimed to perform miracles, and could turn twice two into five, I should give him full marks. It would impress me far more than any other miracle.

But that is not the point. The point is, *why* can we not imagine two twos making five?

There are two possible explanations. (i) We possess some mysterious faculty, given us in a previous life, or by other means. (ii) We cannot imagine twice two being five because in the whole of human history, twice two always has been four, and there has been no need for our minds to imagine it any other way.

The first explanation does not agree with the experience of most teachers. There may be people who possess a faculty of reasoning so perfect as to support this view: it would be interesting to know which schools and colleges they attend. In the works of the greatest mathematicians one finds evidence of blunders, of misunderstanding, of painful groping towards the truth.

Perhaps the greatest blow to the 'mysterious faculty' theory is the fact that mathematicians of today reject as untrue just those beliefs which earlier mathematicians most firmly believed. It was a custom at one time to say that some doctrine was true as certainly as the angles of a triangle added up to two right angles. If Einstein is right, the angles of a triangle do *not* add up to two right angles. Both the theory of relativity and quantum mechanics have destroyed long-cherished beliefs, and forced us to examine again the foundations of our belief.

If you accept Euclid's geometry because it agrees with what you can see of the shapes of things, you will not be unduly alarmed if someone suggests that Euclid may be wrong by a few millionths of an inch in certain places. For you cannot see a millionth of an inch, and Einstein's geometry only differs from Euclid's by millionths. But if you believe that Euclid represents absolute truth – then you are in a mess. Actually, Euclid himself only said, '*If* you admit certain things, then you must admit that the angles of a triangle add up to two right angles.'

On the other hand, there are interesting signs of the way in which human thought has been built up through daily experience. One such sign is to be found in the words we use. Try to imagine, if you can, a cave-man (or whoever it was that first developed language) trying to say to a friend, 'What this writer says about the square root of minus one does not agree with my philosophy at all.' How would he manage to make his friend understand what he meant by such abstract words as 'philosophy', 'minus one', 'agree', and so forth? Every child, in learning to speak, is faced by the same problem. How does it ever come to know the meaning of words, apart from the names of people and objects it can see?

It is instructive to take a dictionary, and to look up such words. Almost always, one finds that abstract words, the names of things which cannot be seen, come from words for actual objects or actions. Take, for instance, the word 'understand'. Both in German and English it is connected with the words 'to stand under'. In French, 'do you understand?' is 'comprenez-vous?', which means 'Can you take hold of that?' rather like the English phrase, 'Can you grasp that?' Still today, people make such remarks as 'Try to get that into your head.'

In learning to speak, a child follows much the same road. It learns the names of its parents and of household objects. It also learns words which describe its feelings, 'Are you hungry?' 'Are you tired?' 'He looks happy.' 'Don't be frightened.' 'Can't you remember?' 'Say you are sorry.'

Every philosopher, every professor, every school-teacher that ever lived began in this way – with words to describe things seen, or things felt. *And all the complicated ideas that have ever been thought of, rest upon this foundation.* Every writer or speaker that ever invented a new word had to explain its meaning by means of other words which people already knew and understood. It would be possible to draw a huge figure representing the English language, in which each word was represented by a block, resting on other blocks – the words used to explain it. At the bottom we should have blocks which did not rest on anything. These would be the words which we can understand directly from our own experience – what we see, what we feel, what we do.

For example, *philosophy*. Philosophy is what a *philosopher* does. Philosopher means '*a lover of wisdom*'. The meaning of *love*, and of being *wise*, we have to learn from everyday life.

What is true of philosophy is equally true of mathematics: its roots lie in the common experiences of daily life. If you can trace the way in which mathematical terms were gradually developed from everyday words, you can understand what mathematics is.

The essential point to grasp is that *mathematical reasoning* is not separate from the other powers of the mind, nor is mathematics separate from the rest of life. Quite the opposite: mathematics has grown from the rest of life, and reasoning has grown from experience.

Another sign of the way our minds are made is to be found in the law, well known to psychologists, 'There is nothing in imagination which was not previously in sense.' For instance, try to imagine a new colour. You will find that you are simply combining the effect of colours that you have already seen. Or try to imagine heaven, or a perfect world. You will find yourself putting together memories of your happiest moments, or turning upside down the things which have aroused your indignation. In a Scottish school, the children (sitting on hard seats) wrote an essay on 'The Perfect School'. Ninety per cent started by stating that the perfect school had cushions on the seats: they then described how the teachers were kept in fear and trembling by the stern rule of the pupils.

Reasoning and Imagination

Earlier we considered the argument, 'Twice two must be four, because we cannot imagine it otherwise.' This argument brings out clearly the connexion between reason and imagination: reason is in fact neither more nor less than *an experiment carried out in the imagination.* In any good detective story, the detective tries to imagine as clearly as possible the background of a crime, and to see how the statements of various witnesses fit into the picture. We are able to follow the story and the reasoning simply by using our own imagination. (*The Mystery of Marie Roget*, by Edgar Allan Poe, is a good example of imaginative reasoning applied to a crime in real life.)*

It is by no means necessary that reasoning should proceed by clearly stated steps. If you hear a rumour which means that your friend Smith has been involved in some particularly dirty business, you may say, 'I do not believe this story. Smith would never do a thing like that.' You may not be able to quote stories of heroic deeds performed by Smith, or to give evidence of any definite kind at all. You just feel that Smith is a decent person. Yet this is a perfectly good example of reasoning. Whether your conclusion is correct or not will depend on how long, and how well, you have actually known Smith. You will find it very hard to make the public share your faith in Smith. They have not your experience of Smith: therefore they cannot imagine him as you do: therefore they reason differently about him.

It is said that European explorers who told tropical peoples of

*See notes and introduction to Dorothy L. Sayers, *Great Short Stories of Detection, Mystery and Horror*, Part I (Gollancz).

the northern winter, when water became like a stone and men could walk on it, were met with polite disbelief. The natives looked at the warm sea waves rolling beneath the palm-trees, and refused to believe in ice. It was outside their experience: they were familiar with the tales of travellers.

People often make mistakes when they reason about things they have never seen. Children imagine kings wearing crowns; in real life, the odds are that a king wears a military cap or a bowler hat. Before the first locomotives were made, people refused to believe they would work. It was thought that the wheels would slip, and the train would remain motionless. A certain Mr Blenkinsop went so far as to invent a locomotive with spiked wheels to overcome this purely imaginary difficulty.

If anyone in the year 1700 had prophesied what the world would be like today, he would surely have been considered mad.

Imagination does not always give us the correct answer. We can only argue correctly about things of which we have experience or which are reasonably like the things we know well. If our reasoning leads us to an untrue conclusion, the fault lies with our reasoning. We must revise the picture in our minds, and learn to imagine things as they are.

When we find ourselves unable to reason (as one often does when presented with, say, a problem in algebra) it is because our imagination is not touched. One can begin to reason only when a clear picture has been formed in the imagination. Bad teaching is teaching which presents an endless procession of meaningless signs, words and rules, and fails to arouse the imagination.

The main aim of this book is not to explain how problems are solved: it is to show what the problems of mathematics *are*.

Abstraction

Let us now consider an example of reasoning applied to objects which everyone has seen and can therefore imagine correctly. Two railway stations, A and B, are connected by a single-track line. Owing to some mistake, a train leaves A for B at the same time as another train leaves B for A. There are no signals or safety devices on the line. Apart from exceptional happenings (such as a storm tearing up the railway track) one expects that there will be a collision.

You will agree that you could have reached this conclusion by the use of your own imagination. But now notice what a dim picture your imagination gave you. In what sort of country did you imagine the line to lie? Among woods, or through towns, or

1.

2.

STAGES OF ABSTRACTION
1. The rough impression of a scene as it might exist in a person's imagination.
2. A diagram, which leaves out all details except those needed for a particular purpose – namely, to show that the two trains are about to collide.

Most diagrams in mathematics are like '2'. All the details except those needed for a particular purpose are left out. But behind every diagram is a picture, like '1'. If you can discover what the picture is, you will find the diagram much easier to understand.

on the top of a precipice? Did you see clearly in your mind the movements of the pistons and the crowd of little devices on the wheels of the engines? How did you imagine the expression on the faces of the drivers, the colour of their hair, the build of their bodies? Did you imagine goods trains or passenger trains? One could continue thus for ever. It is certain, however vivid your imagination, there were points which you overlooked. But this did not in the least affect your answer to the question: will there be a collision? If you had thought of the two trains as two beads threaded on a wire (and the movement of trains might well be shown in this way when a timetable was being planned), you would still come to the correct conclusion. *For the purpose of this question* the trains and the railway-line might just as well be two beads and a wire. Of course for other purposes – if you had to provide ambulances for the wounded, or if you wanted to paint a picture of the event – it would be necessary to know further details.

It is impossible to imagine any event in perfect detail. In attacking any problem, we simplify the situation to a certain extent. We do not bother about those facts which seem un-important. The result of our reasoning will be correct if the picture in our imagination is, *not* exactly correct, but *sufficiently correct for the purpose in hand.*

This process of forgetting unimportant details is known as *abstraction*. Without abstraction, thought is impossible. We should spend all our lives collecting information if we tried to make a *perfect* picture even of a simple event. Some mis-educated people continually interrupt sensible discussion by wailing, 'But you have not defined exactly what you mean by this word.' The great majority of words cannot be defined exactly (for instance, the word *red*.) The important thing is not exact definition: it is to know what you are talking about.

Serious misunderstanding can arise if one forgets the nature of abstraction, and tries to apply a picture of the world, which is entirely sufficient for some purpose, to another purpose for which it is entirely insufficient. Two examples of difficulties which arise in this connexion may be mentioned.

The Mechanical View of Life

At one time there was a great craze for explaining everything in terms of machinery. It had been discovered that many facts of nature, in particular the movements of the planets, the tides, and of solid objects on the earth's surface, could be explained by supposing the universe to be made up of hard little balls, attracting each other according to certain definite laws. Instead of saying, 'We have a theory sufficiently correct for certain purposes', philosophers and scientists leapt to the conclusion that they had the whole truth about the universe. Not only the sun and moon, but our brains also, were made out of these hard little balls, and everything we did was a consequence of the way they pulled each other about. Thought and feeling must therefore be pure illusions – this in spite of the fact that the theory itself was the result of thought!

The whole procedure was entirely unscientific. It is obvious to anyone that courage, loyalty, determination, affection are *facts*, just as much as pound weights or spring balances. Without these qualities, it is very unlikely that any race of men or animals could long survive. The scientific conclusion would have been: our theory gives us true results about the movement of the moon and the planets, therefore there is some truth in it, but it does not lead us to foresee the possibility of atoms coming together and being organized into living creatures, *therefore* it is incomplete, *therefore* it overlooks some of the things which atoms actually do.

The root of the matter is perhaps a superstitious feeling that results obtained by looking through a microscope or a telescope are in some mysterious way superior to the knowledge we get in everyday life. We have at times come near to the worship of scientists, to believing that men who work in laboratories can solve all our problems for us. The views of a great scientist on his own science are indeed worthy of respect, for they are based on facts. But by the very act of shutting himself inside a laboratory, a scientist shuts himself out from much of the daily life of human beings. If a scientist realizes this, if he tries to overcome his isolation by paying special attention to current events and by learning the history of mankind, he may be able to apply his scientific training to other departments of life. But if he rushes straight out of his laboratory, full, like any other human being, of prejudice and ignorance, he is likely to make a rare fool of himself.

Euclid's Straight Lines

Beginners in geometry are sometimes puzzled by being told that straight lines have no thickness. We shall never, we are told, meet a straight line in real life, because every real object has a certain thickness. One of Euclid's lines, however, has no thickness. Two lines meet in a point, and a point has no size at all, only position. We shall never meet a point in real life, either, for all real objects have a certain size, as well as a certain position. It is not surprising that pupils wonder how we know anything about objects which no one has ever seen or ever can see.

This difficulty is a good example of the confusion which can come from misunderstanding the methods of abstract thought. We have seen that Euclid's geometry grew out of the methods used for building, surveying and other work in ancient Egypt. This work was done with actual ropes or strings, real 'linen threads' with actual thickness. What does Euclid mean when he says that a line has no thickness, although he is using results suggested by the use of thick ropes? He means that in laying out a football field or in building a house you are *not interested in the size or the shape of the knots* made where one rope is joined to another. If you allowed for the fact that ropes possess a definite thickness, if you carefully described all the knots used by a bricklayer, you would make the subject extremely complicated, and no advantage would be gained. Euclid therefore says, if an actual rope has thickness, *neglect this* in order to keep the subject reasonably simple.

The position is not that Euclid's straight lines represent a perfect ideal which ropes and strings strive in vain to copy. It is the other way round. Euclid's straight lines represent a rough, simplified account of the complicated way in which actual ropes behave. For some purposes, this rough idea is sufficient. But for other purposes – such as teaching Boy Scouts how to tie knots – it is essential to remember that rope has thickness: for such purposes you will obtain wrong results if you think of ropes as Euclidean straight lines.

Similar illustrations might be drawn from any science. Scientific laws are true, within certain limits, for certain types of object. For other types the truth becomes doubtful, and after a certain point, positively misleading.

Some books on mechanics give a very good explanation of the word *particle*. They say: an object is spoken of as a particle when its size is small compared to the distances in which we are interested. The earth sweeps round the sun at a distance of about 90,000,000 miles. Compared with this, the diameter of the earth, say 8,000 miles, does not amount to much, and we might speak of the earth as if it were a point. On a map of the world London might be regarded as a point. According to the atlas, London is $51\frac{1}{2}$ degrees north of the equator. It is not necessary to say whether this refers to Hampstead or the Isle of Dogs.

Readers will find some statements in this book very puzzling if they treat every sentence as being true (so to speak) to ten places of decimals. Particularly within the limits of a small booklet, it is impossible to hedge every sentence round with the remarks and cautions that would be necessary in a text-book. In any case, I do not wish to present people with ready-made opinions. It is up to the reader to approach this book in a mood of sturdy commonsense, with a readiness to criticize and reject anything which, through stupidity, carelessness or lack of space, or through the essential difficulty of saying anything with 100% truth, is misleading. My aim has been to convey a general impression, sufficient to show how mathematicians think.

The Mathematicians on the Second Floor

At this stage there will be a protest from the pure mathematicians, who will say that engineers and other practical mathematicians may think in this rough instinctive way, but that my statements neglect the very important body of people who work on mathematics itself, and neither know nor care what practical applications their work may have.

It is true that pure mathematicians, working in this way under the inner compulsion of an artistic urge, have not only enriched mathematics with many interesting discoveries, but have also created methods of the utmost value for practical men. It is very shortsighted (from the practical point of view) to discourage all work which has no *immediate* practical aim. It pays humanity to encourage the artist, even if the artist does not care in the least about humanity.

What is pure mathematics *about*? It does not seem to deal with any definite thing, yet there is no doubt about its truth, and its discoveries can be used with confidence for practical tasks.

Perhaps the square root of minus one will serve as an illustration. How do we come to study such an unearthly idea? The history of this idea is briefly sketched at the beginning of Chapter 15. Mathematicians first used the sign $\sqrt{-1}$, without in the least knowing what it could mean, *because it shortened work and led to correct results*. People naturally tried to find out *why* this happened and what $\sqrt{-1}$, really meant. After two hundred years they succeeded.

This suggests that pure mathematics first appears as *the study of methods*. Pure mathematicians do not appear on the scene until late in human history: they represent a high level of civilization. The first comers are the practical men, who study the world at first hand, and discover methods which work in practice. Pure mathematicians do not study the natural world. They sit, as it were, upstairs in the library, and study the writings of the practical men. Sometimes the practical men get taken in by a method which usually gives the correct result, but not always (see Chapter 14). The job of the pure mathematicians is then to sort out the methods which are logical (that is, which give correct results) from those which are not.

Pure mathematicians are in touch with the real world, but at second hand. They do not sit by themselves and think. The material they study consists of the books in the libraries of the world. These books do not consist solely of the writings of engineers. The chain is often very long. An engineer consults an 'applied mathematician' (one who studies the applications of mathematics to everyday problems): the applied mathematician consults a pure mathematician: the pure mathematician writes a paper on the question: another pure mathematician points out that the question could be solved if only we knew the solution to some more general problem, and so it goes on. A great literature arises, showing the connexion between different problems. A subject becomes so large that it is impossible to remember all that has been written about it: it becomes an urgent necessity to boil all the various results down into a few general rules. After a century or two, problems are being discussed which seem to have no connexion with the worries of the original engineer. But the connexion is there, even if it is not easy to see.

Is pure mathematics, then, merely the study of how mathematicians think? It certainly is not. Pure mathematicians take very little account of how people actually think. If all the applied mathematicians in the world suddenly went mad, pure mathematics would remain unchanged. Pure mathematics is the study of how people *ought* to think in order to get the correct results. It takes no account of human weaknesses. It would perhaps be more true to say that pure mathematics is the study of how we should have to construct calculating machines, if we decided to do without human mathematicians altogether.

Pure mathematics appeals to those who, like Rupert Brooke, appreciate

> 'the keen
> Unpassioned beauty of a great machine,'

but this is a taste that comes late both in the history of the human race and in the life of most individuals. For the purpose of teaching, it is essential to master the primitive methods of practical mathematicians before attempting to introduce the strict methods of the pure mathematician. The emphasis in this book is laid on practical mathematics, not because practical mathematicians can claim any superiority over pure mathematicians but simply because teaching experience shows that it is necessary to do so.

Nor would I claim any infallibility for the view I have suggested as to how it has come about that men can reason. I have had less time than I would have wished to study the history of mathematics, and of mankind generally. These views I merely believe to be on the right lines. But that most human beings think, and need to be taught, as this theory would lead one to expect – this, from direct experience, I know to be true.

Practical Conclusions

To sum up – successful reasoning is possible only when we have a clear picture in our minds of what we are studying. Imagination is developed, and is made reliable, through practical contact with the real world. Mathematics is difficult when it is presented as something quite apart from everyday life. Mathematical reasoning can grow gradually and naturally, through practical work with real objects. This holds both for elementary and 'higher' mathematics. Only for the 'highest' pure mathematics is the connexion with daily life rather indirect.

CHAPTER 4

THE STRATEGY AND TACTICS OF STUDY

'I have taught mathematics and applied science or engineering to almost every kind of boy and man ... In my experience there is hardly any man who may not become a discoverer, an advancer of knowledge, and the earlier the age at which you give him chances of exercising his individuality, the better.' – John Perry, 1901.

THE two main conditions for success in any sort of work are interest and confidence. People usually pay little attention to these two factors, because they feel (quite rightly) that they cannot make themselves confident or interested by an effort of will.

It is quite true that you cannot increase confidence by an act of will. But neither can you increase the size of your muscles or make your heart beat more vigorously by sitting in a chair and willing it. This does not mean that it is impossible to change your muscular strength or the rate of your heart-beat. If you skip for half an hour you will do both.

Confidence and interest can also be changed *by taking the proper measures.*

The proper measures do not consist in rushing at work like a bull at a gate. It is well known that the effect of too intensive physical training is to destroy the body, not to build it up. The same is true of the mind.

In physical training, some of the vital organs lie beyond the control of our conscious minds. We cannot send direct orders to our heart, our liver, our glands. We have to find exercises depending on the movement of our limbs, on the efforts of muscles which we can control, that will produce the desired effect on the other organs. After a few months of proper training, we do not know what changes have taken place in our bodies, but we feel the benefit and know that changes must have occurred.

In mental training also the decisive changes take place outside consciousness. The test of any system of coaching is not whether it turns out students capable of doing certain tricks, like performing dogs. Such a method is futile and fundamentally degrading. It merely enables people to pass examinations in subjects which they do not understand, and to qualify for posts in which they will be unhappy and inefficient. The real test of any teaching method lies far deeper. With the correct approach, a student finds his whole feeling about the subject changing. He begins to understand what the subject is about, he feels confident that he can master it, he begins to take pleasure in it and to think about it outside working hours. Only when such an attitude has been created does the mind really *grasp* the subject. People show a greater degree of intelligence and knowledge in connexion with their hobbies than in any other department of life.

Lack of Interest

Is it possible to transfer the kind of interest we feel for a hobby, and to use it for the purpose of work? It depends on the reason for your lack of interest.

There are people whose interest is concentrated on one subject. If you feel that you have one single purpose in life, whether it be to paint pictures or to find a cure for cancer – if you feel that this one thing alone matters for you, that everything else – comfort, wealth, respectability, safety, family ties or social obligations – are without significance compared to it – then obviously you have no doubt what you are to do.

Only a few people are thus clear cut in their aims. Most men and women are prepared to fit in, more or less, with the customs they find around them, to work at any job by which they can earn a reasonable living.

There are probably some who fall between two stools – people who could be happy and efficient in some particular type of life, but who lack the self-knowledge or the courage or the determination needed to break away from the life which other people expect them to lead. The war has produced many cases in which people, who had previously been making a rather half-hearted effort to qualify for learned professions, found themselves doing practical work, putting out fires, driving lorries and so on. It was obvious that they had found the type of work for which nature designed them. In a perfect world they would be encouraged to do such work, without a war being necessary. For such people the question is not how to learn mathematics, but how to drop mathematics at the first possible moment.

This then is your first question: to which type do you belong? Are you a person with such a keen interest in some special type of activity, that you can afford to drop other subjects (including mathematics) and succeed as a specialist expert? Or do you belong to the more usual type, that is ready to tackle whatever comes along?

You must decide definitely one way or the other. Either your interests are so far from mathematics that you could never have

308

any use for or amusement from mathematics, or there is something which you accept as worth doing, for which mathematical knowledge is necessary. In answering this question you must make allowance for the fact already mentioned – that the educational system seems specially designed to take all life and interest out of the subjects taught. By mathematics is meant the living subject, not what is taught in many schools.

In some cases, then, the lack of interest goes right down to the roots of personality. But the vast majority of people who hate mathematics do not come under this heading. By far the commonest cause of dislike is the way mathematics has been presented. You can test this for yourself. Do you like puzzles? Do you listen to the Brains Trust, or do crosswords? Do you play bridge, or chess, or draughts? Do you take part in the heated arguments one sometimes hears, such as the question what would happen if passengers in a motor-car threw a cricket ball straight up into the air – would it fall into the car again? Do you take an interest in any sort of scientific or mechanical development, such as radar or aeroplane working? If so, your basic interests are not very different from those of the mathematician. I know a family (by no means high-brow) that was divided into warring factions one Christmas by the car and cricket-ball question. At school, it was the most normal boys who felt most strongly about their own solutions to such problems. This interest in what would happen is close to the interest a scientist feels, and science soon leads to mathematics.

The Removal of Fear

Probably most people would be interested in mathematics, as most people would be interested in music, if they were not afraid of it. Interest and confidence are closely connected. If you find that you can do something, you are pleased. You like the feeling of having mastered nature and the feeling that other people will admire you. You want to do some more of it, and the more you do, the better you become. On the other hand, if you start off with a defeat, the effect is the opposite. Nobody likes to appear a fool. You avoid the subject, or try to make out that you do not bother about it. You decide that you never will be any good, so why waste energy? In any case, you convince yourself, it is no use. All of this has nothing to do with the facts of the case: it is the desperate attempt of a human mind to keep its balance and its self-respect. You probably concentrate on some other subject, or play hard at some game, and say to yourself, 'Well, I may not be able to do algebra, but I am pretty hot at cricket and chemistry.'

In some schools, the excellent custom is followed, when a boy is a complete failure at lessons, to put him on to some useful activity such as carpentry or ploughing. He then becomes sure that he can do *something* well, and he no longer needs to deceive himself about his lessons. He can take the risk of really trying to succeed, since his self-confidence will not be destroyed should he fail.

It is essential, if you are trying to overcome your dread of a subject, to realize what is your first objective. Your first job is *not* to learn any particular result. It is to get rid of fear. You must go back a certain way, and start with work which you are absolutely sure you can do. In learning a foreign language, for instance, it is helpful to get a book written in that language for children just learning to read. However badly you have been taught, you will almost certainly be able to read it. This is your first victory – you have read a book genuinely written for the use of someone speaking a foreign language.

In mathematics it is even more important to go back to an early stage. It is impossible to understand algebra if you have not mastered arithmetic: it is impossible to understand calculus if you have not mastered algebra. If you attempt the impossible, without realizing what you are doing, your morale will suffer.

Apart from this logical necessity, there is also a psychological reason. The chances are that you are still carrying around with you all the feelings of uncertainty that have troubled you during all the different stages of your education. You are still *feeling* the setbacks that you had when you were eight or nine. This feeling will immediately disappear if you go right back to the beginning, and read again the text-books that you then had. You will often

310

find that the difficulties have vanished without your realizing it.

It is for this reason that there are chapters in this book dealing with such things as the multiplication table. You will read these chapters without difficulty. At some stage of the book you will find yourself again puzzled. This means that you have reached the stage where your knowledge of the subject begins to show gaps – at this point, or at some earlier point, your revision must begin. It is nothing unusual to be puzzled by the things you have just learnt. If you keep revising, and are perfectly clear about everything which you have done more than a year or more than six months ago, you need not worry.

A good way to revise is to take a text-book, and look through the examples in it. If you can do them easily, you need not read the book. The examples on some chapters may give you difficulty. If the text-book is one which you first read several years ago, you will probably know whether the results of these particular chapters are much used in later work. If so, you have found out the source of your difficulty in the later work. If they are not important, you may leave them for the time being.

In mathematics it is often necessary to work backwards. If you find a difficulty on page 157 of some book, try to find out why. See if page 157 uses the results of other, earlier pages in the book, or if it uses some fact explained in an earlier text-book. If page 157 depends on pages 9, 32, and 128, read these pages again and make sure that you understand them. If you do not understand them, you cannot possibly understand page 157.

If you still have difficulty, ask someone else to explain the page to you. Notice very carefully if he uses any word, any sign, or any method which is strange to you. If so, ask where this word, sign, or method is explained.

If you can find out what your difficulty is, you are half-way to overcoming it. People often go about with a fog of small diffi-culties in their heads: they are not quite sure what the words mean, they are not quite sure what has gone before, they are not quite sure what is the object of the work. All these difficulties can be dealt with easily, if they are taken one at a time. Provided the book is written in reasonably simple language, a few minutes with a dictionary should clear up that difficulty.* The next thing is to find out what knowledge you are expected to have before you attempt to understand the proof of a new result. It is possible to make a diagram showing how a book hangs together, how one section depends on previous sections. One should learn a book both backwards and forwards: one should know that the result on page 50 is proved by the result on page 29, and that it is used to prove the result on page 144. (Of course no sane person will learn the numbers of the actual pages on which results occur. But it may be worth while to write in the margin of page 50, 'See p. 29; used, p. 144') Many people learn separate results, but never link them together in this way.

In this book it has not been possible, in every single sentence, to give references to all the remarks, made earlier in the book, that may help towards understanding. If you cannot understand some sentence, underline it. The chances are that somewhere earlier in the chapter, or in the book, a remark has been made that was especially intended to prepare for the difficult sentence. At the first reading you may not have noticed this remark at all. It seemed pointless. Look back for such remarks. If you succeed in finding them, put a note in the margin, 'This explains sentence underlined on page ...'

It may seem to you that this advice does not amount to much, that it is obvious. It may be obvious – but people need a lot of persuading before they do it. As a rule, someone who has difficulty with calculus or trigonometry is not prepared to believe that the real trouble is ignorance of algebra or arithmetic. There is always an examination coming in six weeks, or a year, or whatever it is, and this examination is on calculus or trigonometry – not on algebra and arithmetic. Trying to learn higher mathematics without a firm grasp of the earlier part is like trying to invent an aeroplane without knowing anything about motor-car engines. Until the motor industry had been developed, all attempts at aeroplanes were complete failures.

*I have tried to keep words in this book as short as possible. One or two words may not be known to everyone. It is only fair that readers should take the trouble to look these up.

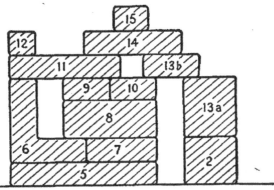

COMMON SENSE & EVERYDAY EXPERIENCE

THE GENERAL PLAN OF THIS BOOK

In this diagram each block represents a chapter. Chapters 1, 3, and 4 are of a general nature, and are not included in the diagram.

Each block depends upon the blocks below. Thus, it is impossible to understand Chapter 11 without first having read Chapters 6, 9, and 10, and Chapters 9 and 10 in turn cannot be understood without Chapter 8, etc.

In some cases, the upper block depends only on a small part of the lower one. For instance, Chapter 8 can be understood without understanding the whole of Chapter 6. In fact, it is only the part of Chapter 6 explaining the meaning of the signs 4^3, 10^5, etc., that is needed for Chapter 8. It is not possible to show this on the diagram.

Chapter 13 is split into two parts. 13a represents the greater part of the chapter, which is quite elementary. 13b represents the end of the chapter, which is more advanced.

If a reader finds difficulty, say in Chapter 10, he may find it worth while to leave Chapters 10, 11, and 12, for the time being, and to read the easier part of Chapter 13.

To revise elementary mathematics takes much less time than people imagine. How many text-books has a student of eighteen used? One on arithmetic, one on algebra, several perhaps on geometry, an elementary trigonometry, perhaps a book on calculus. Geometry we may leave on one side for the moment. How long does it take to look through an arithmetic book and one on algebra, and find out if there is any important result which you missed at school? How long does it take to write down on a sheet of paper a list of the contents of these books, and to put a tick against the results which you thoroughly understand? Not very long. The advantage of doing this is that you begin to see how much (or how little) you have to learn. One tends to think of algebra as a vast jungle of confusion, in the midst of which one wanders without map or compass. It is much better to think of algebra (or that part of algebra which you need to know) as being half a dozen methods, and twenty or so results, of which you probably already know 60%. Nor need you revise the whole of this at once. Suppose for instance you are finding difficulty with calculus because you do not properly know the Binomial Theorem. Get down your book of algebra, and look up *Binomial Theorem*. Never mind about the proof for the moment. First get quite clear what the Binomial Theorem is. It is full of signs such

as ^nC_r or $\binom{n}{r}$ – different signs are used in different books. These

signs are explained in the chapter on Permutations and Combinations. Again, do not bother about proof. See what these signs mean. Work out a few examples – $^4C_1$ $^4C_2$ and $^4C_3$, for instance. Work these right out, as numbers. Come back to the Binomial Theorem, and take particular examples of it. Put $n = 4$, for instance.* The binomial theorem deals with the expression $(x + a)^n$. Put $x = 10$ and $a = 1$. Work out 11^2, 11^3, 11^4. What is the connexion between 11^4 and the numbers worked out above? Work out 101×101 and $101 \times 101 \times 101$. What do you notice about 11×11 and 101×101? What do you notice about $11 \times 11 \times 11$ and $101 \times 101 \times 101$? The same numbers turn up both times? Do you think the same numbers will turn up in 1001×1001 as in 11×11? In $1001 \times 1001 \times 1001$ as in $11 \times 11 \times 11$? If so, you are not far from discovering the Binomial Theorem for yourself. (If you are not clear what 11^4 stands for, the remarks above will be meaningless to you. What 11^4 means is explained in Chapter 6.)

*If you are in the fortunate position of having never been taught algebra, and therefore having no mistaken ideas about it, take no notice of this paragraph. The meaning of algebraic signs is explained in Chapter 7.

In this way, tracing back and back, you get to know the parts of algebra which are useful for calculus. You know at least what the Binomial Theorem is, and how it helps you to write down $(1001)^4$, even if you cannot prove it. When a book or a lecturer refers to the Binomial Theorem, you will be able to follow the use that is made of it. When you are thoroughly familiar with the usefulness and the meaning of the Binomial Theorem, it *may* be worth your while to study the proof. (Some books contain very dull proofs. Look for a book with a proof that is short and that appeals to you.)

Reading with a Purpose

We have just been using an algebra book in a special way – with a purpose. We have not tried to read the whole book. We have taken no notice of any chapters, except those which are necessary for an understanding of the Binomial Theorem. You may not think this is much of a purpose, but it is better than none at all. You will be surprised how much more sensible a text-book becomes if you use it in this way. You have a definite interest in getting this information – it will save you from getting any further behind with your work. You are not littering your mind with all the information in the book. You are learning only things which you need to learn.

All mathematics grew rather in this way. Someone wanted to do or make something: it was impossible to do it without mathematics: so mathematics was studied, and the *purpose* gave meaning and unity to the work done. A very simple example – try to make a model mansion with gables and attics in the roof, by cutting out pieces of cardboard or paper and sticking them together. You will find it is not so easy as it looks to draw the shapes that will be required. From such a problem, scientifically investigated, can arise geometry and spherical trigonometry. By working and experimenting with this problem of the toy-maker and the architect, you will unconsciously acquire the type of imagination necessary for studying geometry, trigonometry and solid geometry.

Interest is a peculiar thing. There are hundreds of things in which you feel you *ought* to be interested – but for which (to be honest for once) you do not give a hang. There are hundreds of other things – odd remarks, pointless little stories, tricks with matches, stray pieces of information – which seem to have no use in life, but which stay in your memory for years. At school we read a history book by Warner and Marten. No one remembered the history (this was no fault of the authors). But there were certain footnotes in it: one about a curate who grew crops in the churchyard and said it would be turnips next year; a lady who blacked out a picture and said, 'She is blacker within'; a verse about someone longing to be at 'em and waiting for the Earl of Chatham – everyone knew these years after they left school. These were the things that really interested us.

If you want to remember a subject and enjoy it, you must somehow find a way of linking it up with something in which you are *really* interested. It is very unlikely that you will find much entertainment in text-books. If you read only the text-books, you will find the subject dull. *Text-books are written for people who already possess a strong desire to study mathematics: they are not written to create such a desire.* Do not begin by reading the subject: begin by reading *round* the subject – books about real life, which somehow bring in the subject, which show how the subject came to be needed.

In any reasonably large town, a public library gives an easy way of finding good books. Nearly all libraries use the same method of indexing books, the Dewey Decimal System. Take a look at the books between 501 and 531. On the open shelves of Manchester Central Reference Library, inside an hour and a half, I found the following books, and glanced through their contents. I give them just as I jotted them down – pass rapidly over any book which does not appeal to you. The reference numbers are given.

510.8 Horsburgh: *Modern Instruments of Calculation.* Do not try to read this straight through. Photographs of calculating machines, round about page 26. If you hate arithmetic, why not make a calculating machine for yourself?

510.2 Mellor. *Higher Mathematics for Students of Chemistry or Physics.* An excellent book, but do not try to read it until you are ready for it.

515. Abbott. *Practical Geometry and Engineering Graphics.* A book full of illustrations. It covers problems rather like that of the model house. How do you cut a flat sheet of metal to make a stove-pipe with a bend in it? What curve is best for making gear wheels? Glance through the whole book, see what subjects interest you, then trace backwards, and see what type of mathematics is needed for each. Fairly technical language. Beginners should rest content with a general impression.

523. Serviss. *Pleasures of the Telescope.* Very simple indeed. Well illustrated. Contains star maps. Will appeal to artistic people. Useful for airmen and sailors, who may steer by the stars in emergencies.

522.2 Bell. *The Telescope.* Intended for the makers of telescopes and field-glasses. Only a small part of the book consists of mathematics. Best method – read through the book: note anything you cannot understand; then consult an elementary book on Optics (under the number 535). Try your hand at designing a telescope, a microscope, a magic lantern or cinema projector, an epidiascope, a camera obscura. The advantage of doing your own design is that you can use any 'scrap' – old spectacles, magnifying glasses, etc. – that you may have. Very simple geometry is sufficient for this purpose, if you find the right method.

526.8 Hinks. *Maps and Survey.* Chapter 2 explains why it is necessary to have maps. Chapter 8 deals with the kind of map made by an explorer, and Chapter 10 with the rough survey made by the first settlers in a frontier town. Chapter 12 shows how maps are made from aerial photography. By reading *the right parts* of this book, a beginner in trigonometry can get a useful background – how to make a rough plan of a field, etc. The book also brings out some unexpected connexions between practical life and scientific questions: the exact shape of the earth and observations of stars are needed to make a map of a big country like Africa; it is hard to make a proper map of India, because the Himalayas are heavy enough to exert a noticeable pull on a plumb-line, and cause it not to point straight at the centre of the earth.

While on the subject of maps, *A Key to Maps*, by Brigadier H. St J. L. Winterbotham, may be mentioned. Among other things, it tells hikers how to see from a map what the view from any place will be like. Many libraries have, or can obtain, this book.

530.2 Saunders. *A Survey of Physics*. In the words of the author, 'The reader will be introduced to some of the mysteries of nature, as well as to many ingenious inventions of mankind.'

531. Goodman. *Mechanics Applied to Engineering*. Contains a great amount of information. I am not sure how it will appear to beginners. As with all other books, look through it, learn anything you can, but do not be distressed if there are parts of the book you cannot follow at all.

You may find something to interest you under 385, Railways; 620.9, History of Engineering; 626, Canals. If you are particularly interested in any subject, the library assistants will tell you where to look. Look right through the catalogue, under any section that interests you. It pays to spend a long time searching for an interesting book on the subject, rather than to read half a dozen books that will bore you.

It is often good policy to read a book of which nine-tenths merely reminds you of things you already knew, while the remaining one-tenth is new. Your mind will then have plenty of energy to learn the new facts. Do not make a great effort to remember every detail. Anything that interests you will stick in your mind. If you find some useful piece of information that may be needed later, write it down in a note-book kept for the purpose. Your aim should be to have in your mind a general view of the subject, in your desk a collection of exact facts that you can use for any particular problem.

Books on the History and Teaching of Mathematics

If you find these suggestions of any use, if by browsing in a library or by looking about you in the street you hit on anything which you genuinely like and want to know more about (where there's no will, there's no way), you will soon find yourself becoming a specialist in this. It may be anything from radar to how drains are fitted, provided it beckons you on. As you get to know more about this question, you will get impatient with popular introductions, you will find yourself wanting a complete answer to questions, the professional way of dealing with the subject. You will find yourself pulling down bulky volumes that seemed infinitely dry a year ago. You will not read them from cover to cover. You will search with a skilful eye for the paragraph or two that deals with what you want to know at the moment. And you will realize that, while you may not now be interested in other subjects, if you were to become interested in anything, however complicated, you could deal with that too in the same professional way. This confidence, this freedom from fear, is the main thing that distinguishes the expert. An expert does not need to know much. He must know *how* and *where* information can be found.

As the subject you have chosen for your hobby becomes better known to you, you will begin to realize how much like yourself were the men who worked at it and discovered it. When you reach this stage, you may find it useful to have some idea of the dates at which these men lived. There are various reasons for this. (i) By noticing the dates you can get an idea of how much of the subject you know. For instance, if you find that the mathematics you know was all discovered before 1800, you will realize that there is much yet to learn. The nineteenth century saw tremendous mathematical activity. You will not make the mistake of trying to research on questions for yourself without first making some effort to find out if the problem that puzzles you has already been solved. (ii) If you know how much of the subject was known at any time, it is often much easier to see how particular discoveries were suggested by things already known. This helps you to understand the subject. (iii) If you are baffled by something, reading the history of that discovery may help you. The life of the actual discoverer is often very helpful: the attempts he made, the experiments he carried out may supply the clue. In this way you can outflank your difficulty by reading round it – much better than battering your head against it. Far too little use is made of history in teaching mathematics.

In choosing an historical book, as with any other book, look for one which appeals to you, and do not be worried if you cannot read the whole book. Read what you can.

It may also help you to read a book on the teaching of mathematics. There is no ideal way of teaching. What suits one student is useless to another. A teacher who has to deal with a class of fifty has an almost impossible job. If you read a book on teaching, you will find that there are several entirely different ways of tackling the subject. You may feel that you would·have done much better if you had been taught by one of these methods. Note the names of the people who developed this method, and see if there are any books by them in your library. *The Teaching of Mathematics*, by J. W. A. Young (1911), contains a description of several movements in mathematics teaching, and the author is human and enlightened. In it will be found a great number of references, on which further reading can be based. One of the reformers mentioned by Young is Professor John Perry, whose *Address to the British Association*, 1901, is the source of the quotation at the head of this chapter. It is well worth reading, both for Perry's speech and for the remarks (mainly approving) of the leading mathematicians of the day. Anything by Perry is worth reading. His book *Calculus for Engineers* may be mentioned. It is forty years since Perry gave this lead. If parents, teachers, and teaching authorities today were fully aware of what was said in 1901, much mental suffering among children would be prevented. The tide is undoubtedly flowing in that direction. It still has a long way to flow.

PART II
ON CERTAIN PARTS OF MATHEMATICS

CHAPTER 5

ARITHMETIC

'One, two, plenty.'
– Tasmanian Method of Counting.

ARITHMETIC plays a very small part in mathematics, especially in the higher mathematics. Geometry, as we have already seen, can be studied direct from diagrams, in which simple numbers – 3, 4, 5, etc. – occasionally occur. The higher one goes, the less arithmetic is likely to be used. This is why there are so many stories about famous mathematicians quarrelling with tram conductors about their change, and being wrong.

Arithmetic does depend on certain things which have to be learnt by heart, such as the multiplication table, addition and subtraction tables. These operations can be carried out by machines, and to a certain extent anyone who learns arithmetic has to become a machine. For instance, a clerk adding up long sums of figures does not need to think deep thoughts about the nature of a number. It is sufficient for him if the sight of 7 and 8 immediately bring the number 15 into his mind.

Whilst it is possible to teach arithmetic in a purely mechanical manner, it is certainly not desirable to do so. Even for the simplest operations, it is easier to remember what has to be done if one knows the reason. For anyone who wants to go on to the other branches of mathematics, mechanical learning is fatal. No one has yet invented a machine that will think for itself. It is a pity that there are still schools (especially girls' schools) where arithmetic is still taught on the lines of 'You do this, then you do that' – as though the subject were some form of religious ritual.

Arithmetic is not a difficult subject to discover for oneself. There are many things which lie on the edge of arithmetic. For instance, when an operation is being carried out in hospital, a nurse has a board with hooks, holding all the things that will go into the patient and must come out again. Before the patient is sewn up, the nurse must see that no hook is empty. This procedure is not counting, but it is very near to it. When we count on our fingers (the original method!) we are simply using fingers instead of hooks.

Counting with fingers (or fingers and toes) will do only for numbers up to ten (or twenty).* Team-work is needed to go further. If a friend is willing to be nudged each time you reach ten, and to count the nudges on his or her fingers, it is possible to reach a hundred. With six people, a million can be counted thus, though the sixth person can go to sleep most of the time. (I do not see why counting by this method should not actually be carried out in classes for young children, in order to explain what is meant by a number such as 243. In playing hide-and-seek children of their own free will count up to quite large numbers, and seem to enjoy it.)

The same idea, in essentials, is used in the devices which measure how far a motor-car or bicycle has gone. Each wheel, on reaching ten, 'nudges' the next. Adding machines are made on similar lines.

The imagination can be further aided if actual objects (say matches) are being counted. The first person ties the matches into bundles of ten. The second person takes ten bundles, and puts them into a box. Ten boxes go into a bag, ten bags into a sack, ten sacks into a truck, ten trucks form a train – the latter stages in imagination only! At the same time, the progress of the work could be exhibited, as on a cricket score-board. Quite soon, the symbol, 127: the sound, 'one hundred and twenty seven': the picture, one box, two bundles, seven matches: would be welded together in the mind of each child.

All the operations, such as adding together 14 and 28, subtracting 17 from 21, dividing 84 into three equal parts, can be

---

* Some entertaining details of primitive methods of counting may be found in E. B. Tylor, *Primitive Culture*, Chapter 7; Tobias Dantzig, *Number, the Language of Science*, Chapters 1, 2.

carried out, first by experiments with the actual objects: secondly with the objects and with 'score-boards' simultaneously: finally, by written work alone.

In the Montessori method, the tables of addition are taught in some such way. The children have sticks, representing the numbers one to nine, and have to arrange these so as to get ten units in each row: thus –

X   X⎯X⎯X⎯X⎯X⎯X⎯X⎯X⎯X $1 + 9 = 10,$

X⎯X   X⎯X⎯X⎯X⎯X⎯X⎯X⎯X $2 + 8 = 10$, etc.

It is quite useful to have squared paper, cut into strips, ten squares in breadth. The squares are numbered –

1	2	3	4	5	6	7	8	9	10
11	12	13	14	15	16	17	18	19	20 etc.

The addition table can then be worked out, by pasting on strips of correct length. If two numbers, such as 7 and 6, require more than one complete row, the extra squares are cut off and go to the next row.

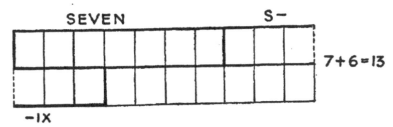

I have heard successful mathematicians say that in adding 7 and 6 the thought was present 'in the back of their minds' that 3 of the 6 units were needed to bring 7 up to 10, so that 3 was left over to provide the odd units.

This method can be extended to the multiplication table, by repeatedly sticking on strips containing the same number of squares. Quite striking patterns emerge. How crude the table for two times –

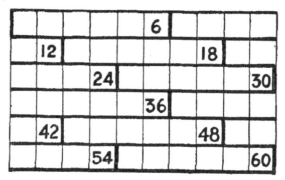

is, compared to 6 times! –

The crudest of all (and the easiest to learn) is 10 times: then 5 and 2; then 9 and 3; then 4, 6, 8; the most subtle is 7 – it would make a good wall-paper.

The appearance of pattern appeals to the artistic side, which is strong in children. Good mathematicians are very sensitive to patterns.

Patterns also suggest questions. Why does '3 times' have a pattern rather like that of '9 times'? Why are '5 times' and '2 times' arranged in upright lines?

It was said of Ramanujan that every number seemed to be his personal friend. One should try to present arithmetic to children in such a way that they come to realize the 'personality' which each number possesses.

Owing to the accidental fact that we possess ten fingers, the multiplication tables depend on this number 10. If we had eight or twelve fingers, the patterns would be different.   .

One can, however, represent multiplication, quite apart from the question of fingers, by means of rectangles. A piece of linoleum, 3 yards by 2, costs six times as much as a piece 1 yard square. We can, if we like, think of 2 times 3 as the area of a rectangle 2 by 3.

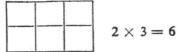

$2 \times 3 = 6$

This idea may be helpful in connexion with fractions. We may explain the meaning of $\frac{2}{3} \times \frac{5}{7}$ by saying that it represents the area of a piece of linoleum that measures $\frac{2}{3}$ yard by $\frac{5}{7}$ yard.

Multiplication of fractions seems to cause trouble. Children are often puzzled why two-thirds *of* five-sevenths should be the same as two-thirds *multiplied* by five-sevenths. They see no connexion between 'of' and 'times'. This difficulty is very largely one of language. It is quite natural to say that one field is 3 times or 4 times or $3\frac{1}{8}$ times as large as another. It is perhaps less usual to say a field is $\frac{7}{8}$ times as large as another, more usual to say it is $\frac{7}{8}$ of the size of the other. It is at any rate clear that to draw an area $3\frac{1}{8}$ *times* as large as this page one would take 3 pages, and add this to $\frac{1}{8}$ *of* a page.

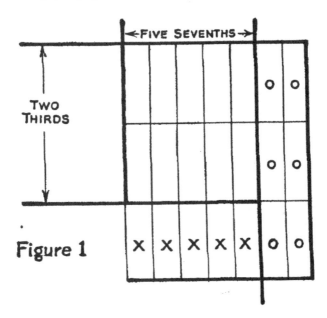

Figure 1

Multiplication of fractions is often taught purely by rule, but it is easy to show why the rule works. Consider for example, $\frac{2}{3}$ of $\frac{5}{7}$. Let us take 1 square yard of linoleum and see what two-thirds of five-sevenths of a square yard looks like. To obtain five-sevenths we must first divide the linoleum into seven equal pieces – by the upright lines in Fig. 1 – and take five of these pieces. If we cut along the heavy upright line, the piece to the left contains five-sevenths. We now require two-thirds *of this*. The level lines divide the whole figure into three equal parts. By cutting along the heavy flat line we shall obtain a piece which is two-thirds of five-sevenths. After the first cut the pieces marked with noughts are removed: after the second cut, those marked with crosses.

This figure shows how to represent $\frac{2}{3}$ times $\frac{5}{7}$ as a single fraction We have divided our square yard into 21 pieces – all the same size and shape. The rectangle, $\frac{2}{3}$ by $\frac{5}{7}$, contains 10 of these little pieces. Each piece is $\frac{1}{21}$ of a square yard, so our answer is $\frac{10}{21}$. In fact, we have found the rule for multiplying fractions –

$$\frac{2}{3} \times \frac{5}{7} = \frac{2 \times 5}{3 \times 7}$$

A common mistake found in examination papers is due to pupils mixing up the rule for adding and for multiplying fractions. They write, for instance –

$$\frac{1}{3} + \frac{3}{5} = \frac{1 + 3}{3 + 5}$$

which is complete nonsense, since the answer thus obtained, $\frac{4}{8}$, reduces to $\frac{1}{2}$, which is *less* than $\frac{3}{5}$.

With parrot learning, such a mistake is quite natural. ' $\times$ ' has been turned into '$+$': that is all. Such a mistake is much less likely in a pupil who has made experiments with $\times$ and $+$, and has come to *feel* the entirely different meanings of these two signs.

The reader may care to work out a diagram which illustrates the correct way of adding $\frac{1}{3}$ and $\frac{3}{5}$.

Decimals

No difficulty at all should be found in teaching or learning decimals. Decimals can be demonstrated by exactly the same 'team work' as was suggested for whole numbers.

The measurement of a line is a convenient illustration. A metre is a French measure, not much different from a yard. A decimetre is one-tenth of a metre; a centimetre one-tenth of a decimetre; a millimetre one-tenth of a centimetre. A line whose length is 1 metre, 3 decimetres, 2 centimetres, and 5 millimetres is written for short as 1·325 metres.

While in English measure it is not simple to turn 2 yards 1 foot and 3 inches into inches, it is at once obvious in French measure that 1·325 metres is 1325 millimetres, or 132·5 centimetres, or 13·25 decimetres.

An ordinary school ruler has millimetres, centimetres, and decimetres marked on it. It is therefore quite easy to build up the length mentioned above – one strip a metre long, three strips of a decimetre, two of a centimetre, five of a millimetre.

Addition of decimals is the same as addition of whole numbers. Multiplication of decimals can be illustrated by means of rectangles, just as was done with ordinary fractions.

Negative Numbers

A picture in *Punch* during the 1914–18 war showed an official saying to a farmer, 'My dear sir, you cannot kill a whole sheep at once!'

This absurd remark illustrates the fact that *fractions* have no meaning for certain things: you cannot have half a live sheep: you cannot tear a sheet of paper into $3\frac{1}{2}$ pieces. But fractions have a meaning in other connexions: it is quite easy to have $3\frac{1}{2}$ feet of lead piping.

In the same way, there are times when you cannot speak of numbers less than 0: there are other times when you can.

A man may have no children, but he cannot have less than none. A box may have nothing in it: it cannot have less than nothing.

But there are examples where we can go below 0. For instance, in the Fahrenheit system of temperatures, water freezes at 32 degrees, a mixture of water and salt freezes at 0 degrees, and it is possible to have temperatures much colder than this. These temperatures are written with a *minus* sign. Thus —10 degrees means the temperature 10 degrees colder than 0 degrees. A temperature of —22 degrees is met with in refrigerators using ammonia. Note that —22 degrees is *colder* than —10 degrees.

In the same way, we may deal with heights and depths. If a bomb falls into the sea from a height of 50 feet we can trace its descent from 50 feet, to 40, 30, 20, 10, and 0 feet above sea-level. But the bomb need not stop at sea-level. It may descend 10 feet below sea-level, and we may speak of this as a *height of* —10 *feet*.

A man who is in debt to the extent of £1 is worse off than a man who has no money and no debts (like a tramp). The tramp at least is free. If we call the tramp's fortune £0, we may call that of the other man £(—1). When you own £(—1), someone has to give you £1 before you reach the position of owning nothing. To own £(—100) means to be bankrupt to the extent of £100. Again —100 is *worse* than —1. If a minus sign is in front of a number, the order of the numbers is turned right round. £(—1) represents a *better* fortune than £(-10,000).

In the same way, an army retreating at 10 miles an hour might be spoken of as 'advancing at —10 miles an hour'. If the army is moving at '—1 miles an hour', that is *better* than moving at '—10 miles an hour'.

A minus sign turns everything upside down, like the reflection of trees and houses in a river.

For a long time, mathematicians felt that it was unfair to use minus numbers (also called *negative numbers*), but it was found in the course of time that minus numbers could be used, added, subtracted, multiplied and divided, and useful results obtained.

30°

20°

10°

0°

10°

20°

Working With Negative Numbers

We may see how to use minus numbers, if we think of ordinary numbers as meaning something *given*, minus numbers as something *taken away*. We might think of 5, for instance, as a five-pound note, or as something given five times: —5 would then mean a bill for £5, or something taken away five times.

Very often we put brackets round minus numbers. For instance, if we want to say 'add —4 to —3', it looks rather queer if we write simply —4 + —3. So we write (—4) + (—3). This means that the thing in the first bracket, —4, has to be added to the thing in the second bracket, —3. (—4) — (—3) would mean that we had to take —3 away from —4.

What would these things mean in practice? We might say that —4 added to —3 meant that a man already owed £4, and then he got a further bill for £3, so that he would be altogether £7 in debt. Or an army might have lost 4 miles of territory, and then lost another 3 miles. The second *loss* has been *added* to the *first*. In either case, we see that a *loss of* 4 together with a *loss of* 3 is the same as a single *loss of* 7. In the signs of arithmetic, (—4) + (—3) = (—7).

In the same way, if we have to add 4 and —3, this means a *gain* of 4 followed by a *loss* of 3, which is clearly the same as a single gain of 1. In short, 4 + (—3) = 1. In fact, 4 + (—3) means exactly the same as 4 —3.

There is nothing new in this, except the signs, and these signs are often used in ordinary life, to show the changes in trade, in unemployment, in the state of parties at elections, + for increases, — for decreases.

Subtracting minus numbers is sometimes a little confusing at first. It is well first to be clear what subtraction means. 7 —3 = 4 means that a man with £7 as compared with a man having £3 is £4 better off. Subtraction means comparing two things. And we can compare losses as well as gains. An army which has lost 200 men is better off than an army which has lost 1,000 men to the extent of 800 men's lives saved. A *loss* of 200 is written for short —200. A *loss* of 1,000 is written —1,000. To *compare* the two we subtract. $(-200) - (-1,000) = 800$. Note that there is no *minus* sign with the 800. If two opposing armies begin by being equal, the one that loses 200 men is *stronger* than its opponent, who loses 1,000, by 800 living men.

We could instead interpret $(-200) - (-1,000) = 800$ as meaning that a man bankrupt for £200 is better off than a man bankrupt for £1,000 by £800. Or we could say that a wreck 200 feet below sea level is higher up than one 1,000 feet down by the amount of 800 feet. It would be correspondingly easier to salvage.

Multiplication? We can only mention this briefly. We may think of 4×5 as meaning, 'Give someone four £5 notes.' This is the same as giving £20, and $4 \times 5 = 20$.

What would $4 \times (-5)$ mean? -5 stands for taking away £5, or for a bill for £5. $4 \times (-5)$ means 'Four bills for £5', the same then as 'A bill for £20'. So $4 \times (-5) = -20$.

$(-4) \times 5$ comes to much the same thing. It would correspond to 'Take away four £5 notes', that is, 'Take away £20.' So $(-4) \times 5 = -20$.

The trickiest case is $(-4) \times (-5)$. Treating -5 as meaning 'A bill for £5' and -4 as 'Take away 4 times', $(-4) \times (-5)$ would mean 'Take away 4 bills for £5'. If the postman comes to you and says, 'I think you have four bills for £5. They should have been delivered to the family next door,' you find yourself £20 better off than you would have been, had the bills really been meant for you. 'Better off' means $+$. So the effect of two minuses, *multiplied together*, is to give $+$. We conclude that $(-4) \times (-5) = 20$.

You may very likely feel that this is a tremendous song-and-dance about nothing at all. Everyone knows that you are better off if your creditors destroy your I.O.U.s. Why make all this fuss about $+$ and $-$ signs? The answer is that we are not going to use minus signs simply to find out what happens to people in debt. Rather we are going to be concerned with formulae, such as $y = x^2 - 3x$, or $y = (x-1)(x-2)$, in which $-$ signs may occur. That is why we have to know how to handle minus signs. What formulae are, and what uses can be made of them, will appear in later chapters.

Imaginary Numbers, or Operators

You will notice that 3 × 3 is 9, and —3 × —3 is also 9. There is no ordinary number (either + or —) which, when multiplied by itself, gives —9. 'Two minuses make a plus.'

It is usual to call 3 × 3 'the square of 3': 9 is the square of 3. 9 is also the square of —3. 3 and —3 are called the 'square roots' of 9.

Every possible number has two square roots: one +, one —. The square roots of 4 are +2 and —2. The square roots of 10 are (very nearly) 3·16 and —3·16.

But negative numbers do not seem to have any square roots. —9 has not, nor has —4 or —10. So far as square roots are concerned, negative numbers are the Cinderellas of mathematics. But mathematicians have succeeded in finding a sort of substitute. If they have not found a man for Cinderella, they have at least found a robot. These robots are called Operators. Operators are not Numbers, but they can do many things which real numbers do, just as robots do *some* things that men do. For instance, you can multiply operators. And a particular operator, called '3i', is such that 3i times 3i is —9, while another, called 'i', is such that i × i = —1.

This 'i' sounds like a mathematical fairy story. The interesting thing is that for many very practical purposes – such as wireless or electric lighting – 'i' is very useful indeed. We shall later on explain what 'i' is, and show that there is nothing mysterious about it at all.

EXERCISES

Questions of Pattern

In questions 1–4, squared paper can be used, as was done in connexion with the multiplication tables. For each question, the reader should consider what is the best number of squares to have in each row. For instance, in the first question, if we take 9 squares in each row (as illustrated) what is happening becomes clear.

1. Albert Smith and his wife Betty are both in the forces. Albert is off duty every ninth evening: his wife is off duty every sixth evening. Albert is off duty this evening: Betty is off duty tomorrow evening. When (if ever) will they be off duty the same evening?

A	B					B	
A			B				
A	B					B	
A			B				
A	B					B	
A			B				

In the pattern, each square represents an evening. It is marked A when Albert is free, B when Betty is. It will be seen that the Bs always come in the 2nd, 5th or 8th column – never in the 1st, where the As are. The answer is: They are never free together.

2. In Question 1, would it have made any difference, if Betty had been free every fifth night, instead of every sixth?

3. On a fire-watching rota Alf watches every third night, Bill every fourth night, Charlie every fifth night, Dave every sixth, and Edward every seventh night. All the men begin their duties on the same night, a Friday.

How long will it be before Alf and Bill are again on duty together? Alf and Charlie? Bill and Charlie?

Will Alf and Charlie ever be on duty together without Dave being there?

On Fridays, when not fire-watching, the men attend a club. How often does Alf miss club night? How often do the others miss it?

Is there any night of the week for which Alf can make a regular appointment? Or does he, sooner or later, do duty on every day of the week? How are the others placed in this respect?

(Use squared paper, with 7 in a row, so that all the Sundays come in one column, etc.)

4. Can you see any principle underlying the answers to Question 3? Can you answer the question – How long will it be before Alf, Bill, Charlie, Dave, and Edward are all again on duty the same night? What night of the week will this be?

5. Two men are walking side by side. One takes four steps in the same time that the other takes three. At the beginning they step off together. In what order will the sound of their footsteps be heard?

(Draw a line, representing the passing of time, and mark on it the moments when the feet of the two men strike the ground.)

6. Question 5 may be varied as much as desired – 5 steps against 4, 7 steps against 5, etc. – and the diagrams drawn.

7. A box has to be made, which can be exactly filled, *either* with packages 6 inches long, *or* with packages 8 inches long, placed end to end. What is the smallest length that the box can be made?

Two Questions for Research

A mathematician does not usually just solve a problem and then forget all about it. If he has solved a problem, he starts altering the conditions of the problem, and sees if he can still solve the problem. He wants to make sure that he will be able to answer any question *of that type* that may confront him in future. He wants to discover if there is any simple principle or rule underlying the problem. You can see from the two examples below how a mathematician goes to work.

The Cup-Tie Problem. If 7 teams enter for a knock-out competition, how many matches will have to be played? (It may be assumed that there are no draws or replays.)

In the first round, one team must be given a bye, and 3 matches will be played. This will leave 4 teams for the second round, the semi-final. There will be 2 matches in the semi-final. There is 1 match in the final round. The total number of matches is $3 + 2 + 1$. The answer is therefore 6.

The particular problem is easily answered. But suppose, instead of 7 teams, 70 or 700 had entered. How many matches would be necessary then? It would take rather a long time to work out directly. It would help us a lot if we could find a simple rule that saves working out all the rounds separately.

To see if there is any simple rule, a mathematician would start

333

working out the simplest possible cases. If only 1 team entered, no matches at all would be necessary. 2 teams could settle the question by playing 1 match. Work out how many matches would be necessary in the cases where 3, 4, 5, 6, etc., teams entered. You will soon see that there is a simple rule connecting the number of teams with the number of matches.

Lastly, can you see the reason *why* there is this simple rule? How many matches would have to be played if 2,176,893 teams entered a competition?

The Income Problem. There is a well-known puzzle, as follows.

Two clerks are appointed in an office. Smith is to be paid yearly, starting at £105, and rising by £10 each year. Jones is to be paid half-yearly, starting with £50, and rising £5 each half-year. Which has made the better bargain?

Most people are rather surprised when they see how this works out. All one needs to do is to write down what each receives, as follows –

	SMITH	JONES		
		January–June	July–December	Total
	£	£	£	£
1st Year	105	50	55	105
2nd Year	115	60	65	125
3rd Year	125	70	75	145
4th Year	135	80	85	165

One naturally thinks that a rise of £5 every half-year is the same as a rise of £10 every year. But it is not. The yearly salary of Jones rises by £20 each year. He has made a much better bargain than Smith.

This question naturally suggests others. A rise of £5 every six months is as good as a rise of £20 a year. What would have happened if the payment had been quarterly? What is a rise of £5 a quarter worth, in terms of yearly salary? Or monthly pay? What is £1 a month rise worth, in yearly pay? What is 1s. a week's rise in weekly pay equal to?

Or the other way round – what rise every six months is the same as a rise of £10 each year? Every quarter? Every month? Every week?

What is the principle involved? Why do things work out this way?

CHAPTER 6

HOW TO FORGET THE MULTIPLICATION TABLE

'My lord, I have undertaken this long journey purposely to see your person, and to know by what engine of wit or ingenuity you came first to think of this most excellent help in astronomy, viz. the logarithms; but, my lord, being by you so found out, I wonder nobody found it out before, when now known it is so easy.'

– Briggs to Napier (From F. Cajori, *History of Mathematics*)

IF you ask an engineer, 'What is 3 times 4?' he does not answer at once. He fishes a contraption known as a slide-rule out of his pocket, fiddles with it for a moment, and then says, 'Oh, about 12'. This may not impress you very much. But if you say to him, 'What is 371 times 422?' he will give you the answer to this, in just about the same time, and without needing to write down any figures.

What is a slide-rule? How is it made? How was it invented? How is it used?

A slide-rule consists of two scales, on each of which can be seen the numbers 1, 2, 3, 4, 5, etc. These numbers are not spaced evenly, like the numbers on a 12-inch ruler. The distance between

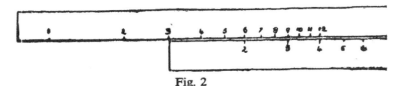

Fig. 2

2 and 3 is less than that between 1 and 2, and the further you go the more closely the numbers are crowded together.

Fig. 2 shows how the engineer would set his slide-rule to find 3×4. He pushes the lower scale along, until the 1 on it is opposite the 3 on the upper scale. Now notice how the numbers stand opposite each other. Above 2, there stands 6: above 3, 9: above 4, 12. Above every number on the lower scale, one finds three times that number on the upper scale. So we read off the number above 4, and that gives us our answer 12.

What principle lies behind the working of this instrument? How could anyone have been led to invent it? Why is it possible to make a multiplying machine at all?

We are all familiar with machines which man uses to *multiply* his own strength – pulleys, levers, gears, etc. Suppose you are fire-watching on the roof of a house, and have to lower an injured comrade by means of a rope. It would be natural to pass the rope round some object, such as a post, so that the friction of the rope on the post would assist you in checking the speed of your friend's descent. In breaking-in horses the same idea is used: a rope passes round a post, one end being held by a man, the other fastened to the horse. To get away, the horse would have to pull many times harder than the man.

The effect of such an arrangement depends on the roughness of the rope. Let us suppose that we have a rope and a post which multiply one's strength by ten, when the rope makes one complete turn.

What will be the effect if we have a series of such posts? A pull of 1 lb. at A is sufficient to hold 10 lb. at B, and this will hold 100 lb. at C, or 1,000 lb. at D (Fig. 3).

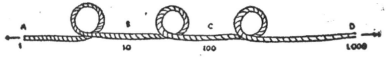

Fig. 3

Each extra post multiplies by 10. One post magnifies by 10: two by 10×10: three by $10 \times 10 \times 10$.

As it takes too much space to write long rows of tens, an abbreviation is usually written. 10^2 is written for 10×10. 10^3 for $10 \times 10 \times 10$, and so on. (In the same way, 8^5 would mean $8 \times 8 \times 8 \times 8 \times 8$.)

Thus 10^8 *will represent the effect of 8 posts*, and 10^{11} the effect of 11. This is a *multiplying* effect. If we pass a rope round 8 posts and then round a further 11 posts, the effect will be $10^8 \times 10^{11}$. But 8 posts and 11 posts add up to 19, so that this must be exactly the same thing as 10^{19}.

The number of turns required to get any number is called the logarithm of the number. For instance, you need 6 posts to multiply your strength by 1,000,000. So 6 is the logarithm of 1,000,000. In the same way, 4 is the logarithm of 10,000.

So far we have spoken of whole turns. But the same idea would apply to incomplete turns. If you gradually wind a rope round a post, the effect also increases gradually. At first you must bear the entire weight yourself: as the rope winds on to the post, friction comes to your aid, and there will be stages at which you can hold twice, three times, four times the amount of your pull. When one complete turn is on, you will have reached ten times.

Accordingly, $10^{\frac{1}{2}}$ will mean the magnifying effect of half a turn, $10^{2\frac{3}{8}}$ will mean the effect of $2\frac{3}{8}$ turns. And so for any number.

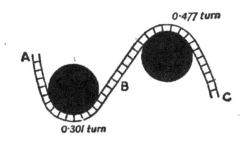

Fig. 4

The logarithm of 2 will be that *fraction of a turn* which is necessary to magnify your pull 2 times. This number is usually called 'log 2' for short. Actually, $0 \cdot 301$ of a turn is required to

337

magnify 2 times. 0·477 of a turn magnifies 3 times: so that log 3=0·477. (These numbers could be found by experiment.)

We can put this another way round. 2 is the effect of 0·301 of a turn. So $2=10^{0.301}$. In the same way, $3=10^{0.477}$.

Now what will happen if we wind 0·301 of a turn on one post, and then 0·477 on the next?

We know that the effect of the first post is to double our effort. If we pull A with a force of 1 lb. it will be sufficient to balance a tension of 2 lb. in the rope at B (Fig. 4). The second post multiplies by 3: 2 lb. at B will balance 6 lb. at C. So 1 lb. at A will hold 6 lb. at C. And, on the two posts together, we have 0·301+ 0·477 = 0·778 of a turn.

0·778 of a turn is needed to multiply 6 times. 0·778 is the logarithm of 6. The logarithm of 3 × 2 has been found by *adding together* log 3 and log 2.

It is not necessary to use separate posts. We can economize in timber by winding the rope again and again round the same post. The only thing that matters is the length of rope *in contact* with the wood. (The post itself must be round. Corners would cause complications.)

If we were given two pieces of rope, and knew that one piece was sufficient to multiply 7 times, and the other sufficient to multiply 8 times, we should only have to join these pieces end to end, to get a piece that would multiply by 7 × 8.

It is exactly this principle of joining *end to end* that is used in the slide rule. On the slide rule, the distance between 1 and 3 is equal to the length of rope required to multiply 3 times; the distance between 1 and 4 is equal to the length of rope required to multiply 4 times; and in finding 3 × 4 we place these lengths end to end.

1 of course comes at the end of the scale, as you do not need any rope at all to multiply your strength by 1.

You will now be able to see why numbers crowd together on the slide-rule as we go farther along. 1 corresponds to no rope; 10 to 1 turn; 100 to 2 turns; 1,000 to 3 turns. The distance on the slide-rule from 1 to 10 is the same as that from 10 to 100, or from 100 to 1,000: each of these is equal to 'one complete turn'. But we have only 9 numbers to fit between 1 and 10: there are 90 between 10 and 100, 900 between 100 and 1000. This accounts for the overcrowding of the larger numbers.

If we want to get a set of evenly spaced numbers we have to take a set like 1, 10, 100, 1000 . . . or 1, 2, 4, 8, 16, 32 . . . In the first set, each number is 10 times the previous one: there is 1 turn between each and the next. In the second set, each number is twice the previous one: at each step we add a length of rope equal to 0.301 of a complete turn.

How Logarithms are Calculated

We have explained what a logarithm is, but we have not shown how to calculate it. We have said that, on a slide-rule, the distance between 1 and 7 is the length of rope needed to magnify a pull 7 times – i.e., log 7. But to make an actual slide-rule we should need to know log 2, log 3, log 4, etc., so that we could mərk 2, 3, 4 . . . at the corresponding distances.

The only logarithms that have been found so far are those of 10, 100, 1000, etc. We know that these are 1, 2, 3 . . . All this tells us about log 70 is that it must lie somewhere between 1 and 2: for we need more than one turn, but less than 2, to produce any numbers between 10 and 100.

There is one other thing that is vague. We have spoken all along of so many complete 'turns'. But the size of the post has not been specified. We could in fact take a circular post of any size, and pass a rope round it. This arrangement might multiply our pull by less than 10: we could correct this by making the post more rough. If it magnified our pull too much, we could correct this by polishing the post. So that we may suppose 'one turn' to represent any length we like. A slide-rule can be made any size we like. We could, for instance, mark 1 at the end of the scale, and 10 at a distance of one foot. 100 would have to come 2 feet from 1, 1000 3 feet – and by this time we should feel that the whole thing had got quite large enough. Notice that our simple argument has only helped us to mark four points on a yard stick – 1, 10, 100, 1000.

But we could go about the question another way. If we start from 1 and keep *doubling*, we shall also get a set of evenly spaced points: the distance between each point and the next is log 2. (Earlier, we stated that log 2 was 0·301. But *no reason* was given for this statement.) Instead of fixing our scale by taking 10 at 1 foot, suppose we fix it by taking 2 at a convenient distance. We might choose it at an inch from 1. 4, being 2 × 2, must now come at 2 inches; 8, being 2 × 4, will come at 3 inches; 16 at 4 inches; 32 at 5; 64 at 6; 128 at 7; 256 at 8; 512 at 9; 1024 at 10. This slide-rule has turned out to be smaller than the last one: 1000 this time has come just below 10 inches from 1. But that is not the important point. The chief thing to notice is that the first slide-rule had only four points on it – 1, 10, 100, 1000. But our second attempt has given us *eleven points* – 1, 2, 4, 8, 16, 32, 64, 128 256, 512, 1024. This suggests that we shall get still better results by taking, instead of 10 or 2, some number closer to 1, such as $1\frac{1}{8}$, or 1·1, or 1·01. It will take more work, with the smaller numbers, to get from 1 to 1000; but once the slide-rule has been made, we shall be able to use it whenever multiplication has to be done, and the work is thus repaid.

Before we leave our slide-rule with eleven points, we may notice that it enables us to get a rough idea of the value of log 2. We saw that 1024 was marked at a distance of 10 inches, so that 10 inches of rope around the post multiply our effort by 1024. But we know that three complete turns multiply by 1000. So that 10 inches must be slightly more than three complete turns. One inch must be slightly more than $\frac{3}{10}$, or 0·3, of a turn. But the figure 2 is marked at a distance of 1 inch. So that 2 corresponds to slightly more than 0·3 of a turn, which is the same as saying that log 2 is just over 0·3. So that our earlier statement that log 2 was 0·301 was at least near to the truth.

How Logarithms were Invented

We made our second slide-rule by a process of continual doubling. We shall now make a better one, using 1·1 instead of 2.

Suppose, then, that we mark on our scale two points, to

represent 1 and 1·1. The distance between them could be, say, $\frac{1}{10}$ inch. We then know that moving $\frac{1}{10}$ inch down the scale (if you prefer, adding $\frac{1}{10}$ inch to the length of the rope) represents multiplication by 1·1. We shall thus be able to mark the points 1, 1·1, 1·21, 1·331, etc., each number being one and one-tenth times the previous one.

This set of numbers is exactly the set that you get if you allow £1 to accumulate at compound interest of 10% over a number of years. Each year that passes increases the sum invested by one-tenth – that is, every year multiplies the amount by 1·1. It was probably the study of tables of compound interest that originally suggested the idea of logarithms to their inventor, Napier.

Some of the numbers found in this way, and the distances at which they have to be marked, are shown in the following table.

Number	Distance (inches)
1·948	0·7
2·143	0·8
2·852	1·1
3·137	1·2
5·053	1·7
6·725	2·0
7·397	2·1
9·846	2·4
10·831	2·5

This shows us that the figure 2 has to be marked somewhere between 0·7 and 0·8 inch; 5 just below 1·7 inches; 7 somewhere between 2·0 and 2·1 inches; 10 a little above 2·4 inches. So 'one turn' corresponds to a little more than 2·4 inches.

This information is still not sufficient for making a really good slide-rule. For instance, we cannot find an accurate position for the figure 7. Our table contains no number between 6·725 and 7·397. We can only guess where 7 lies, between these two numbers. Our slide-rule would, in fact, be liable to errors of about 10%: owing to the fact that the numbers are obtained by adding on 10% at a time – we cannot expect any higher degree of accuracy.

We can use this table to find the logarithms of the numbers 2, 3; 4, etc., but the results for this also are likely to be crude. 'One turn' is the distance corresponding to 10: we guess it to be 2·42 inches. To 2 corresponds a distance between 0·7 and 0·8 inch – perhaps 0·73. If we express 0·73 as a fraction of a 'turn', we shall have an estimate of log 2. 0·73 divided by 2·42 gives 0·3016 – a suspiciously good result for a guess!

The reader will easily see how accurate slide-rules and tables of logarithms can be made, by using a number such as 1·000001 for repeated multiplication. Napier, in making the first tables of logarithms, used 1·0000001.

It is not, of course, necessary for us to make our own tables of logarithms. This work has been done once and for all. The only advantage to be gained from making your own table of logarithms and your own slide-rule is the insight this gives into the underlying principles.

The method of making logarithm tables, described above, shows clearly why such tables can be used for multiplication. We found, for instance, that multiplying by 1·1 seven times was the same as multiplying once by 1·948; while multiplying seventeen times by 1·1 was the same as multiplying once by 5·053 (see the table above). So 1·948 × 5·053 corresponds to 7 multiplications by 1·1, followed by 17 more – that is, it corresponds to 24 multiplications. And this (from our table) corresponds to 9·846. So 1·948 × 5·053 = 9·846.

The method is clear. 1·948 is the 7th number; 5·053 is the 17th; 7 + 17 = 24; the 24th number in the table gives the answer.

In making our slide-rule, we put 1·1 a tenth of an inch from 1, 1·948 seven times as far away, and so on. It does not matter how far 1·1 is from 1, so long as 1·948 is seven times that distance, 5·053 seventeen times as far, etc. The argument will still hold.

In ordinary logarithm tables, log 10 is 1. We saw, on our slide-rule, that 10 came between 24 and 25 times the distance of 1·1. If we choose a distance for 1·1 which lies somewhere between $\frac{1}{24}$ and $\frac{1}{25}$ inch, we shall get 10 coming at a distance of 1 inch. The distance corresponding to any number will be its logarithm.

This change of scale rather camouflages the simple relation,

$7 + 17 = 24$. In the logarithm tables, $1 \cdot 1$ corresponds to $\cdot 0414$; $1 \cdot 948$ to $\cdot 2896$; $5 \cdot 053$ to $\cdot 7036$. In the surface, there is nothing simple about these numbers. But notice these facts. (i) log $1 \cdot 1$ lies between $\frac{1}{24}$ and $\frac{1}{25}$, as we expected, (ii) log $1 \cdot 948$ is seven times log $1 \cdot 1$, and log $5 \cdot 053$ is seventeen times log $1 \cdot 1$. The simple relations are still there. The change of scale does not in any way alter the method: to multiply numbers we add their logarithms.

If we are asked to calculate an expression such as 12^{35} – i.e., the effect of multiplying by 12 thirty-five times – this is easily done. To multiply by 12, one has to add log 12 to the logarithm of the number being multiplied. If one multiplies by 12 thirty-five times, one will thus add log 12 thirty-five times; log 12 is $1 \cdot 0792$. Thirty-five times this is $37 \cdot 772$. $37 \cdot 772$ is the logarithm of 5916 followed by 34 noughts! So this, roughly, is the effect of multiplying by 12 thirty-five times. It would take rather long to find this result by any other method.

A Musical Slide-Rule

One well-known object is in effect a slide-rule – a piano keyboard. The strings at the bottom end of a piano vibrate slowly: as one goes up the keyboard, the rate increases. An octave corresponds to doubling the rate of vibration. Each note vibrates about 6% more rapidly than the note immediately below it. Every time one goes a certain distance along the keyboard, one multiplies the rate by a corresponding amount. This is just the same thing as happens on a slide-rule.

EXERCISES

1. If you can get hold of a slide-rule and a book of Logarithm Tables, verify the statement made in the text, that every number is marked on the slide-rule at a distance proportional to its logarithm.

2. Make a slide-rule for yourself, using tables of logarithms to tell you at what distance each number should be marked.

3. Make a slide-rule by the method explained in Chapter 6.

4. Where is the square root of 10 marked on a slide-rule?

5. Check the accuracy of your slide-rule by finding on it 2×2, 2×3, 4×5 and other simple multiplications.

6. The logarithm of 2 is $0 \cdot 301$. The logarithm of $1 \cdot 05$ is $0 \cdot 0212$. How many years will money invested at 5% require to double itself?

7. An Eastern monarch sends 10,000 golden vessels to a brother monarch, whose kingdom is many days march distant. The gift is carried on camels. Each merchant, who supplies camels for some part of the journey, demands as commission 10% of what passes through his hands. Thus the first merchant hands over to the second not 10,000, but 9,000 golden vessels. Altogether, the vessels pass through the hands of twenty merchants. How many vessels does the brother monarch receive at the end?

CHAPTER **7**

ALGEBRA – THE SHORTHAND
OF MATHEMATICS

'*Mathematics* is *a language*.' – J. Willard Gibbs.

ALGEBRA plays a part in mathematics which may be compared to that of writing or of shorthand in ordinary life. It can be used either to make a statement or to give instructions, in a concise form.

Shorthand, of itself, does not make new discoveries possible. In the same way, most problems that can be solved by algebra can also be solved by common sense. Statements in algebra can be translated into ordinary speech, and vice versa. The statement in algebra is much shorter: some facts or instructions, which are easily written in algebraic form, are too long and complicated in ordinary speech. This is the advantage of algebra: while results *could* be got without it, it is unlikely that they *would*.

We shall consider some simple questions – perhaps not very

344

useful ones – to illustrate the form given to common-sense arguments, when the symbols of algebra are used.

The Cakes and Buns Problem

Most books on algebra, in a chapter headed 'Simultaneous Equations', deal with some such question as this. 'I visit a tea-shop on two occasions. The first time I order two buns and a cake; my bill is for 4*d*. The second time I order three buns and two cakes; the bill is for 7*d*. What are the prices of buns and cakes?'

I have tried this problem on people who know nothing about algebra, and they usually solve it. They argue: the second bill is 3*d*. more than the first. So 3*d*. represents the cost of the extra bun and cake. A bun and a cake cost 3*d*. But two buns and a cake cost 4*d*. So the difference, 1*d*., is the cost of a bun. A cake must cost 2*d*.

This problem may not sound important, yet in one form or another it repeatedly occurs in mathematical investigations of a very practical type. We shall ourselves need to solve such a problem in Chapter 8.

Mathematicians have therefore been forced to apply the argument outlined above on many different occasions. And – like other people – they have gradually introduced abbreviations to shorten the work. One can imagine the argument soon being written –

	2 buns & 1 cake	4*d*.
	3 buns & 2 cakes	7*d*.
So	1 bun & 1 cake	3*d*.
But	2 buns & 1 cake	4*d*.
So	1 bun	1*d*.
And	1 cake	2*d*.

Later one might begin to write '*b*' where 'bun' comes, '*c*' for 'cake'. If we replace '&' by '+', we have the modern form

$$2b + c = 4$$
$$3b + 2c = 7$$

345

So	$b + c = 3$
But	$2b + c = 4$
So	$b = 1$
And	$c = 2$

In this, b stands for the number of pence paid for a bun, c the number paid for a cake. You will notice that we write $2b$ for twice the number b. We do not write any multiplication sign between the 2 and the b. It is no use arguing whether a multiplication sign ought to be written here. If you feel happier with $2 \times b$, by all means write it that way. It is open to the objection that we often use x to represent a number, and $\times$ might easily be confused with x.

Of course $12b$ means *twelve* times b, not $1 \times 2 \times b$. You may feel it is confusing to have this distinction – but every shorthand system has its faults. In algebra, numbers such as 123 placed together have the same meaning as in arithmetic, but $2bc$ mean $2 \times b \times c$.

Try translating into ordinary language the following statements:

$$b + c + t = 6$$
$$2b + 3c + t = 11$$
$$4b + 8c + t = 23$$

b and c here have the same meanings as before, but each meal now contains a pot of tea costing t pence. This problem is also quite simple to solve. If you consider the difference in cost between the first meal and the second, you will obtain an equation which contains only b and c. Comparing the second meal with the third, you will get another statement, in which the price of tea does not appear. You now have two statements about buns and cakes:

$$b + 2c = 5$$
$$2b + 5c = 12.$$

If a bun and 2 cakes cost $5d.$, 2 buns and 4 cakes – twice as much – must cost $10d.$ So $2b + 4c = 10$. But we have above $2b + 5c = 12$. Comparing these, we see that $c = 2$. So $b = 1$. Going back to the first meal, we see that $t = 3$.

ALGEBRA – THE SHORTHAND OF MATHEMATICS

WORDS	PICTURE	ALGEBRA
I. Think of a number.		n
II. Add 6 to it.		$n+6$
III. Multiply by 2.		$2(n+6)$ or $2n+12.$
IV. Take away 8.		$2(n+6)-8$ or $2n+4$
V. Divide by 2.		$\dfrac{2(n+6)-8}{2}$ or $n+2$
VI. Take away the number you first thought of.		$\dfrac{2(n+6)-8}{2}-n$ or 2.
VII. The answer is 2.		$\dfrac{2(n+6)-8}{2}-n$ $=2.$

Each bag is supposed to contain as many marbles as
the number you thought of, whatever that was.

The same picture can often be described in different ways. Thus we
might describe the picture III as 'A bag and six marbles, twice,' or
simply as 'Two bags and twelve marbles.' In algebraic shorthand, these
descriptions are $2(n+6)$ and $2n+12$.

As a rule, there is no difficulty is solving problems of this type.
This shorthand can also be used to state truths. An old trick
runs as follows. 'Think of a number. Add 6 to it. Multiply by 2.
Take away 8. Divide by 2. Take away the number you first

347

thought of.' Whatever number you think of, the answer is always 2. Why?

We could deal with this by thinking in pictures. You think of a number – any number. We will think of this as marbles placed in a bag. 'Add 6 to it.' This gives us one bag and six loose marbles. 'Multiply by two' – two bags and twelve marbles. 'Take away 8' – two bags and four marbles. 'Divide by 2' – one bag and two marbles. 'Take away the number you first thought of' – that is, take away the bag. Two marbles remain – whatever the number in the bag.

In algebra, we need not talk about bags of marbles. We say, let n stand for the number you think of. 'Add 6'; we get $n + 6$. 'Multiply by 2', $2n + 12$. 'Subtract 8', $2n + 4$. 'Divide by 2', $n + 2$. 'Take away n', 2 is the answer.

We can express the whole process, and the fact that the answer is always 2, by writing the single equation

$$\frac{2(n + 6) - 8}{2} - n = 2.$$

The expression on the left-hand side indicates that you take twice $(n + 6)$, subtract 8, and divide by 2, finally subtract n. One line of symbols replaces a paragraph of talk.

This example shows that two apparently different expressions may in fact represent the same thing. An important part of algebra therefore consists in learning how to express any result in the simplest possible way: this is known as Simplifying.

It is sometimes possible for a question to have two answers which at first sight appear different, but which are actually both correct.

Suppose, for instance, you were asked to discover the rule by which the following numbers have been chosen: 0, 3, 8, 15, 24, 35, 48, 63. You might notice that these numbers are given by the rule 1^2-1, 2^2-1, 3^2-1, 4^2-1, 5^2-1, 6^2-1, 7^2-1, 8^2-1. (You will remember from Chapter 6 that 5^2 is short for 5×5.) In short, the n^{u} number is n^2-1.

But you might also notice that 63 is 7×9, that 48 is 6×8, and so on. The eighth number is the number before 8 (that is, 7) multiplied by the number after 8 (that is, 9). The first number, 0, is the number before 1 (i.e., 0) multiplied by the number after 1 (i.e., 2). This suggests the rule for the nth number: multiply the number before n (which is $n - 1$) by the number after n (which is $n + 1$). This gives us the formula $(n - 1)(n + 1)$.

Both these rules are correct. Whatever number you may choose for n, you will always find that $(n - 1)(n + 1)$ is the same as $n^2 - 1$.

Here we have used algebraic signs as a shorthand for writing *instructions*, how to find the numbers in a certain set. This use of algebra is very common. The person who uses a formula need not understand why a formula is right. For instance, a sapper who has to blow up a railway bridge will work out how much explosive to use by means of a formula: he does not need to know how the formula is obtained in the first place. In the same way, there is a rule which says, if you wish to see n miles out to sea, you must have your eyes $\dfrac{2n^2}{3}$ feet above sea-level. This formula is found by means of geometry: but without knowing any geometry you can use this formula, and discover that a tall man on the beach can see nearly 3 miles out to sea (since $\dfrac{2 \times 3^2}{3}$ gives 6 feet as the height needed), while to see 12 miles, you need a cliff 96 feet high. Such a formula could be used in designing a battleship, to tell how high an observer must be to see the effect of the ship's guns.

Most formulae contain several different letters. For instance, we might wish to know how much metal is required to make a circular tube. We must be told how long the tube is, how thick the wall is, and the measurement around the tube. Let us call the *length L* inches, the *thickness T* inches, the outside *measurement* around the tube M inches. A formula tells us the tube will then contain $LT(M - 3 \cdot 14T)$ cubic inches of metal. Thus a tube 10 inches long, $\frac{1}{2}$ inch thick, and 15 inches round will contain $10 \times \frac{1}{2} \times (15 - 3 \cdot 14 \times \frac{1}{2}) = 5 \times 13 \cdot 43 = 67 \cdot 15$ cubic inches. A rule such as this could be stated in words, but would be much longer. The shorthand is so simple – L for length, T for thickness,

M for measurement – that no difficulty can arise in learning it. Yet many people are terrified by the sight of a page of algebraic symbols, and others have a reputation for immense intelligence because they understand algebra.

In bygone ages, a man who could read and write counted as a scholar. Today we think nothing of reading and writing. Algebra too is a language – neither more nor less mysterious than ordinary print, once its alphabet and its grammar have been learned.

EXAMPLES

1. We may express the instructions, 'Think of a number (n), double it, and add 5' by the shorthand sign $2n + 5$. Translate into algebraic shorthand the following sentences –

>   (i) Think of a number, add 5 to it, and double the result.
>   (ii) Think of a number, multiply by 3, and add 2.
>   (iii) Think of a number. Write down the number after it. Add the two numbers together.
>   (iv) Multiply a number by the number after it.
>   (v) Think 'of a number, and multiply it by itself.

2. Translate the following shorthand signs back into sentences such as those of Question 1.

>   (i) $4n + 4$.   (iii) $3(n + 1)$.   (v) $\frac{1}{2}n(n - 1)$.
>   (ii) $n - 1$.   (iv) $\frac{1}{2}(4n + 8)$.

Work out what these signs would give if the number thought of, n, happened to be 6. Also what they would give if the number n was 3.

3. To see n miles out to sea you must have your eye $\dfrac{2n^2}{3}$ feet above sea-level. Make a table showing how high your eye would have to be, in order to see 0, 1, 2, 3, ... 10 miles.

4. We have seen that $(n - 1)(n + 1)$ gives exactly the same number as $n^2 - 1$. We tested this by putting n in turn equal to 1, 2, 3, ... 8. This did not prove that the two expressions were

always the same, but it made it likely. By this test you can show that some of the statements below are *probably true*, while others are *certainly untrue*. Which are which? Here *n* means 'any number.'

(i) $(n + 1) + (n - 1) = 2n$.

(ii) $n = 2n$.

(iii) $2(n + 3) = 2n + 6$.

(iv) $n^3 - 1 = (n - 1)(n^2 + n + 1)$.

(v) $4n + 2$ is always an even number (*n* being a whole number).

(vi) $n(n + 1)$ is always an even number (*n* being a whole number).

(vii) $(n + 1)(n + 1) = n^2 + 1$.

(viii) $\dfrac{2n}{n^2 - 1} = \dfrac{1}{n + 1} + \dfrac{1}{n - 1}.$

5. If it takes *a* minutes to set up a certain machine, and *b* minutes to make a single article on the machine, how long does it take to set up the machine and make 10 articles?

How long would it take to set up the machine and make *n* articles?

Write down in turn the time needed to set up the machine; the time needed to set it up and make 1 article; the time to set it up and make 2 articles, etc.

6. In question 5, the time taken to make *n* articles after setting up the machine is $a + bn$ minutes. The last part of the question requires us to put *n* in turn equal to 0, 1, 2 ... in the formula $a + bn$, giving $a, a + b, a + 2b, \ldots$ etc. Putting a definite value for *n* in the formula is called *substituting* for *n*.

Thus, $a + 2b$ is the result of substituting $n = 2$ in the formula $a + bn$.

Again, if in the formula $n^2 - 1$ we substitute $n = 7$, we get $7^2 - 1$. In question 3, we substituted in turn 0, 1, 2 ... for *n* in the formula $\dfrac{2n^2}{3}$. You will be able to follow the argument of Chapter 8 only if you are familiar with this idea. That is the point of the following examples.

(i) If a train travels at v miles an hour, it goes nv miles in n hours.

Make a table showing how far it goes in 0, 1, 2, 3, 4 and 5 hours.

(ii) What does this table become if $v = 30$, i.e. if the train travels at 30 m.p.h.?

(iii) What does it become if $v = 10$?

(iv) What is the result of substituting $n = 4$ in the expression $5n - 1$?

(v) What is the result of substituting $n = 1$ in $2n^2 + 3n + 5$?

(vi) If you substitute in turn, 0, 1, 2, 3, ... etc., for n in the formula $n^2 + 4n + 4$, what do you notice about the answers?

(vii) What is the result of substituting in turn $n = 0, 1, 2, ...$ in the expression $an^2 + bn + c$?

Note – This last question seems to trouble students, but we need the answer to it for Chapter 8. Compare it with section (v). Putting $n = 1$ in $2n^2 + 3n + 5$ gives 10. For when $n = 1$, n^2 becomes 1^2, that is, 1, and the expression $2n^2 + 3n + 5$ becomes $2 \times 1 + 3 \times 1 + 5$, that is, $2 + 3 + 5$. So that when $n = 1$, the three numbers that occur in the expression (2, 3, and 5) *are simply added together*. This would happen whatever these numbers were. If you put $n = 1$ in the expression (say) $10n^2 + 17n + 35$, you would get the result $10 + 17 + 35$, which adds up to 62. If you put $n = 1$ in any expression of this type (so much n^2, so much n, and a number added together), you get the answer by adding together the three numbers that occur in the expression. So, if you put $n = 1$ in $an^2 + bn + c$ you get the answer $a + b + c$.

In the same way, you will find that the result of putting $n = 0$ is simply to give you the third number.

For instance, when $n = 0$ the expression $4n^2 + 173n + 45$ becomes 45.

When we substitute $n = 0$, $an^2 + bn + c$ becomes c.

You will also find that the result of substituting $n = 2$ is to give you

4 times the first number in the formula.

+2 times the second number in the formula.

+ the third number in the formula.

In shorthand, this result is $4a + 2b + c$.

Find for yourself the rules for what you get when you put $n = 3$, or $n = 4$, or $n = 5$.

If you find great difficulty with this chapter, try to get hold of an engineer, who will tell you just what he does when he uses a formula for a practical problem. The earlier part of Chapter 8 may also help you to see how a formula is used in practical life. It is only towards the end of Chapter 8 – 'The Calculus of Finite Differences' – that we have to do problems similar to Question 6, above.

CHAPTER 8

WAYS OF GROWING

'*When it is considered how essential is their use in a vast range of trades and professions – from plumbing to* Dreadnought *building – it is hardly extravagant to say that facility in the working, interpretation and application of formulae is one of the most important objects at which early mathematical studies can aim.*' – T. Percy Nunn, *The Teaching of Algebra.*

WE are very often interested in knowing how quickly a thing grows. If one skyscraper is twice as high as another, it must have a stronger framework to support the extra weight. It will cost more than twice as much to build. How much more? Four times? Eight times?

As an army advances into hostile territory, the difficulty of bringing up supplies and maintaining communications increases. To cover 1,000 miles requires more than ten times the lorries necessary for 100 miles: how many, then?

If you are fire-watching on a high building, you may need to jump off in an emergency. Is it twice as dangerous to jump from 40 feet as from 20? Or more than twice? Or less than twice?

If a housewife is buying firewood, and pays 6*d.* for a bundle measuring 1 foot around, how much should she pay for one measuring 6 inches?

In all these questions, we are interested in the different ways in which something grows. The answer may be quite important for practical purposes. Anyone who tries to provide housing economically has to know the answer to the first question: otherwise he may find that a saving in ground-rent has been altogether swallowed up in extra costs for building material.

Again, many would-be inventors have been disappointed through ignorance of the effects of change in scale. Many people have, in the past, invented flying-machines and successfully made small models which flew very well. They then enlarged their model, and built a full-size machine – and it would not fly at all. The reason was that the weight of a machine and the lifting-power vary in entirely different ways. If one constructed a flea, enlarged to the size of an elephant, its performance would be entirely different from that of an actual flea – as you can well imagine.

It is therefore quite natural that engineers and scientists expect mathematicians to supply them with a simple way of writing down the manner in which any quantity grows.

Of course, things grow in a great variety of ways. If, for instance, one considers the population of Manchester during the last 150 years, this is a quantity which has changed in a very complicated way. A mathematician can study it, and describe it, but you, must not expect the description to be very short or simple. Many things will enter into it – the Industrial Revolution, the varying fortunes of the cotton trade, evacuation of children in war-time, and so on. On the other hand, some things vary in a very simple way. We shall give examples below. In between these two extremes come a great variety of types of growth, which can be studied and written down with greater or less difficulty. You must not expect mathematics to make a complicated question simple. Mathematics may help us to discover the underlying causes of things, but if the causes are many and intricate, then the mathematical description too will be far from simple. We shall here study simple cases only: do not make the mistake of supposing that every problem, however profound, can be forced into these simple forms.

The Simplest Form of Growth

An example of a simple relation is the cost of any article bought by the yard. If one yard of lath costs 2*d.*, 2 yards will cost 4*d.*, *x* yards will cost 2*x* pence. If *p* stands for the price in pence of *x* yards, we have $p = 2x$.

We can make this formula more general. A yard of lath need not

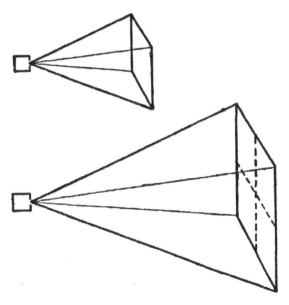

THE SIZE OF CINEMA SCREENS

In the lower diagram the screen is twice as far from the projector as in the upper diagram. The lower screen is twice as broad and twice as high as the upper one. The dotted lines show that the lower screen could be cut into four screens, each as large as the upper screen.

cost 2*d*. Suppose it costs *a* pence, where *a* may stand for any number. Then the price of *x* yards is given by $p = ax$. We assume that the price of each yard does not depend on the number of yards bought: there is to be no reduction for quantity. In mathematical language this is stated by saying that *a* is *constant*.

Such relations are common. For instance, the circumference and diameter of a circle – *C* and *D* – are connected by the relation $C = 3 \cdot 14 \, D$. Again, in a spring-balance the spring stretches by a distance proportional to the weight hung on it. If I lb. causes the spring to stretch *k* inches, than *x* lb. will cause it to stretch *kx* inches. This fact was discovered by Hooke, about 1660. Hooke was led to study the properties of springs by his work on clock-making. His invention of the balance-wheel – by which a hair-spring replaces the pendulum of a clock – was a practical consequence of his investigation. Hooke's Law is true only for reasonably small weights. A very heavy weight will stretch a spring too far: when the weight is removed the spring does not return to its original length.

Other formulae of the type *ax* will be found in almost every branch of mathematics, engineering or science.

Powers of x

Another type of growth occurs when a cinema projector, or magic lantern, is moved further away from the screen. If you double the distance of a magic lantern from the screen, the picture will take up – not twice, but – four times as much space. If you treble the distance, the amount of material needed for the screen will be nine times as much.

The rule is clear: 4 is 2×2, or 2^2, 9 is 3×3, or 3^2. If we put the lantern *n* times as far away, we need n^2 times as much material for the screen.

In the same way, if we enlarge a photograph or a map *n* times, n^2 times as much paper will be necessary.

We have here the answer to our earlier question about fire-wood. The bundle tied with a 12-inch string contains four times as much firewood as the 6-inch bundle. You can see that the large

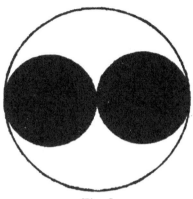

Fig. 5

bundle must contain more than twice the amount of the small one, by looking at Fig. 5. The black part represents two small bundles: the large circle represents one large bundle.

If a stone is dropped from the top of a cliff, you will find that it falls about 16 feet in the first second; after two seconds it has fallen 64 feet; after three seconds, 144 feet. These results can be expressed by the formula that, in x seconds, the stone falls about $16x^2$ feet. Thus in 5 seconds the stone would fall 16 times $5^2 = 16$ times $25 = 400$ feet. If you can remember this formula, and have a watch with you, it is easy to find the height of a cliff, or the depth of a well, by dropping a stone, and noting how many seconds it takes to reach the bottom.

Another formula gives the speed with which it strikes the bottom. This is $v^2 = 64\ h$. In this formula h is the height of the cliff in feet, and v is the velocity, in feet per second, with which the stone lands. If the cliff is 100 feet high, h is 100, so $v^2 = 6,400$, and $v = 80$. To produce a speed twice as big, the cliff would have to be *four* times as high. (This answers the question about fire-watching.) It is easily worked out that a speed of 3 feet a second is roughly the same as 2 miles an hour. So 80 feet a second is about 53 miles an hour. Jumping off a house 100 feet high is as dangerous as a car crash at 53 miles an hour.

In the same way, we could discuss the way of growing represented by x^3. You would need 8 cubes of sugar to make 1 cube with twice the normal measurements. To make a cube x times the usual size, you would need x^3 ordinary cubes. If you enlarge any solid object x times – it need not be a cube – you multiply the material contained by x^3. For instance, if you double all the measurements of a drawer, or a box, or a trunk, you multiply by 8 the amount that can be contained.

357

When a model of any object is enlarged, all these different kinds of growing may be involved. Suppose, for simplicity, we have a box in the form of a cube, made out of cardboard. If the side of the cube is 1 foot, the box will hold 1 cubic foot, 6 square feet of cardboard will be sufficient to make it, and a string 4 feet long could extend round it. If we make instead a box in the form of a cube, but with each side 2 feet long, we find that it holds eight times as much, but that it needs only four times as much cardboard, and a piece of string only twice as long can extend round it. It is cheaper to pack goods in large boxes than in small ones – so long as the cardboard does not burst.

It is easy to see why the early aeroplane inventors had disappointing results, when they tried to enlarge the scale of their models. If the scale is doubled, the weight is multiplied by 8, but the wing-surface is multiplied by only 4.

x, x^2, and x^3 thus turn up naturally enough, when we consider changes in the scale of models and plans. In other applications, we make use of x^4, x^5, x^6 and so on.

For instance, a common device for storing energy is a flywheel. Suppose we make two flywheels by cutting circular pieces out of a sheet of metal – one circle having twice the radius of the other. Suppose both wheels are turning at the same rate – say, one revolution a second. Will the large wheel have twice, or four times, or eight times the energy of the small one? No. Experiment shows that it has *sixteen* times as much, 2^4 as much, that is. If we enlarge the radius x times, we increase the energy x^4 times. Aeroplane engines can be started by means of a flywheel. The flywheel is made to rotate by hand, and is then suddenly connected to the aeroplane engine. If you were using the larger flywheel, mentioned above, you would have sixteen times the energy at your disposal, as compared with a man using the small one: as it would take you sixteen times as long to get your flywheel spinning, you would obtain a vivid picture of the meaning of 2^4!

If you double not only the radius of the flywheel, but also the thickness of the metal, you multiply the energy by 2^5, or 32. In this case, the bigger flywheel is twice as large *in every direction* as the smaller one. The effect of enlarging a flywheel x times in every direction, is to increase its energy (at a given speed or rotation) x^5 times.

x, x^2, x^3, x^4, x^5 are called the first, second, third, fourth and fifth powers of x. Instead of 2, 3, 4 or 5, we could have any number. Using n as an abbreviation for 'any number', we may say that x^n is called the nth power of x.

Powers of x may occur mixed with each other, and with constants. For instance, a tennis club might charge 5s. entrance fee, and 1s. for every afternoon on which a member actually played during a season. The cost of one afternoon's play would thus be 6s., of two would be 7s., of x would be $(5 + x)$ shillings.

Again, if a ball is thrown straight up with a speed of 40 feet a second, after x quarter seconds its height is given by the formula $10x - x^2$ feet. (Quarter-seconds are used instead of seconds partly to give simpler numbers, partly because a ball spends such a short time in the air.) We could make a table as follows –

Number of quarter-seconds.	0	1	2	3	4	5	6	7	8	9	10
Height in feet.	0	9	16	21	24	25	24	21	16	9	0

Examine the set of numbers in the lower row of this table. You will notice that it reads the same backwards as forwards. Do you notice anything else about it?

Write down the change between each number and the next one. Thus –

Numbers.	0		9		16		21		24		25		24		21		16		9		0
Change.		9		7		5		3		1		−1		−3		−5		−7		−9	

There is a very simple rule to be seen in this set of numbers: each number is 2 less than the number before it. This is due to the steady downward drag which gravity exerts on the ball. In the first interval of a quarter-second the ball rises 9 feet. But it is being slowed down all the time. In the second interval it covers only 7 feet, in the third 5 feet, and so on. In the fifth it rises only 1 foot. In the sixth it descends 1 foot. (As usual, + 1 means one foot *up*, − 1 one foot *down*.) Now it comes down faster and faster: 3, 5, 7, 9 feet in successive intervals.

We can keep on writing down such rows of numbers – each row giving the changes in the row above. We should thus get the following table –

TABLE I

0		9		16		21		24		25		24		21		16		9		0
	9		7		5		3		1		−1		−3		−5		−7		−9	
		−2		−2		−2		−2		−2		−2		−2		−2		−2		
			0		0		0		0		0		0		0		0			
				0		0		0		0		0		0		0				

All the numbers in the third row are the same, −2. There is no change as we go from one to the next. So all the numbers in the fourth row are noughts. We can go as far as we like: we shall merely get more noughts, in the fifth, sixth and following rows.

Let us try this on some other expressions we have already had. If we write down the numbers corresponding to x^2, we obtain –

TABLE II

0		1		4		9		16		25		36		49		64		81
	1		3		5		7		9		11		13		15		17	
		2		2		2		2		2		2		2		2		
			0		0		0		0		0		0		0			

If we try x^3 we find

TABLE III

0		1		8		27		64		125		216		343		512
	1		7		19		37		61		91		127		169	
		6		12		18		24		30		36		42		
			6		6		6		6		6		6			
				0		0		0		0		0				

Try for yourself x^4 and x^5. Make up expressions such as $2x + 3$, $x^2 + 5x + 7$, and try it on these. You will find that, after a certain number of rows, you always get noughts. What is the rule giving the number of rows that occur, before the noughts are reached? The answer to this question is given later. But try to guess it for yourself. Work out a large number of different examples: group together those which have one row, then noughts: in another group put those with two rows, and so on. The rule is quite a simple one.

Exponential Functions

We have just seen that any expression, made up by mixing together powers of x, will lead to rows of noughts at a certain stage of the process described above.

Not all ways of growing have this property: in fact, expressions formed by mixing powers of x are the only type that possess this characteristic.

If you try some other rule, you will soon see that this is true. Take, for instance, the set of numbers 1, 2, 4, 8, 16, 32, 64, 128, etc., where each number is formed by doubling the previous one. This set corresponds to the formula 2^x. (Remember that we start with $x = 0$. If a sum of money doubled itself each year, a high rate of interest, £1 would become £2 after 1 year, £4 after 2 years, etc. After x years it would be £2^x.) If we make a table for this set of numbers, using the same method as before, we get –

```
1   2   4   8   16   32   64   128  . . . . .
    1   2   4   8    16   32   64   . . . . .
        1   2   4    8    16   32   . . . . .
```

Each row is exactly the same as the one before! However long we go on, we shall never find a row all noughts.

Try 3^x. This gives us the table –

```
1   3   9   27   81   243  . . . . .
    2   6   18   54   162  . . . . .
        4   12   36   108  . . . . .
```

Here each row is *twice* the previous one. However long we go on, we shall never find a row all noughts.

2^x, 3^x are called *exponential functions*. If we use a as shorthand for 'any number', a^x is an exponential function.

The Calculus of Finite Differences

It very often happens that we want to know the rule by which a certain set of numbers has been formed. An engineer might find, by experiment, the pressure required to burst boilers made from sheet metal of various thicknesses. It would be helpful to other engineers if he could express his results in the form of a simple rule. A scientist might measure the size of a plant each day, and try to find the rule by which it grew.

A great part of science consists of the attempt to find rules by studying the results of experiments.

When one quantity depends on another, it is said to be a *function* of the latter quantity. Thus, the bursting pressure of a boiler depends on the thickness of the boiler walls. Calling the pressure p and the thickness t, we say that p is a function of t; the pressure needed to burst a wall of thickness t may be written $p(t)$. Thus $p(2)$ would mean the pressure needed to burst a boiler built with metal 2 inches thick, $p(\frac{3}{8})$ would mean the pressure to burst a boiler with $\frac{3}{8}$-inch walls. Naturally, we suppose that the design of the boiler is fixed, and that the same metal is used for all the experiments.

In the same way, if we denote 'the number of days' by x, and 'the size of a plant in inches' by y, y is a function of x. $y(17)$ will mean the size of the plant after 17 days: $y(x)$ the size after x days.

If we say, 'What function is y of x? we mean, 'By what particular rule is y connected with x?'

This question is used in intelligence tests. A child is shown the numbers 1, 2, 3, 4, 5 and is asked, 'What is the next number?' Of course 6 is the answer. An older child might be shown 2, 4, 6, 8 and expected to guess the next number as being 10.

Such simple cases can be guessed without any special method. But suppose you were shown the table below –

x	0	1	2	3	4	5	6	7	8	9	10
y	1	3	7	13	21	31	43	57	73	91	111

How is the number y in the second row found, corresponding to any number x in the first row? A child might be forgiven if, shown the numbers 1, 3, 7, 13, 21, 31 it failed to guess that the next number was 43! But how quickly our method – of writing down the change from one number to the next – supplies a clue. It gives the table –

TABLE IV

1		3		7		13		21		31		43		57		73		91		111
	2		4		6		8		10		12		14		16		18		20	
		2		2		2		2		2		2		2		2		2		2	
			0		0		0		0		0		0		0		0		0		

We have noughts in the bottom row: the formula must be a simple one, containing only powers of x.

But how many powers of x shall we need? Shall we have to bring in x^5 as was necessary in the case of the flywheel? Or need we not go so far?

Perhaps you have already discovered the answer to the question asked earlier.* If not, here is the answer, Any formula, such as $2x + 3$, which contains no power higher than x, gives us two rows of numbers, and then noughts. If x^2 comes in – as in $5x^2 + 3x — 2$, for instance – we have three rows, then noughts. If x^3 comes into the formula, we have four rows, then noughts. And so on. If x^n occurs, we have $(n + 1)$ rows before the noughts come. This works also the other way round. If we have four rows before the noughts, it will be possible to find a formula which does not use any power above x^3. If we have $(n + 1)$ rows, the formula will contain powers up to x^n.

This helps us to find the formula which gives the numbers 1, 3, 7, 13, etc. This set of numbers, as we have just seen, leads to a table containing only three rows. The formula cannot contain any power of x higher than x^2. It will be sufficient to take a certain amount of x^2, together with a certain amount of x, and with some number added. In algebraic shorthand, our formula will be $ax^2 + bx + c$, where a stands for the number that goes with x^2, b for the number that goes with x, c for the number that is added. (Thus, in the formula $5x^2 + 3x — 2$, a is 5, b is 3, c is —2.) We do not yet know what a, b and c have to be. All we

*Page 94

know is that it is possible to get the right formula by choosing the proper values for a, b and c. This of course is a great help. When we started this problem we had to be prepared for *any* formula: it might have been $x + 2^x$, or x^9, or even worse expressions.

Once we know that the formula is of the type $ax^2 + bx + c$, it is very easy to find a, b and c. We know that the numbers 1, 3, 7, 13, etc., result if, in the proper formula, we replace x by the numbers 0, 1, 2, 3, etc., in turn.

If in the formula $ax^2 + bx + c$ we replace x by 0, we get c: if we replace it by 1, we get $a + b + c$: if we replace it by 2, we get $4a + 2b + c$. (If you like, you can turn these results into words by reading $4a$ as 'four times the number that goes with x^2 in the formula', and so on.)

We can now compare these two sets of results. If y is given by the formula $ax^2 + bx + c$, $y(0) = c$. But $y(0)$, the value of y corresponding to $x = 0$, is 1. c must be 1. Again the formula gives $y(1) = a + b + c$. But $y(1)$ is 3. So we must choose a, b and c in such a way that $a + b + c = 3$. In the same way, comparing the formula for $y(2)$ and what it ought to give, we get the equation $4a + 2b + c = 7$. Altogether we have three equations:

$$c = 1$$
$$a + b + c = 3$$
$$4a + 2b + c = 7.$$

This is exactly similar to the problem of the cakes and the buns and the pot of tea. It is easily solved by the method described in Chapter 7, and leads to the result $a = 1$, $b = 1$, $c = 1$. So that we have the formula $y = x^2 + x + 1$. This is the rule by which the numbers in the table were found.

In the subject known by the imposing name of the Calculus of Finite Differences, the method we have just used is further developed, and proofs of its correctness are given.

It has been found convenient to introduce certain abbreviations. We have had to keep on referring to 'the second row in the table', 'the third row', and so on. To avoid this, certain signs are used, as names for these rows. The first row (which, in our last example, contained the numbers 1, 3, 7, 13 ...) we have already called y. The second row (the numbers 2, 4, 6, 8...in that example) are called Δy. The sigh Δ is short for 'the change in'. As each row represents the changes that occur in the previous row, we get one more sign Δ every time we go down a row. The third row, for instance, represents the changes in Δy, and could be written $\Delta\Delta y$. Note that Δ does not stand for any number as did a, b and the other letters. Δ stands for '*the change in*' – that and nothing else. It can always be replaced by these words. Usually $\Delta\Delta y$ is still further shortened to $\Delta^2 y$. This is especially convenient when large numbers of Δ are involved. For instance $\Delta^5 y$ is much more convenient than $\Delta\Delta\Delta\Delta\Delta y$ as an abbreviation for the numbers in the sixth row.

Sometimes we want to refer briefly to a particular number in one of the rows. We have already used the sign $y(x)$ to describe the number in the first row which corresponds to the value x: so that the numbers of the first row are $y(0)$, $y(1)$, $y(2)$, $y(3)$ and so on. We use similar signs for the numbers in the following rows. The numbers in the second row are called $\Delta y(0)$, $\Delta y(1)$, $\Delta y(2)$ and so on; in the third row, $\Delta^2 y(0)$, $\Delta^2 y(1)$, $\Delta^2 y(2)$ etc.; and so on for any row.

You will find these signs in any book on the Calculus of Finite Differences. At first they may seem strange, but once you are accustomed to them, and have realized that $\Delta^2 y(1)$ means nothing more terrifying than 'the second number in the third row' of a table such as Table III or Table IV, you will find the subject quite a good one to experiment with. You may try your hand at the following problems.

(1) A car drives past a lamp-post. One second later it is 3 yards away from the lamp-post; after 2 seconds, 10 yards; after 3 seconds, 21 yards; after 4 seconds, 36 yards. How far away is it after $\frac{1}{2}$ second, $1\frac{1}{2}$ seconds, $2\frac{1}{2}$ seconds? Is it speeding up or slowing down?

(2) What is the missing number in the following set?

$$3, 4, \ldots 24, 43, 68.$$

If you succeed in guessing the right number, the table for Δy, $\Delta^2 y$, etc., will make it quite clear that you are right. You will not be in any doubt about it, once you have tried the right number. And it must be a number between 5 and 23. If the worst comes to the worst, you can try all of these in turn.

Binomial Coefficients

It is possible to work out a table similar to Table IV, if we suppose the first row, y, to contain *any* set of numbers. In fact, we may represent the numbers in the first row by algebraic symbols. Let a stand for the first number (whatever that is), b for the second, c for the third, d for the fourth and so on. The row y then reads –

$$a, b, c, d, e, f \ldots$$

How are we to form the next row Δy? The first number in it shows the change from a to b. It is obtained by subtracting a from b, and may therefore be written $b - a$. In the same way, the next number may be written $c - b$. (Check these statements for yourself. In Table IV, what numbers are a, b, and c? Is it true that the row Δy begins with numbers equal to $b - a$ and $c - b$?) The second row in fact is $b - a$, $c - b$, $d - c$, $e - d$, $f - e$, etc.

From the second row the third row can be found. The first number in it is $(c - b) - (b - a)$, which simple algebra shows to be equal to $c - 2b + a$. The second number in this row is $d - 2c + b$.

Continuing in this way, we obtain the expressions collected in Table V.

TABLE V

a		b		c		d		e
	$b-a$		$c-b$		$d-c$		$e-d$	
		$c-2b+a$		$d-2c+b$		$e-2d+c$		
			$d-3c+3b-a$		$e-3d+3c-b$			
				$e-4d+6c-4b+a$				

You will notice certain things about this table. A particular set of numbers appears in each row. In the row $\Delta^4 y$, for instance, we have the numbers 1, 4, 6, 4, 1. In the row $\Delta^3 y$ we find the numbers 1, 3, 3, 1. In the row $\Delta^2 y$ we find 1, 2, 1, and in the row Δy we find simply 1, 1. (No notice has been taken of whether these numbers appear with a + or — sign.) You will notice that these sets of numbers read the same backwards as forwards. For example, 1, 3, 3, 1 is the same, whether read backwards of forwards. You will notice that the first and last numbers are always 1. What else do you notice? What is the rule that gives the number next to the end? Can you find the formula for the number next to that? (You will need to work out a few more rows of Table V to do this.) Apply the method already explained, for finding the formula of a set of numbers.

These numbers are known as the *Binomial Coefficients*. Mathematicians came to know them in exactly the way you have done – by noticing that they turned up in the course of work. They turn up, for instance, if you work out 11^2, 11^3, and 11^4, which are, in fact, 121, 1331, 14641. (After this point *carrying* comes into the arithmetic, and the simple connexion does not hold. The numbers in $\Delta^5 y$ are 1, 5, 10, 10, 5, 1, and of course the number *ten* cannot appear as a single figure in 11^5. 11^5 is actually 161,051, which does not read the same backwards as forwards.) They appear, too, in $(x + 1)^2$, $(x + 1)^3$ and $(x + 1)^4$, etc. We may write them in a table, as below –

TABLE VI

```
1 1
1 2  1
1 3  3   1
1 4  6   4   1
1 5 10  10   5   1
1 6 15  20  15   6  1
1 7 21  35  35  21  7  1
```

Now you can measure your place among the great mathematicians. This table was known as early as 1544. Gradually people noticed all sorts of odd facts about it. But it was not until 1664, 120 years later, that the greatest of English mathematicians found *a formula* giving the numbers in any column of Table VI. The first column is obvious enough – always 1. The second column contains 1, 2, 3, 4, 5, 6, 7 – a simple law here. But what is the rule for the third column, 1, 3, 6, 10, 15, 21? You will find this problem quite easy if you use the method outlined earlier in this chapter – make a table on the lines of Tables I-IV, and then hunt for a formula.

The rule that Newton found (and that I hope you will find for yourself) is known as the *Binomial Theorem*. That is all the Binomial Theorem is – a rule for writing down the numbers in Table VI.

The object of explaining Δy, $\Delta^2 y$, etc., to you is that you may see how theorems are discovered, and may be able to discover results for yourself.

EXERCISES

1. If the temperature of L feet of steel is raised T degrees Fahrenheit, the length of the steel increases by an amount 0·000006 LT.

If the temperature of a mile of steel (say, on a railway) rises 10 degrees Fahrenheit, how much extra room will it need?

2. In scientific work temperature is measured in degrees Centigrade. This can be changed to degrees Fahrenheit by means of the formula

$$F = \frac{9C}{5} + 32,$$

where F degrees and C degrees stand for the temperature Fahrenheit and Centigrade respectively. What temperature Fahrenheit corresponds to 15 degrees Centigrade? What is the temperature 90 degrees Fahrenheit in terms of degrees Centigrade?

3. 10 feet of common 2-inch-bore lead piping weighs 50 lb. What is the formula for the weight of x feet of such lead piping?

4. One square foot of ordinary brickwork will support with

safety a weight of 6 tons. How many tons will a piece of brick-work x feet square support?

With particularly good bricks, 1 square foot of brickwork will support 54 tons. What weight will a block x feet square support?

A brickwork foundation capable of bearing a weight of 1,000 tons is required. The foundation is to be square in shape. How large must it be if it is made (i) of ordinary brick, (ii) of particularly good bricks?

5. When a train moves at x miles an hour, the total pressure on the front of the locomotive, due to air pressure (y lb.), is given by the following table.

x	0	20	40	60	80	100
y	0	79·5	318·0	715·5	1272·0	1987·5

Is there a simple formula connecting x and y? If so, what is it?

6. One sometimes sees on trams a table giving the fare between any two points on the route, as in the illustration.

It is clear that no diagram at all is necessary unless the tram has at least two stations to connect. With 3 stations, the diagram contains 3 squares. Work out the number of squares in the diagram when there are 4, 5, 6, etc., stopping stations. How many squares are needed if there are x stations? Is there any connexion with the numbers in Table VI?

7. If n teams enter for a knock-out competition, how many matches will be played? (See the question at the end of Chapter 5.)

8. In Britain and the United States the horse-power rating of a motor-car is found from the formula –

$$H = \frac{2Nd^2}{5}$$

where

H = horse-power rating

N = number of cylinders

d = bore of cylinder in inches.

What bore would be necessary, for a four-cylinder car, to give 40 H.P.? What for 10 H.P.? What would give a horse-power just below 23 H.P.?

9. The breaking strength of three-strand Manila rope is given by the formula –

$$L = 5000\ d(d+1)$$

where L lb. is the load needed to snap a rope d inches in diameter. How many lb. will be required to snap a rope $1\frac{1}{2}$ inches in diameter? What rope will just snap under a load of 60,000 lb.?

10. The safe load, S hundredweight, for a rope measuring C inches in circumference is given by the formula –

$$S = C^2.$$

How many hundredweight may safely be put on ropes of circumference 2, 3, and 4 inches? What size of rope is needed to carry safely $\frac{1}{4}$ ton? How many ropes 2 inches in circumference would be needed to support $\frac{1}{4}$ ton? (Fractions of ropes are not used.) How many ropes 3 inches around would do the same job?

Further formulae, on which to practise, can be found in Kempe's *Engineer's Yearbook*, from which many of the examples used here have been drawn. Formulae will be found covering subjects varying from the amount of sludge deposited by sewage to the amount of rainfall in Northern India.

CHAPTER 9

GRAPHS, OR THINKING IN PICTURES

'Care is taken, not that the hearer may understand, if he will, but that he must understand, whether he will or not.'
— Henry Bett, *Some Secrets of Style.*

THE great problem of every teacher is to present facts in such a way that the students cannot help *seeing* what is meant. A bald statement is soon forgotten. Vivid images remain in the memory. Many people must have noticed the difference between reading a history text-book and seeing an historical film. Whatever the relative accuracy of the book and the film, the film certainly makes one realize events more intensely, and remember them longer.

In films it is sometimes necessary to explain quite complicated ideas, not to a class of students, but to an audience which represents the whole population of a country. Cinema audiences, too, are in no mood for concentrated thought. They want to relax, to be amused. It is extremely instructive to examine how film directors go about the job. They rarely fail to make their point understood – a fact which should be seriously considered by those defeatists in education whose perpetual alibi is the stupidity of pupils.

In our last chapter we considered the different ways in which any quantity can grow. Suppose we wished to present this idea to a cinema audience. How could this be done? We might wish to represent the fact that a man's wealth began to grow – perhaps an inventor's first success. We might show him storing sovereigns in a safe. The first week he puts a sovereign in. Next week he adds two more sovereigns. Then he adds a pile of three sovereigns. The earnings of each week form a pile, and each pile contains one sovereign more than the previous pile.

Very good – in the xth week he saves £x, and the steadily rising heaps of coin show at a glance the meaning of this fact.

But the plot need not end there. The inventor has a friend who lives by fraud and violence, a gangster. The gangster is determined to prove that it does not pay to be honest. He urges the inventor to come where the big money can be made. Scornfully, each week, he places a pile of coins behind the inventor's. The first week, £1; the second, £2; the third week, £4; the fourth week, £8 – doubling each week. The steady rise of the inventor's earnings sinks into insignificance. He may save £x – the gangster saves £2^{x-1}, each week. (Fig. 6).

These figures not only show that the incomes of the inventor and the gangster are growing. They bring out the significance of the different ways in which they are growing. Here we have the essential idea of a *graph* – that is, a diagram which will show to the eye the meaning of a mathematical expression such as x or 2^{x-1}.

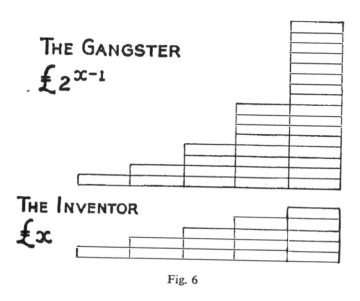

Fig. 6

In this particular illustration we have been considering something which grows by steps, by sudden jumps. For instance, the gangster's weekly savings rise from £4 to £8 without passing 'through the values between £5, £6 and £7. It is also possible for a thing to grow steadily, like a plant, without jumps. We can, and usually do, draw graphs to illustrate this steady growth. For instance, if a plant grows continuously according to the formula $y = x$ (where y means the height of the plant in inches after x weeks), this not only means that the plant is 1 inch higher after 1 week and 2 inches after 2 weeks. It means that it is $1\frac{1}{4}$ inches high after $1\frac{1}{4}$ weeks, $1\frac{1}{2}$ inches after $1\frac{1}{2}$ weeks, and so on. We show this by a diagram in which the steps have been smoothed out (Fig. 7.).

Whether one draws a continuous curve, or one which rises by steps, is decided by the nature of the process which the graph is intended to illustrate. The size of a plant, the distance travelled by a train, the weight of a child – these give continuous graphs. The number of children in a family, the seats held by a party in Parliament, the number of battleships in a navy – these change by steps.

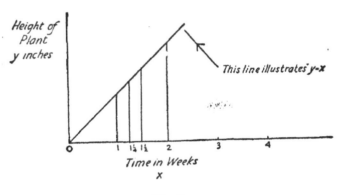

Fig. 7

There are certain cases in which one may use either a continuous curve or a graph with steps. Suppose, for instance, we wish to represent the growth of the population of Great Britain from 1800 to 1900. Strictly speaking, this changes by jumps – increases by one whenever a child is born and decreases by one at every death. But the population itself is measured in millions: to get our graph a reasonable size, we must take a scale such that a million people are represented by not more than an inch. Each individual birth or death corresponds to a change of not more than a millionth of an inch. This is far less than the thickness of a pencil line – even if we could draw each little step, we should be unable to see the effect. So the population curve would appear as a continuous curve – not as a staircase.

Graphs have become so much a part of everyday life that it is not really necessary to explain them. People entirely without mathematical training are usually able to see the significance of the temperature chart over a patient's bed, of the curves showing changes in unemployment or the history of Lancashire's cotton exports. Graphs are used to show the progress of a campaign to raise money, or the output of a factory. Business journals contain graphs showing the trend of prices. Wireless valves are marketed with graphs to show their characteristics. At some holiday resorts one can see instruments which record curves, showing how the barometer has risen and fallen, and charts of the rainfall and sunshine from day to day. The general idea of a graph is already widely understood.

It may be useful to explain exactly how a graph is drawn. A graph illustrates the connexion between two sets of numbers. For instance, we have already considered the possibility that a plant might grow as shown in the following table:

Number of weeks (x)	0	$\frac{1}{4}$	$\frac{1}{2}$	$\frac{3}{4}$	1	$1\frac{1}{4}$	$1\frac{1}{2}$	$1\frac{3}{4}$	2
Height in inches (y)	0	$\frac{1}{4}$	$\frac{1}{2}$	$\frac{3}{4}$	1	$1\frac{1}{4}$	$1\frac{1}{2}$	$1\frac{3}{4}$	2

We drew a level line, along which we marked the number of weeks. We then drew lines upwards, representing the height of the plant corresponding to any number of weeks. In Fig. 7 such lines have been drawn corresponding to 1, $1\frac{1}{4}$, $1\frac{1}{2}$ and 2 weeks. The upright line corresponding to 1 week is 1 inch high – the size of the plant after 1 week. The upright line corresponding to $1\frac{1}{4}$ weeks represents the height of the plant after $1\frac{1}{4}$ weeks. So one can go on, drawing as many upright lines as one likes. These upright lines show the growth of the plant, in the same way that the piles of coins show the growth of the inventor's weekly savings. After drawing a large number of these upright lines, we can see that the tops all lie on a certain straight line. (In other examples the tops lie on a curve.) Drawing the line (or curve) joining the tops of the upright lines, we obtain *the graph of the plant's growth*. As the plant grows according to the formula $y = x$, this line is also called *the graph of $y = x$*.

Any other process, or the mathematical formula which describes it, can be graphed by this method. On page 93 there is a table showing the motion of a ball thrown into the air. Draw for yourself a graph to illustrate this table. The tops of the upright lines will lie not on a straight line, but on a curve. Notice how this curve rises so long as the ball is going up, and descends as the ball comes down. What would the graph of a bouncing ball look like?

In both these examples, y has been a mathematical function of x. For the plant, $y = x$. For the ball, $y = 10x - x^2$. But do not suppose that graphs can be drawn only when a simple formula exists. One can graph the temperature of a patient or the price of milk: it is extremely unlikely that a simple formula can be found to fit either of these.

The Uses of Graphs

Graphs have a great advantage over tables of figures, when information has to be taken in at a glance. It is quite easy to run an eye down a row of figures, and fail to see that one number is much larger than the rest. On a graph, such a number would stand out like a mountain peak. A sudden bend in a graph is easily seen – a casual glance at the corresponding figures would certainly not reveal its existence. Graphs are particularly useful for busy men who want to know the general outlines of a situation but do not want to be bothered by going into every small detail.

This is the simplest use of a graph – to convey a general impression. An historian or an economist may simply want to know that Lancashire was prosperous in 1920 and that a sharp crash

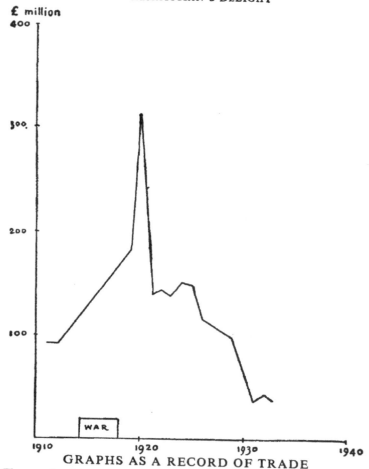

£ million

GRAPHS AS A RECORD OF TRADE

The graph shows the exports of cotton cloth, in million pounds, during the years in question. One can see in a few seconds the general outline of Lancashire's fortunes in this period. One would grasp far less from seeing the actual figures. Try for yourself taking a column of figures from an encyclopedia or year-book. Glance at them for fifteen seconds, put them away and write down the things you have noticed — when the figures are largest, when they are small, when they are growing, when they are getting less, etc. You will not notice very much in a short time. Now make a graph of the figures, and notice how the graph brings out things you have missed.

came in 1921. One glance at a graph of cotton exports will remind him of this fact.

Again, graphs can be used to bring out the connexion between two events. Most books on Germany point out how the distress in Germany during the world slump created a mood of extremism and desperation, and helped the rise of the Nazi party. How far can we accept this view as being true? Let us draw, on the same piece of paper, two graphs, one showing the amount of unemployment in Germany, the other showing the number of Nazi M.P.s, between 1926 and 1933 (Fig. 8).

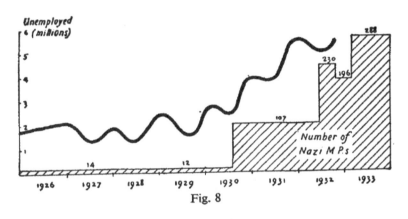

Fig. 8

This graph immediately shows that there is some truth in the idea. During the boom years, the elections returned negligible numbers of Nazi M.P.s: 14 and 12. The two curves, in the main, rise together.

It would, however, be absurd to try to find a mathematical formula connecting the two things. The number of M.P.s changes by steps, at every general election. Unemployment and insecurity are not the only causes acting. For instance, the setback to the Nazis in the second election of 1932 was due to political causes – quarrels among the Nazis, a belief that the Army would oppose Hitler, and so forth.

You will notice how a graph calls your attention to unexplained

GRAPHS USED TO DETECT UNDER-NOURISHMENT

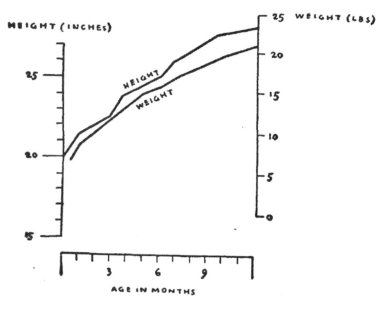

The two graphs show the height and weight of a baby in the first year of its life. If the graph for weight does not keep pace with the graph for height, something is wrong.

facts, and urges you on to further enquiry. We drew the graph to see how far the slump explained the rise of Hitler. The graph not only gives us an indication of the probable answer to this question: it brings to our notice the fall in the Nazi vote at the end of 1932, which is in no way connected with the curve for unemployment, and sets us searching for further facts to explain the setback.

Again, one can hardly help noticing the wave-like shape of the unemployment curve, which rises every winter and falls every summer. This reminds us that there are some trades – such as building – which cease work during bad weather. The summer of 1926 seems to have been an exception. One wonders why. The longer one looks at a graph, the more questions it suggests and the more information it helps one to remember.

It is worth while to collect graphs on any subject in which one is interested. One often hears remarks, and wonders what evidence there can be for their truth. A visit to a public library will often establish the truth or expose the falsehood of a statement. If it is possible to illustrate the question by means of a graph, one has a way of recording much information in a little space. One need not look up the same facts again. As time passes, the collection of graphs is likely to contain some interesting facts.

Quiller-Couch, in *The Art of Reading*, mentions a girl who kept a graph of the attendance at a village church, and tried to account for every rise and fall that occurred. She must have gained an amazing knowledge of the qualities of the preachers and the habits of the village.

Graphs are used by doctors, to show whether children are being properly nourished. The weight of a child, and its height, are graphed on the same piece of paper. For a healthy child, the two curves go up together. If the child is not getting the food it needs, the curve for weight fails to keep pace with that for height. The doctor need not wait until there is a big gap between the two curves. If he notices that the curve for weight begins to bend downwards, this may be the first sign that something is going wrong. If, after special treatment or extra food, the curve begins to bend upwards again, the doctor knows that good effects are beginning to be felt. Part of the science of interpreting graphs consists in knowing how a graph looks when something is increasing, when it is increasing very fast, when it is increasing faster and faster, when it is increasing but increasing slower and slower. (Draw graphs, to illustrate these different possibilities.)

In all these examples the conclusions drawn from the graph have been of a rather general nature. The doctor sees that a child is getting healthier or less healthy, but he does not attempt to *measure* how healthy it is. He cannot say that it is 80% healthy, any more than we can say that someone is 80% happy or 80% honest. Such things as health, happiness and honesty can be measured only indirectly: statistics of deaths, suicides, thefts, may throw some light on these matters. But it is quite possible to know a lot about how healthy, happy or honest a person is, without being able to give a single figure of anything that can be measured.

There are some departments of life, on the other hand, in which measurement plays a large part. This is particularly true of such subjects as engineering, chemistry, physics. Quite a small bump on a railway track may be sufficient to derail a train: if a ball-bearing is one-thousandth of an inch too large, it may take all the weight that should be spread over several ball-bearings and wear out too fast. In such matters very exact calculations are frequently necessary. For this reason engineers and scientists cannot be content with rough statements. They sometimes want to say, not merely that a curve rises slowly, but that it rises at a rate of 1 in 100, or 1 in 87. Much of mathematics has developed in an attempt to satisfy such demands of engineers: mathematicians have been led to invent a whole set of numbers, by means of which one can not only describe, but measure, exactly what a curve is doing at any point. The next chapter – on the study of speed – explains how this is done.

Mathematicians and Graphs

Mathematicians use graphs for many different purposes, some of which are indicated in the following paragraphs.

Graphs may be used to help us to know what we are talking about. It often happens when long calculations are being made with algebraic symbols that we lose sight of the meaning of these symbols; we have at the end a formula, which has been obtained by using the rules of algebra, but we have no way of feeling what it means. It deepens our understanding of the subject if we do not rest content with having found a correct formula, but try to realize what this formula means.

For instance, the formula –

$$P = 364\ V - \frac{V^3}{270,000}$$

gives the power (P) transmitted when a shaft is driven by means of a leather belt. V represents the velocity in feet per second at which the leather belt is travelling. The formula holds in certain conditions which do not concern us at the moment.

What does this formula mean? It contains a quite striking result. It would be natural to suppose that, by turning the driving pulley sufficiently fast, one could transmit as much power as one wished. But draw the graph of P, taking V for values between 0 and 8,000. You will find that P rises until V is 5,700, after which it decreases. If you drive the belt faster than 5,700 feet a second, you do not transmit more power but *less*. One glance at the graph shows this. If, however, one did not draw the graph, but used the formula blindly, one might make serious mistakes, such as designing a plant which worked at a speed too high to be economical.*

Graphs can be very helpful to anyone learning mathematics. Many people can follow all the steps in the solution of a problem, when the solution is shown to them, but they are unable to discover the solution for themselves. They understand each separate step, but they do not know which series of steps will bring them out of the wood. This difficulty can be overcome only if one learns to *see* the meaning of mathematical formulae. Many mathematicians think about their problems all day, wherever they may be. They do not remember all the formulae: they remember a *picture* which the problem has created in their minds. They keep thinking about this picture, until a *method* of solving the problem occurs to them. Then they go home to their pens and paper and collections of formulae, and work out the solution in full. Graphs are one of the ways by which it is possible to form a picture of a problem.

It is a good practice to collect, and to become familiar with, the graphs of the more common functions, such as $y=x$, $y=2x+1$, $y=3-2x$, $y=x^2$, $y=x^2+2x+5$, $y=x^3$, $y=x^4$, $y=2^x$, $y=\frac{1}{2}x$, and so on.

In scientific work one often obtains a set of results by

* Both the formula and the graph can be found in J. Goodman, *Mechanics Applied to Engineering*, Vol. 1, page 355, 9th edition.

experiment, and then tries to find a formula to fit these results. This can be very difficult, since there are many different types of formula, any one of which *might* be the correct one. It is often helpful to represent the experimental results by means of a graph. If one is familiar with the graphs of many functions, one may at once recognize the type of function which produces such a graph. For instance, all functions which have straight lines as graphs are of the type $y = ax + b$.

Of course, small errors always creep in, and one does not expect the points to lie exactly on a smooth curve. Such small errors in measurement are due to various causes – the thickness of the lines on a ruler when a length is being measured, for instance. Occasionally a big mistake occurs – for instance, one might copy 7197 as 7917, or forget to close a switch when an experiment was being done. Such big mistakes are easily detected on a graph. All the other readings cluster around a smooth curve, but the big mistake is far away from the curve, and one suspects it immediately.

This way of detecting errors is useful not for scientific work only, but also for mathematics itself. For instance, in calculating a set of numbers we may make slips in one or two of the numbers. By drawing a graph it is usually possible to see which numbers are incorrect. When all the numbers are correct, the graph will be a smooth curve – at any rate, this is true in the great majority of cases.

Graphs not only enable us to express a formula by a curve: they enable us to describe a curve by a formula. For instance, when there is no wind, a jet of water from a hose or a small pipe forms a simple curve. If a board is held near the jet of water, the curve can be traced. One can then study this curve, and try to find the formula of which it is the graph. The formula, once found, provides a sort of name for the curve. The part of mathematics known as *Analytical Geometry* is based on this idea of describing every line or curve by the formula corresponding to it. If you want to learn analytical geometry, but find the text-books difficult, the best thing to do is to experiment with graphs for yourself. Draw graphs of the type $y = ax + b$, taking all sorts of values for a and b, positive and negative, large and small. Verify the statement made earlier that all these graphs are straight lines. What do you notice about the graphs of $y = x$ and $y = x + 1$? Can you find a formula which gives a straight line at right angles to $y = x$? Experiment on these lines, record your experiments, and try to reach general conclusions: see how long it is before you can tell, simply by looking at the formulae, that two lines are at right angles. *Then* read the chapter in the text-book headed 'The Straight Line' or 'The Equation of the Straight Line', and you will find your own results, in another person's language. Since you already know what the author is trying to say, it will not be long before you come to understand his language.

EXAMPLES

1. Draw the following graphs. What do you notice about them? How would you describe in words the figure they form?

(i) $y=2x$. (ii) $y=2x+1$. (iii) $y=2x+2$. (iv) $y=5-\frac{1}{2}x$.

2. Draw and describe, as in question 1, the four graphs following.

(i) $y=3x$. (ii) $y=3x+1$. (iii) $y=3x+2$. (iv) $y=4-\frac{1}{3}x$.

3. What do you notice about the following two graphs?

(i) $y=x^2+2x$. (ii) $y=x^2+4x+3$.

4. Draw the graph $y=x(9-x)$. For what value of x is y largest, and what is the largest value of y?

5. What do you notice about the graphs following? –

(i) $y=25-x^2$. (ii) $y=x^2$?

Minus Numbers on Graphs

Often we want to draw a graph, in some part of which x or y or both are minus numbers. For instance, we may want to draw a graph showing the length of an iron rail for temperatures which are *below zero*. If x degrees is the temperature, this means that x is a minus number. If in our graph $x=1$ is one inch to the right, $x=-1$ will be one inch to the left. $x=-2$ will be two inches to the left, and so on.

In the same way, if $y=1$ is one inch up, $y=-1$ will be one inch down.

For instance, we may draw the graph of $y=x-1$, for values of x lying between -3 and 3. We first make the table –

x	-3	-2	-1	0	1	2	3
y	-4	-3	-2	-1	0	1	2

We mark the values of x on a level line. $x=3$ is marked 3 inches to the right of 0, -3 three inches to the left of 0, and so on. The corresponding values of y are then shown as upright lines. When $x=3$, $y=2$, so that a line 2 inches high is drawn from the point where $x=3$ is marked. When $x=-3$, $y=-4$, so a line 4 inches *downwards* is drawn from the point where $x=-3$ is marked. The ends of these lines give us the line PQ, which is the required graph of $y=x-1$.

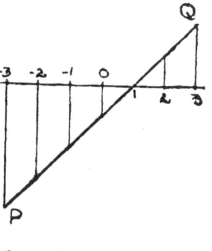

One of the advantages of using minus numbers will be seen in the examples on the shape of bridges. Very often the formula is much simpler if we take $x=0$ at the middle of the bridge, than if we take it at the end.

6. Draw the graph of $y=x-2$ for values of x between 2 and 6.

This gives part of a straight line. With a ruler extend this straight line in the 'south-westerly' direction. Check that this line now passes through the points given by the table for x between -4 and 2.

7. Draw the graph $y=5-x$ for x between 0 and 5. This gives part of a straight line. Extend this line, using a ruler. Read off the

values of y corresponding to $x=6$ and $x=7$. For what values of x is y equal to 6 and 7? Does this agree with the way of finding $5—(—1)$ and $5—(—2)$ explained in Chapter 5?

8. *Graphs to Describe Shapes*. – The book *Building with Steel* by R. B. Way and N. D. Green contains sketches of various famous bridges. The curves there shown seem to agree with the graphs given below –

(i) The Langwies Viaduct, Switzerland. The central arch, of reinforced concrete, resembles the curve –

$$y=2-\frac{2x^2}{9}.$$

(ii) The long low arch of the Royal Tweed Bridge at Berwick,

$$y=1-\frac{2x^2}{37}, \text{ from } x=—4\cdot3 \text{ to } x=4\cdot3.$$

(iii) The lower cable on the suspension bridge at the side of Tower Bridge,

$$y=\frac{9x^2}{80}.$$

The Outline of Victoria Falls Bridge

(iv) The arch of Victoria Falls bridge,
$$y=\frac{116—21x^2}{120}.$$

The upright lines are to be marked at $x=2\cdot35$ and $x=—2\cdot35$. The level line is at the height $y=1\cdot25$.

9. In each of the following sets of numbers a mistake occurs. On a graph, all the numbers of each set ought to give a smooth curve. Which numbers are incorrect? What are the correct numbers that ought to be in place of the wrong ones? (Only a *rough* answer is expected to the second question.)

    (i) 10, 13, 61, 19, 22.
    (ii) 4, 11, 13, 19, 20, 19, 16.
    (iii) 0, 0, 5, 9, 12, 14, 15, 14.
    (iv) 23, 34, 41, 49, 50, 52, 53.
    (v) 3610, 4000, 4410, 4640, 5290, 5760.

10. One of the following numbers is wrong, but not much. Can you find which one it is?

    3844, 3969, 4096, 4252, 4356, 4489, 4624, 4761.

(Probably you will not be able to do this by the method of question 9. The point of this question is to show what *cannot* be done easily by graphs. The point of question 9 is to show what *can* be done with graphs. Somewhere in this book you will find a method that supplies a clue to the question just asked.)

11. Even if you answer question 10 by graphs, you will certainly need another method to find the wrong number in the set below –

    6724, 6889, 7065, 7225, 7396, 7569.

CHAPTER 10

DIFFERENTIAL CALCULUS – THE STUDY OF SPEED

'When I was an apprentice, I wanted to know engineering theory, and the only two books available contained unknown mathematical symbols ... Other boys might sigh for luxuries, but to me the one thing wanting was a knowledge of $\frac{dy}{dx}$ and $\int$. Looking back, I seem

to have panted for a knowledge of the use of these symbols for years.' – John Perry.

ONE of the commonest words in modern life is 'speed'. It is therefore natural that mathematicians, who have had a hand in most of the scientific and industrial advances on which modern life is based, should have a special set of symbols to describe speed, and a special subject dealing with the use of these symbols. Like the sellers of patent medicine, mathematicians have not been able to resist the lure of high-sounding titles. The subject is known by the name of the Differential Calculus.

In any subject dealing with things that move, or grow, or change, you are likely to find the symbols of differential calculus. Even in subjects where nothing seems to be moving, these symbols turn up. We say that a road bends 'very suddenly'; we can discuss how 'quickly' the direction of a railway line changes. Neither the road nor the rail is moving at all. Yet we do mean something when we use such phrases. Words originally meant to describe motion – 'quickly', 'suddenly' – can be used to describe motionless objects. It is the same with the symbols which take the place of words in mathematical work. They too can be used to describe the curve of a road, or a railway, or of any similar object.

Differential calculus is therefore a subject which can be applied to anything which moves, or has a shape, or changes – and this does not leave much out! It is useful for the study of machinery of all kinds, for electric lighting and wireless, for economics and for life insurance. For two hundred years after the discovery of the differential calculus, the main advance of mathematics lay in applications of it. Very few really new ideas came into mathematics. Once the basic ideas of differential calculus have been grasped, a whole world of problems can be tackled without great difficulty. It is a subject well worth learning.

The Basic Problem

The basic problem of differential calculus is the following: we are given a rule for finding where an object is at any time, and are asked to find out how fast it is moving.

For instance, we might be given the following table, for a stone rolling down a hillside.

TABLE VII

Time in seconds	0	1	2	3	4	5	6
Distance gone (feet)	0	1	4	9	16	25	36

This rule, of course, is a very simple one: $y=x^2$, x meaning the time in seconds required to go y feet.

We are now asked: You know where the stone is at any time, find out how fast it is going. Let us try to find out how fast it is going after one second.

First of all, it is easy to see that the stone continually goes faster and faster. In the first second it goes only 1 foot; in the next 3 feet; in the third second 5 feet, and so on, 2 more feet for every second that passes.

But this does not tell us how fast it is going after 1 second, though it helps us to get an idea of the answer. In the first second the stone goes 1 foot. It is *averaging* a speed of 1 foot a second, during this second. This does not mean that its speed is 1 foot a second. A car which travels 30 miles in an hour does not travel at a speed of 30 miles an hour. If its owner lives in a big town, the car travels slowly while it is getting out of the town, and makes up for it by doing 50 on the arterial road in the country. The rolling stone is doing the same sort of thing – it starts slowly, but (so to speak) keeps its foot on the accelerator the whole time. As it covers 1 foot in the first second, its speed at the end of that second must be *more* than 1 foot a second, for it reaches its highest speed (for the first second) right at the end.

Its speed still goes on increasing during the second interval, in which it covers 3 feet. Accordingly, at the beginning of the second interval its speed must have been *less* than 3 feet a second.

Accordingly, after 1 second its speed is somewhere between 1 foot a second and 3 feet a second.

This is the best we can do, if we merely consider the figures for whole seconds. But there is no need to keep to whole seconds.

Our rule, $y=x^2$, applies equally well to fractions. If we work out the distances corresponding to 0·9 second and 1·1 seconds, we have the little table:

TABLE VIII

x	0·9	1	1·1
y	0·81	1	1·21

Just the same argument can now be applied again. In the tenth of a second between 0·9 and 1 the stone covers 0·19 of a foot. This represents an average speed of $\dfrac{0·19}{0·1}$ feet a second – that is, 1·9 feet a second. In the same way, the average speed in the tenth of a second just after 1 second is 2·1 feet a second. The number we want therefore lies between 1·9 and 2·1. In getting this result, we have not had to carry out any process more complicated than ordinary division.

But there is no limit to the accuracy we can obtain by this method. If we consider the hundredth of a second just before, and the hundredth just after, 1 second, we find that the speed lies between 1·99 and 2·01 feet a second. If we take a thousandth of a second, we find the speed lies between 1·999 and 2·001. And there is nothing to stop us considering a millionth or a billionth of a second if we want to. Only one speed will satisfy all these conditions – exactly 2 feet a second. And that is the answer to our question.

In exactly the same way you find the speed after 2 seconds. The little table may then be read:

TABLE IX

x	1·9	2	2·1
y	3·61	4	4·41

which shows that the speed after 2 seconds lies between 3·9 and 4·1. In fact, the speed is 4 feet a second.

So one may work out the speed after any time. The results of doing this are collected in the following table.

TABLE X

Time in seconds	0	1	2	3	4	5	6
Speed (in feet a second)	0	2	4	6	8	10	12

From this table it is easy to see the rule. After x seconds the speed is given by the number $2x$.

By this 'experimental' method it is fairly easy to find the rules for other formulae. First, one finds the speeds corresponding to 1, 2, 3, 4, 5, 6, etc.; then (by the method explained in Chapter 8) one tries to find a formula which will fit this set of numbers, and give the rule for the speed after x seconds. This enables one, at any rate, to *guess* the answer: to *prove* its correctness one has to use algebra.

You should be able to find for yourself the speeds corresponding to the formula $y=x^3$, the speeds corresponding to the formula $y=x^4$, and so on, with $y=x^5$, $y=x^6$, etc. When you have done $y=x^3$ and $y=x^4$, you will notice how simple the answers are. This suggests that the answers for $y=x^5$ and $y=x^6$ will also be simple, and helps you to shorten the work of guessing the rule. To work out the rule by the method of Chapter 8 would otherwise be a rather long piece of work. If you possibly can, work out for yourself the answers for the above cases, without looking at the results below. Anyone can do this work, and it makes all the difference to morale if you can find the results for yourself without ever looking at a text-book.

If you succeed in doing this, you will obtain the results set out in the table below.

TABLE XI

Formula for Distance Gone in x seconds.	Formula for Speed after x seconds.
$y=x^2$	$2x$
$y=x^3$	$3x^2$
$y=x^4$	$4x^3$
$y=x^5$	$5x^4$
$y=x^6$	$6x^5$

It is obvious that these results could be obtained by a simple rule. Where we have x^3 in the first column, we have something containing x^2 in the second; opposite x^4 stands a certain number of times x^3. The power of x in the second column is always one less than in the first. Opposite x^n there will be something containing x^{n-1}. Even simpler is the rule for the number which stands before x: it is the same as the number in the first column: it is n. Our rule is, 'If the formula for the distance is x^n, the formula for the speed is nx^{n-1}.'

Note what a lot of work is contained in this little result. To find the speed corresponding to x^2 we had to do a whole row of calculations; then we had to notice that the formula $2x$ would fit the results. We had to do this work also for x^3, x^4, x^5 and x^6. We then collected the formulae together in Table XI, and noticed that they could all be fused in one general rule.

Once having found the general rule, we can apply it immediately to any other case. To the formula $y=x^{17}$ will correspond the speed $17x^{16}$, the speed corresponding to x^{92} is $92x^{91}$.

In mechanics, and other applications, we often have to deal with formulae which contain several powers of x. For instance, if a ball is thrown straight upwards with a speed of 40 feet a second, its height after x seconds is given by $40x-16x^2$ feet. (We had this formula in Chapter 8 in a slightly different form. There it was given for the height after x *quarter*-seconds.) How is the speed after x seconds to be found?

The best way to deal with such a question is to split it up. We shall consider in turn the different parts which make up the problem.

(i) How quickly does the term $40x$ grow? $40x$ is the distance that a body would go in x seconds if it travelled with a *steady* speed of 40 feet a second. So the speed corresponding to $40x$ is obviously 40.

(ii) How quickly does the term $16x^2$ grow? We could get the table for $16x^2$ by multiplying all the numbers in the lower row of Table VII by 16. In other words, if a body travels according to the formula $16x^2$ after any number of seconds, it will have gone 16 times as far as one travelling according to the formula x^2. At any moment it must therefore be travelling 16 times as fast. But the speed corresponding to x^2 is $2x$. The speed corresponding to $16x^2$ must be 16 times as large: it must be $32x$.

(iii) We now know that $40x$ grows steadily at the rate 40, while $16x^2$ grows at the rate $32x$. How fast will $40x—16x^2$ grow? How are the two rates to be combined?

$40x—16x^2$ is obtained by subtracting $16x^2$ from $40x$. How can we picture this subtraction? We might think of $40x$ as representing a man's income at any moment, $16x^2$ as representing the expense of bringing up his family. Both income and expenditure are growing. $40x—16x^2$ represents the weekly balance which the man has, after meeting his expenses. It is obvious that this balance will increase at a rate given by the rate at which his income rises, *minus* the rate at which his expenses rise. (If the balance is decreasing, this rate will be less than nothing – it will have a minus sign.) The rate of increase of the income is 40; the rate of increase of expenditure is $32x$. The rate of increase of the balance is therefore $40—32x$. So we combine the rates by subtracting the second from the first.

We thus reach our grand conclusion: the speed corresponding to the formula $40x—16x^2$ is $40—32x$.

You will see that the arguments used could equally well be applied to any other expression of a similar type. For instance, the speed corresponding to $4x^3+x^2+3x+1$ is $12x^2+2x+3$. (The number 1 does not change at all: $y=1$ would mean that a body always stayed at a distance of 1 from some fixed point. Its speed would of course be nothing at all. So this 1 in the formula does not add anything to the answer. $4x^3+x^2+3x$ would lead to the same speed. This is quite reasonable. $4x^3+x^2+3x$ is always 1 less than $4x^3+x^2+3x+1$. The first formula neither catches up nor falls behind the second. So the speeds are naturally the same).

If you have any difficulty with this idea, reason out for yourself the speeds which correspond to $5x^2$ and to $2x$; then to $5x^2+2x$. Work out the speeds which correspond to x^2+x, $x^2—x$, $x+1$, x^2+x+1, and other examples which you can make up for yourself. Check your answers by working out the tables for these formulae, and seeing if your answers for the speeds are reasonable.

Signs for Speed

It is inconvenient to keep on saying 'the speed corresponding to the formula'. A sign is therefore used. If we have any formula giving y, the corresponding speed is represented by y'. This enables us to state a rule we had earlier in the shorter form, 'If $y = x^n$, $y' = nx^{n-1}$.' This means exactly the same as 'To the formula x^n corresponds the speed nx^{n-1}.' Just as $y(x)$ is used to represent the distance corresponding to x, so $y'(x)$ is used to represent the speed corresponding to x. Thus $y'(2)$ will mean the speed after 2 seconds.

It is sometimes convenient to use another sign, instead of y'.

This other sign is $\dfrac{dy}{dx}$.

There is a reason why this sign is used. The d in it has a very special meaning, like the Δ used in Chapter 8. In fact, it is only through the sign Δ that you can see why d is used here.

What, after all, is a speed? If you are told that a train has covered 300 miles in 4 hours, you know that its speed has been (on the average) 75 miles an hour. The 75 is found by dividing 300 by 4. If you know that a train has travelled 150 miles by 7 a.m. and 270 miles by 10 a.m., how do you find its average speed between 7 a.m. and 10 a.m.? You find the time that has passed between 7 a.m. and 10 a.m., 3 hours. You find the change in the distance, $270 - 150 = 120$. Then, dividing 120 by 3, you have your answer: 40 m.p.h.

If we call the time x hours, and the distance gone y miles, we have a table, rather like those in Chapter 8.

TABLE XII

Δx	3	
x	7	10
y	150	270
Δy	120	

As before, we have the values of x in one row, the corresponding values of y beneath them, and then a row giving Δy, the change in y. The only new feature is the row labelled Δx, giving the change in x. In Chapter 8, the change in x, between any number and the next, was always 1, so it would have been a waste of time, as well as a complication, to have had a row Δx. But for finding speeds Δx is absolutely essential. The speed of 40 m.p.h. was found by dividing 120 by 3 : that is, by dividing Δy by Δx.

The rule for finding *average speed*, then, is to work out the change in distance divided by the change in time. In our symbols,

average speed $= \dfrac{\Delta y}{\Delta x}$.

But this only gives *average* speed. We are looking for the speed at any moment. If a car runs into you at 60 m.p.h. it is no comfort to your widow to be told that it had averaged only 10 miles over the last hour, because the driver had spent most of the hour in a pub. The thing that matters is not the average speed during the past hour : it is the actual speed at the exact moment when the car hits you that counts.

But the speed at the moment of the collision will not differ very much from the average speed during the previous tenth of a second. It will differ even less from the average speed for the previous thousandth of a second. In other words, if we take the average speed for smaller and smaller lengths of time, we shall get nearer and nearer – as near as we like – to the true speed. For most practical purposes, the average speed during a thousandth of a second may be regarded as the exact speed.

It is for this reason that mathematicians find it useful to represent *speed* by a sign similar to that for *average speed*. The sign Δ is used by the Greeks to represent the capital letter D. We cannot take over the sign $\dfrac{\Delta y}{\Delta x}$, unchanged, to represent the speed : for the average speed over a short interval, however near it may be to the exact speed at any moment, is never quite the same : it would lead to confusion to have the same sign for two different things. But, as it were for old times' sake, to remind us how the idea of average speed has helped us towards finding the exact speed, we replace the Greek Δ by an English d, and use $\dfrac{dy}{dx}$ to represent the speed. For the moment, do not ask what dy and dx mean separately. Just regard $\dfrac{dy}{dx}$ as a sign that can be used instead of y', to represent the speed.

Again, in mechanical problems the speed is usually called by the technical term 'velocity', and we may use v as an abbreviation.

The process of finding how quickly a quantity changes is known as *differentiation*. If we differentiate y, we obtain its *rate of change* (or *speed*), y', $\dfrac{dy}{dx}$, v. If we differentiate x^2 we obtain $2x$.

This process can be repeated. When we considered a stone rolling downhill, according to the formula $y=x^2$, we saw that the velocity v continually increased. One might easily ask, 'How fast does it increase?' There is no difficulty in answering this question. We have seen that the velocity v after x seconds is given by the formula $v=2x$. Thus we have a very simple formula for v, and it is easy to find v'. In fact, $v'=2$. The velocity increases steadily; it increases by 2 for every second that passes. (Check this result from the values of v given in Table X.)

Since v is the same thing as y', it is natural to represent v' by y''. There is nothing new involved in this sign y''. y' represents the rate at which y changes: y'' represents the rate at which y' changes. In Chapter 8 we found $\Delta^2 y$ from Δy by just repeating the process we had already done to find Δy from y. It is the same here. We start with y. How quickly does y increase? The answer is y'. We now start again with a table (or a formula) for y'. How quickly does y' increase? The answer is y''. In many ways y'' resembles $\Delta^2 y$.

The Importance of y' and y''

The quantities y' and y'' have great importance in mechanics. It is obvious that y' (which simply means the speed, or velocity) is important. If anything, y'' is even more important. y'' measures how quickly the speed changes. If you are in a car travelling at 50 m.p.h. and the driver gradually brings the car to rest – say, within 10 minutes – you feel hardly anything at all. If, on the other hand, the car is brought to rest in one-hundredth of a second – by colliding with a stone wall – this is felt as a blow of tremendous force, sufficient to do serious damage. It does not hurt to travel at a high speed, such as 50 m.p.h. What does hurt is *a sudden change of speed*.

Usually, when our speed changes we feel pressure. If you are in a car, and the brakes are suddenly put on, you feel yourself thrown forward. What really happens is that you keep on moving at the same speed, but the car stops. You stop only when you strike the seat in front of you: you feel this pressing you back. In the same way, a bicycle cannot be slowed down if it has no brakes (unless perhaps there is a strong wind blowing against it, or it is going uphill, or it is badly oiled – any of these states can take the place of brakes).

Newton's Laws of Motion express this idea. According to Newton, if a body could get right away from all outside influences – far away from the pull of the earth and the sun, not being pressed or pulled by any other body, away from electric and magnetic forces – that body would keep on moving in a straight line at a steady speed. With a telescope one can observe little bits of matter, such as comets, and it is seen that the farther away they get from the earth and the sun, the more nearly they move in straight paths at a steady speed.

Whenever we find a body moving in a curved path, or with a changing speed, we therefore believe that something else is interfering with it, is acting upon it. We say that a *force* is acting on it and we try to discover what this force is. Is the body tied to a rope or string? Is it nailed to some other body? Is it being pulled by the earth or the sun or (in the case of tides) the moon? Has it been magnetized? Is it charged with electricity? Is it sliding on a rough surface, which is causing it to slow down? Is it moving in some liquid, such as water or treacle, which opposes its motion? Is it passing through the air, like a parachute, or a falling feather?

Next we ask how to measure the force. It is clear that the force needed to alter the speed of a body depends on how massive the body is. It is easy to stop a runaway pram; harder to stop a runaway wagon; very hard to stop a string of loaded trucks; almost impossible to stop an avalanche. Scientists therefore use the word *mass* to express this quality of a body. One cubic centimetre of water is chosen as the unit of mass; it is called a gramme. Anything which is just as easy to stop, or to get going, as a cubic centimetre of water is said to have a mass of 1 gramme. Anything which is as hard to stop as 100,000 cubic centimetres of water is said to have a mass of 100,000 grammes. And so on. For short, we shall call the mass of a body m grammes.

It is then found that the force which changes the speed of a body (mass m grammes) at the rate y'' is given by my''. When the body is going faster and faster, with y increasing, the force pulls the body forward. When the body is slowing down, y'' is negative: this means that the force is acting as a brake – it is pulling the body back.

In scientific work it is usual to measure the distance y, not in feet or inches, but in centimetres. By using the decimal system of measures we save all the complications of having 12 inches one foot, 3 feet one yard, 22 yards one chain, $30\frac{1}{4}$ square yards one pole, and so on. The English system of measurement has been handed down from very ancient times, long before science or modern engineering had been thought of. It is based on such things as the amount of land a team of oxen can plough in a day (furlong=a furrow long, etc.) or the average size of a part of the human body (*e.g.*, a foot). Such measures were convenient for their original uses. The French system, on the other hand, was introduced during the French Revolution of 1789, and was specially designed for modern trade and industry. Any difficulties that are found in changing from feet and tons to centimetres and grammes must be regarded as due to human history: they are not purely scientific problems.

English engineers also use a system of measurement, in which the standard mass is a one-pound weight, and the distance y is measured in feet. The force corresponding to m pounds and a speeding-up y'' (measured in feet and seconds) is then my'' poundals.

We have already considered the formula $y=40x-16x^2$, which gives the height in feet of a body x seconds after it has been thrown-up with a speed of 40 feet a second. What force is acting on this body? $y'=40-32x$. $y''=-32$. If the body has a mass m pounds, the force acting on it is my'', which equals $-32m$. This force does not depend on x. It is the same whatever x may be. The size of the force is $32m$: the sign in front of it is *minus* because the earth drags the weight *down*, as everyone knows. In the case of something which tended to rise (such as a balloon) the force would be $+$.

It is found by experiment that any heavy body thrown into the air moves in such a way that $y''=-32$. We suppose the body is sufficiently heavy for air resistance to be neglected. This law obviously does not hold for a feather, or for a parachute. The whole point of a parachute is that it falls in a way very different from a brick. The law just stated gives good results for a falling stone, cricket ball, or man. It does not work for feathers, raindrops, or mice. Nor does it work for very high speeds. In the motion of a shell or a bullet, the force due to air resistance may well be greater than that due to gravity.

The figure 32 is of course not exact. The earth does not bother to pull us towards itself with a force that is a simple multiple of the length of our feet! But 32 is near enough for most purposes.

Since the pull of the earth causes y'' to have the value -32, the force exerted on a mass of m pounds by the earth must be $-32m$ poundals (found by putting $y''=-32$ in the expression my''). The *minus* sign means that this force acts *downwards*.

Other Useful Subjects*

So far we have dealt with a very special case, that of a body moving in a straight line, and acted on by a single force only.

* The remainder of this chapter contains applications which may interest some readers, but are not necessary for an understanding of the rest of the book. A brief reference to this section is made in Chapter 13.

In nearly all practical studies the problem is more complicated. A lift moves up and down in a straight line, but two important forces act on it – the pull of the earth downwards, and the pull of the supporting rope upwards. We may also need to take into account any device used to stop the lift bumping against the walls of the shaft, friction, air-resistance, etc. – even if we neglect these, we still have *two* forces to consider. In other examples we may have to deal with bodies that do not move in straight lines: a train or motor-car going round a bend, a shell in the air, a piece of metal in a flywheel.

Statics deals with the combined effect of a number of forces. Its laws have to be discovered in the first place by experiment, and can then be used for reasoning.

When several forces act in the same direction, the result is what you might expect. If two men pull a sledge, each hauling with a force of 1000 poundals, the effect is the same as that of a single pull of 2000 poundals: the separate forces are simply added together.

When two forces act in opposite directions, the effect is easy to calculate. If a lift weighs 2500 pounds, the earth will pull it downwards with a force of 32×2500 poundals – i.e., 80,000 poundals. If the wire rope pulls the lift upwards with a force of 100,000 poundals, two forces are acting on the lift, 100,000 poundals upwards, 80,000 poundals downwards. These two forces combined have the same effect as a force of 20,000 poundals (obtained by subtracting 80,000 from 100,000), acting upwards. Note that the rope must be able to stand a strain which is *greater* than the weight of the lift. For it is only when the pull of the rope upwards is greater than the pull of the earth downwards that the total force is upwards. And one must be able to make the total force act upwards in order to start the lift for an upward journey and (equally important) to check it at the end of a downward journey. In a coalmine, the cage lifts and lowers the miners through hundreds of yards in an amazingly short space of time. Very great changes of speed take place, and it is a matter of vital importance that the rope be strong enough, not merely to bear the weight of the cage and the men inside it, but also to exert the extra force necessary for starting and braking. (It is possible to experiment with model lifts, using cotton thread instead of rope, to demonstrate the effect of a sudden jerk.)

An entirely new principle has to be learnt in order to deal with forces which do not act in the same straight line. Suppose we have a force of 2 poundals acting East, and a force of 3 poundals acting North: to what single force is this equivalent? It is impossible to answer this by argument: we can only try to see what happens when a small weight is dragged towards

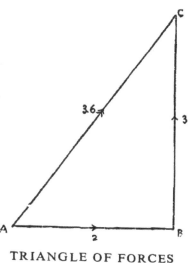

TRIANGLE OF FORCES

the East by one string attached to it, and towards the North by another. (For details of the experiment, see text-books on Statics.) The reader will be able to *feel* what sort of result is likely – the weight will be dragged in a direction somewhere between North and East. Experiments show that the following method gives the correct answer. Draw a line 2 inches long, towards the East. Call this line AB. From the Eastern end of this line (B) draw a line BC, 3 inches long, towards the North. The line AB is drawn 2 inches long, to represent a force of 2 poundals; the line BC is made 3 inches long, corresponding to the force of 3 poundals. If we measure AC, we find it to be 3·6 inches long. The length and direction of AC gives the answer to the question. The two forces, 2 poundals towards the East and 3 poundals towards the North, acting together, will drag the weight in the direction AC, with a force of 3·6 poundals. This principle is known as the Triangle of Forces, for an obvious reason. In the triangle ABC the two sides AB and BC represent the two forces given. The third side, AC, represents the single force produced by these two forces acting together.

In an ordinary catapult two pieces of elastic are fastened to a small piece of cloth. When the catapult is fired, the small piece of cloth moves in a direction that lies between the direction of the two pieces of elastic.

Co-ordinate Geometry

In dealing with graphs we used the idea of fixing the position of a point by measuring the distance across the paper ('to the East') and the distance 'to the North'. The same idea may be used to study the movement of any small weight, when it is not moving in a straight line. We suppose that, after x seconds, the small weight is y feet to the East and z feet to the North of some fixed landmark, O. The small weight might be part of some machine. The rules giving y and z in terms of x will depend on the way in which the machine is constructed. For instance, the weight might be some part of a locomotive. If we know the shape of the railway line, and the speed at which the train is travelling, we know *where* each part of the locomotive will be at any time. In other words, we know what values y and z will have after x seconds.

If no force is acting on a body, the body moves in a straight line. When a locomotive goes round a bend, it is not moving in a straight line, nor is any piece of the locomotive moving in a straight line. So there must be forces acting on each part of the locomotive. You will always notice that a locomotive, in going round a bend, presses against the outer rail, just as a motor-car going round a corner too fast tends to run into the outer edge of the road, if the road is not sufficiently banked. The rail presses back on the wheels, and makes these go round the bend, instead of going straight on, as they would prefer to do. Is it possible to find how large is the force acting on any part of the locomotive? It is possible, though it is not easy to describe the method in a few words.

First of all, in order not to make the problem too complicated, let us choose a part of the locomotive which does not move up and down. As it always stays at the same height, its motion can be described completely by giving a table, showing how far it has moved to the East of the landmark O, and how far it has moved to the North of O. Our first task, then, is to discover formulae, or to make tables, giving y and z corresponding to any time, x seconds. We suppose this part of the job completed.

It would be quite easy to study the motion of the locomotive (or the little part of it) towards the East, *if* there were no motion towards the North. The locomotive would then be moving due East, *in a straight line*. After x seconds its distance to the East would be given by y, and the force pushing the small part (of mass m pounds, say) towards the East would be (by our previous method) my''.

It would also be easy to find the answer, if the locomotive was moving due North. The force pushing the small part to the North would be mz'', by a very similar argument.

At this point we receive a free gift from Nature. *It turns out to be true* – and we had no reason to expect this – that the movement towards the East and the movement towards the North can be treated as if they were quite separate. The actual force pushing the small piece is obtained by combining (by the Triangle of Forces) a force my'' to the East and a force mz'' to the North.

The problem therefore can be completely solved. There is no essential difficulty brought in if we consider movements up and down, as well as to the East and to the North. The forces due to the fact that parts of a locomotive move up and down are very important. Old-fashioned locomotives, if driven fast, would jump into the air.

Of the design of modern locomotives, Kempe's *Engineer's Yearbook* writes, 'The horizontal forces are the most injurious, though American engineers consider the vertical forces to be so; but English practice is to take a medium course between excessive horizontal and vertical disturbing influences.'

The calculation of the forces brought into play by moving weights is a practical question in the design and balancing of machinery. In this short space it has not been possible to explain the method in a satisfactory way, but the fact that the method can be outlined, even vaguely, in so few words shows that the principles involved are both few and simple.

Conclusion

Statics and Dynamics will seem very unreal to you if you have had no experience of handling heavy weights. You can learn more dynamics in an afternoon starting and stopping a heavy (but well oiled) railway truck or garden roller than you can from whole books of dynamics. You can get the benefit of reading a book on dynamics only if such words as 'force' call up a vivid image in your mind. Once you have the necessary feel for the subject, the books can be most valuable, even interesting – but not before.

Calculus does not need the same experimental background. Almost everyone already knows what speed is. The job is rather to study sets of figures, until you realize what sort of motion they represent. Take any formula. Work out a table, showing the distance gone after various times. If you cannot see what the exact speed is, begin to ask questions. Silly ones are the best to begin with. Is the speed a million miles an hour? Or one inch a century? Somewhere between these limits. Good. We now know something about the speed. Begin to bring the limits in, and see how close together they can be brought. Study your own methods of thought. How do you know that the speed is less than a million miles an hour? What definite evidence does the table show to support this view? What method, in fact, are you unconsciously using to estimate speed? Can this method be applied to get closer estimates?

You know what speed is. You would not believe a man who claimed to walk at 5 miles an hour, but took 3 hours to walk 6 miles. You have only to apply the same common sense to stones rolling down hillsides, and the calculus is at your command.

EXAMPLES

It has already been urged that the reader should not try to reason about any problem until he has a perfectly clear picture of it in his mind, and has found some way of bringing the problem into touch with real life, so that he can see and handle the things of which it speaks. This is particularly important in the study of *speed*, which is by no means such a simple thing as we at first think it to be. The reader must find for himself some device by means of which he can observe movement. This may be a pencil rolling down a desklid, a bicycle on a hillside, or a weight hanging by a string. One particular device may be mentioned, on the lines of cinema cartoons. Most school-children are familiar with a way of drawing pictures on the leaves of a book, so that when the leaves are allowed to fall in rapid succession the figures seem to move. The same idea may be used to study the movement of a point. It has the advantage that one can study the movement 'frozen' – by looking at the points marked on the various pages of the book – as well as in action. In questions 1 and 2 it is assumed that the leaves of the book fall at the rate of ten each second.

1. On the first sheet of a book mark a point $0 \cdot 1$ inch from the bottom of the page, on the second $0 \cdot 2$ inch, etc., the point on the nth sheet being $\frac{n}{10}$ inches up the page. This illustrates the movement in which $y = x$ (y in inches, x in seconds). That the point moves with a steady speed is shown by the fact that the mark on any sheet is always $0 \cdot 1$ inch higher than that on the page before.

2. On the nth sheet mark a point at the height $\frac{n}{100}$. This corresponds to the movement $y = x^2$ discussed in this chapter. Notice how slowly the point moves in the first half-second (five sheets), how it gains speed as time passes.

3. A body moves according to the law $y = x$. Make a table for its motion and convince yourself: (i) that it is moving at a steady speed, (ii) that this speed is 1. In fact, when $y = x$, $y' = 1$.

4. Similarly, show that when $y = 2x$, $y' = 2$.

5. And when $y = \frac{1}{4}x$, $y' = \frac{1}{4}$.

6. When $y = x + 1$, $y' = 1$.

· 7. And when $y = x + 2$, $y' = 1$.

8. When $y = \frac{1}{4}x + 1$, $y' = \frac{1}{4}$.

9. When $y = \frac{1}{4}x + 2$, $y' = \frac{1}{4}$.

10. A dog is chasing a cat. The cat moves according to the formula $y = 30x + 2$, the dog according to the formula $y = 30x$. Is it true that (i) both animals are moving at 30 feet a second; (ii) the dog is always 2 feet behind the cat; (iii) $y' = 30$ for both formulae?

11. If the cat moves according to $y=20x+10$ and the dog according to $y=25x$, is it true (i) that the dog starts 10 feet behind the cat; (ii) the dog moves faster than the cat; (iii) the dog will catch the cat within a short time? What is y' for the cat? for the dog? When will the dog overtake the cat?

12. Write down y' in the following cases:

(i) $y=x^2$. (ii) $y=2x^2$. (iii) $y=2x^2+1$. (iv) $y=\frac{1}{2}x^2$. (v) $y=x$. (vi) $y=x^2+x$. (vii) $y=x^2+x+1$. (viii) $y=\frac{1}{2}x^2-1$. (ix) $y=x-x^2$. (x) $y=1-x^2$. (xi) $y=x^3$. (xii) $y=2x^3$. (xiii) $y=2x^3+x$. (xiv) $y=2x^3+1$. (xv) $y=10x^3-20x^2+7x-3$.

13. We have seen that when $y=x^2$, $y'=2x$ and $y''=2$. Make tables showing y, y', y'', Δy and $\Delta^2 y$ for $x=0, 1, 2 \ldots 10$. Is it true that (i) the table for y' is rather like, but not quite the same as, the table for Δy; (ii) $\Delta^2 y$ is exactly the same as y''?

14. If $y=x^3$, $y'=3x^2$ and $y''=6x$. Make tables for y, y', y'', Δy and $\Delta^2 y$. Is it true (i) y' behaves rather like Δy; (ii) y'' behaves rather like $\Delta^2 y$?

15. If you had worked out a problem and found a formula for y' which behaved in a way quite different from Δy (for instance, y' getting steadily larger while Δy got steadily smaller), would you think you had made a slip in your work or not? What about y'' and $\Delta^2 y$? Do you expect them, as a rule, to behave in more or less the same way?

CHAPTER 11

FROM SPEED TO CURVES

'Our townsman, Dr Joule . . . instanced the porpoise, with its bluff figurehead, attaining a velocity of over thirteen miles an hour, whilst voracious fishes are so constructed that they can attain a much greater velocity. He advocated a study of natural proportions to those who wish to be successful shipbuilders.' – Bosdin Leech, *History of the Manchester Ship Canal.*

So far we have considered y' or $\dfrac{dy}{dx}$ simply as a sign for the speed of a moving point. For many important applications this is quite sufficient. But it is only one half of the story. There are many problems for which calculus can be used to describe shape. For instance, it is possible to find the curve in which a chain hangs when its ends are held, or the way in which the strain on a bridge is distributed. Movement does not come into either of these questions at all.

It is very easy to translate our discoveries about movement into statements about shape. Any type of movement can easily be

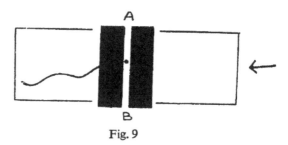

Fig. 9

represented by a curve. Consider the simple arrangement shown in Fig. 9. The point of a pencil is supposed to be moving in the slit AB. Underneath the slit is a sheet of paper, which is made to move at a steady pace towards the left. It is clear that the movement of the pencil will be recorded on the paper as a curve. If we want to see how the pencil was moving, we have only to pass the paper under the slit again. Through the slit we shall be able to see a very short piece of the curve, which will be seen as a point, and will seem to move up and down as the paper passes to the left.

This arrangement is rather similar to a gramophone. The groove of the gramophone record is cut by a vibrating needle. When the record is played, the original vibrations are reproduced. All the peculiarities of the original motion, then, are somehow preserved in the shape of the groove; and any alteration in the shape of the groove would result in some difference when the record was played.

In the same way, the motion of the pencil point and the curve traced on the moving paper are closely connected. Anything that can be said about the movement of the pencil must tell us something about the shape of the curve. Anything that can be said about the curve tells us something about the movement of the pencil.

Now we know that y' tells us how fast the pencil is moving at any moment, and y'' tells us whether the pencil is speeding up or slowing down. It must be possible to find out what y' and y'' represent, what they tell us about the shape of the curve traced by the pencil. To do this is our next job.

The Case of Steady Movement

We will begin by considering the simplest case. Figures 9A to 9E show the traces left on the paper in five experiments. In each of these experiments the pencil moved at a steady speed. The strip of paper is 1 inch wide, and it moved through the slit,

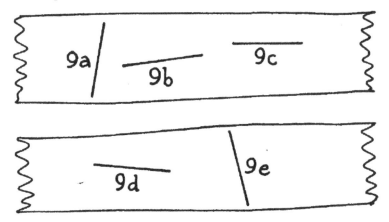

towards the left, at the rate of 1 inch a second. You can, if you like, make an arrangement of the type illustrated in Fig. 9, and pass these strips through it, thus reproducing the original movements.

What happens when 9A passes through? It takes only one-fifth of a second, and during this time the moving point gets right across the paper, a distance of 1 inch. 9A is the track of a point moving at 5 inches a second. For it, $y'=5$.

9B is the track of a point that moves up the slit, but at a much slower rate. In one second the point has risen only one-tenth of an inch. Here $y'=\frac{1}{10}$.

Already, by comparing 9A and 9B, we can see that the line is *very steep* when the point has moved *very fast* (that is, for large y'), but is *nearly level* when the point is moving *slowly* (y' small). In fact, y' *measures how steep the graph is*.

9C is the track left when the pencil-point is *at rest*. The point stays at the same height. It has *no speed*, so $y'=0$.

Accordingly, when $y'=0$, the graph is *level*.

In 9D the pencil-point moves *down* the slit as the paper passes through. When a second has passed, the point has gone down one-tenth of an inch. The change in y during 1 second is therefore $-\frac{1}{10}$, from which it follows that $y'=-\frac{1}{10}$.

Again, in 9E the pencil-point descends 1 inch in one-fifth of a second; it is therefore descending at the rate of 5 inches a second, and $y'=-5$.

We notice that the graph slopes *downhill* when y' is minus (cases D and E) *uphill* when y' is plus (cases A and B).

To sum up: the *steepness* of the graph depends on how *big y' is*: whether the graph goes *uphill* or *downhill* depends on whether y' has a $+$ or a $-$ sign. $y'=0$ means that the graph is *level*.

The General Case

So far we have been considering only what happens when the pencil-point moves at a steady speed. But as a rule this is not the case. We may often have to study things that move with different speeds at different times.

It is, however, still possible to use the conclusions to which we were led by a study of the simpler cases. You should test this for yourself, by means of some arrangement on the lines of Fig. 9. If you move a pencil up and down the slit, varying its speed, you will find that when the pencil is moving fast, the track it leaves is steep; when it is moving slowly, the track it leaves is not very steep. We can still say that *speed* corresponds to *steepness*. If the *speed varies*, then the *steepness* of the graph also *varies*. In this case the graph will be curved, instead of straight, as it was before.

This brings us to the question of y''. y'' tells us how quickly the speed, y', varies. We shall be mainly interested in the sign of y'', whether it is $+$ or $-$. If y'' is $+$, it means that y' is growing (i.e., that y' is changing by having something *added* to it). If y'' is $-$, it means that y' is decreasing (is having something *taken away* from it).

Look at the four sample tracks shown in the figure.

SAMPLE 1.	SAMPLE 2.	SAMPLE 3.	SAMPLE 4.
$y'\ +$	$y'\ +$	$y'\ -$	$y'\ -$
$y''\ +$	$y''\ -$	$y''\ +$	$y''\ -$

What are the signs of y' and y'' in Sample 1? This curve is rising, its slope is uphill; y' therefore must be $+$. The farther you go, the steeper this curve gets. Its steepness (measured by y') is getting bigger. So y' must be increasing. That means y'' must be $+$. It is easy to get a little confused between the meanings of y' and y''. Remember, y' measures how fast y is changing – that is, y' measures the speed of a moving point. y'' measures how quickly y' is changing – that is, how quickly the speed changes.

If this curve were part of a chart showing the course of a military campaign, it would mean (*a*) that the army was advancing, (*b*) that the speed of its advance was continually increasing. (*a*) corresponds to the mathematical statement that y' is $+$; (*b*) to the statement that y'' is $+$.

We have a different state of affairs in Sample 2. True, the slope of the curve is uphill, but the farther you go, the *less* steep it is. This corresponds to the military communiqué 'our advance continues, but is being slowed down by determined resistance'. Since it is an *advance*, y' is $+$. Since the rate of advance is being *slowed down*, y'' is $-$.

One has to be rather careful with Samples 3 and 4, owing to the fact that y' is minus. We have to remember that a change from $y'=-10$ to $y'=-1$ represents an increase in y', owing to the properties of negative numbers.

In Sample 3 the state of affairs at the beginning represents a *rapid descent* – in military terms, a rout. Later on the curve is still doing downhill, but not nearly so fast. The retreat is being checked. To this extent the situation is improving. The *improvement* is reflected by the fact that y'' is $+$. The *retreat* is shown by the downward slope of the curve: y' is $-$.

The reader may remember that the line 9E, going steeply downwards, had $y'=-5$, while 9D had $y'=-\frac{1}{10}$. In Sample 3 the early part of the curve slopes like the line 9E, while the end of the curve is more like 9D. In Sample 3, then, y' begins by being about -5, and ends by being about $-\frac{1}{10}$. You have to add something to -5 to make it into $-\frac{1}{10}$. That is why y'', the rate of change of y', is $+$.

In Sample 4, on the other hand, the situation is going to the dogs faster and faster. The curve is going downhill, becoming steeper and steeper. y' may be about $-\frac{1}{10}$ at the *beginning*, and -5 at the *end*. y' is therefore *changing for the worse* – that is, y'' is $-$.

In these four samples we have covered all the main possibilities. y' must be either $+$ or $-$, and y'' must be $+$ or $-$ (unless y' or y'' should happen to be 0). By combining our four Samples, we can see what the shape of any graph will be, provided we know how y' and y'' behave. Note that it is quite easy to give a simple meaning to y''. When y'' is $+$, the curve *bends upwards* (Samples 1 and 3); when y'' is $-$, the curve *bends downwards* (Samples 2 and 4).

An Example

Suppose you were asked. 'What is the general shape of the graph $y=x^3-3x$?' We will consider the shape of the graph between $x=-20$ and $x=+20$.

First of all we need to know y' and y''. Since $y = x^3 - 3x$, $y' = 3x^2 - 3$, $y'' = 6x$.

Clearly, y'' is $+$ when x is $+$, and $-$ when x is $-$. This tells us that the graph *bends upward* for all positive x, *downward* for all negative x.

If you try a few values for x, you will see that $3x^2 - 3$, the formula for y', is + when x lies between —20 and 1, and also when x lies between 1 and 20. $3x^2-3$ is — when x lies between —1 and 1.

We can collect this information together in a diagram, thus:

x	—20	—1	0	1 20
y'	+ + +	0 — —	— — —0	+ + +
y''	— — —	— — —	0 + + +	+ + +
Curve resembles sample	2 2 2	4 4	3 3	1 1 1

We thus conclude:

From $x = $ —20 to —1 the curve looks like SAMPLE 2.
     —1 to 0   ,,   ,,   ,,   SAMPLE 4.
     0 to 1   ,,   ,,   ,,   SAMPLE 3.
     1 to 20   ,,   ,,   ,,   SAMPLE 1.

Fitting these together, we see that the general appearance of the graph must be as follows:

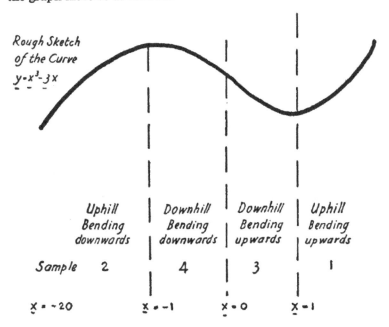

Rough Sketch
of the Curve
$y = x^3 - 3x$

Uphill Bending downwards	Downhill Bending downwards	Downhill Bending upwards	Uphill Bending upwards
Sample 2	4	3	1
$x = $ —20	$x = $ —1	$x = $ 0	$x = $ 1

It would, of course, be possible to make an exact graph of the curve, by working out a table and plotting a large number of points on the curve. We should, of course, get the same curve in the end. But usually the method just explained, using y and y'', is shorter, more instructive and more artistic. Some of the examples at the end of this chapter are intended to illustrate this point.

We saw in Chapter 10 that y' measured the *speed*, y'' the *force acting* on a moving body. When y'' was $+$, it meant that the body was being pushed *upward* (or, in some cases, *forward*). When y'' was —, it meant that the body was being pulled *downward* (or, in some cases, *backward*).

But, by examining the graph that represents the motion of the body, we can see how y' and y'' are behaving. In this way, by looking at the graph, we are able to say (for example), 'Here the graph is rising very steeply. The body must be moving very fast. But the curve bends downwards. That means y'' is *minus*, some force is putting a brake on the motion.'

It is quite easy, with a little practice, to tell from a graph how the quantities y' and y'' behave, where y' is $+$, where y'' is minus, etc.

But suppose we are not content with a general description: suppose we want to measure the speed at a certain moment? How can we go about this?

We have already seen (in Chapter 10) that the true speed of a body does not differ much (as a rule) from the average speed over a short period of time. If we know how far a body goes in one tenth of a second, we can get *some* idea of how fast it is going.

If we are shown the graph representing an object's motion, can we tell how far it goes in one-tenth of a second?

In Fig. 10 part of a graph is shown, considerably magnified. The distance AB represents one-tenth of an inch, and corresponds to one-tenth of a second. At the beginning of this length of a second the pencil touched the paper at the point C. At the end of the tenth of a second it touched the paper at D. It must have moved upwards through a distance DE during this interval. In other words, DE represents the change in y: that is, Δy. The time that

ROLLING A CRICKET PITCH

The curve on the right records the motion of the roller. To compare this curve with the arrangement of Fig. 9, it would be necessary to turn the page on its side; the roller would then seem to be moving *upwards* (like the pencil-point in the slit).

The motion may be divided into three sections, A, B, and C.

(a) The man has to push hard to get the roller moving. He is pushing *forwards* ($y''+$). But the roller is not yet moving fast (y' not large, curve not steep).

(b) The roller is now under way. The man walks beside it, but lets it roll without pushing or pulling ($y''=0$. *No* force).

(c) To stop the roller running into the wickets, the man has to *pull it back* ($y''-$).

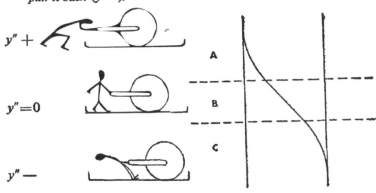

Note that the man is working hardest in sections A and C, but the roller is moving fastest in section B. The *greatest force* (y'' large) does not occur at the same time as the *greatest speed* (y' large).

One can also test this with a bicycle. Use the highest gear, and note that (on a calm day) one works hard in *getting* the bicycle moving, not in *keeping* it moving.

has passed is represented by AB. Thus AB is Δx. The average speed, $\frac{\Delta y}{\Delta x}$, is therefore found by dividing the length DE by the length AB. AB is the same length as CE. DE divided by CE therefore represents the average speed. And it is clear that DE divided by CE gives us a rough measure for the steepness of the curve between C and D.

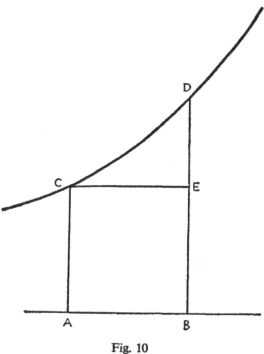

Fig. 10

If instead of a tenth of a second we had taken a hundredth or a thousandth, we should have found a better answer – one nearer to the exact value of y'. So that it is possible to explain what y' is without bringing in the idea of speed at all. Starting with the graph, one takes a point B near to A, draws the figure, and measures DE and CE. One then works out $\dfrac{DE}{CE}$. Then start again: take B still nearer to A, and work out DE divided by CE for the new figure. As B keeps on getting closer and closer to A, the answer keeps on getting closer and closer to some number. The number which it approaches is y': we may regard y' as measuring the steepness of the curve at the point C.

In this way we have given a meaning to y', quite apart from the idea of movement. The same can be done for y'', and these symbols (as was mentioned earlier) can be applied to problems about the shape of a hanging chain, or the arch of a bridge or the best curve for the tooth of a gear-wheel. It need not surprise you if you find still other applications of y' where neither shape nor speed seems to come in. For instance, x might represent the temperature of a body, and y might measure the amount of heat put into the body. It is then possible to give a meaning to y'. Whenever you meet the symbol y' or $\dfrac{dy}{dx}$, there must be in the problem two quantities, x and y, which are connected with each other, so that any change in x automatically produces a change in y.

So that our definition of y' as a *speed* may be regarded as a kind of scaffolding. It was helpful at the beginning, but no one keeps the scaffolding up when the house has been built. When you have had some experience of the different applications of y' you will probably be able to think of it simply as the number which $\dfrac{\Delta y}{\Delta x}$ approaches when Δx is made smaller and smaller. But do not be in a hurry to think of it in this way. Even when you are thoroughly familiar with the idea of y', it will often help you to think of it as a speed, or as the steepness of a graph.

The Use of Rough Ideas

It may not have struck you before what a subtle idea 'speed' is. It was quite easy to explain 'average speed'. A car has gone 30 miles in an hour: its average speed has been 30 m.p.h. This is a simple enough idea. But its speed at the precise moment of a collision? That is a much more difficult idea: it is a much harder thing to measure. We have to perform quite a complicated process. Work out the average speed for the minute before the collision, for the second before, for one-tenth of a second before, and so on. See if the answers approach closer and closer to some number; if so, this number represents the speed at the moment of collision.

Actually to carry out this process, we should have to measure very short periods of time – in turn, a hundredth, a thousandth, a millionth of a second – and the very short distances passed over in these times. And even then we should not be quite sure of getting an exact answer. It would always be possible that in the last billionth of a second the driver pressed the brake harder than before, so that the speed at the last instant was really less than we should have expected from the average speed over the last millionth of a second.

Engineers and pure mathematicians differ in their attitude to this question. The engineer thinks the discussion is a waste of time. He does not mind whether the speed was 50 m.p.h. or 50.00031 m.p.h. He cannot measure speed beyond a certain degree of accuracy, and he does not want to, anyway. Even if the brake is put on harder in the last billionth of a second, it will alter the speed by only a tiny amount. So far as an engineer is concerned, the average speed for the last millionth of a second *is* the speed at the moment of collision.

Why does the pure mathematician not agree with this point of view? It is not entirely due to the passion for hair-splitting which affects some mathematicians. One reason is historical. At first, calculus was treated rather in the spirit of the practical man. Very small periods of time were considered. In working out the average speed, this period of time was supposed to be some definite number, bigger than nothing. But in the answer certain parts came which were not wanted, and mathematicians then turned round and said that the little period was so small that it could be treated as nothing. So that at one time a millionth was a millionth, and at another time (when it gave a more convenient answer!) a millionth was treated as being nothing. Naturally students felt that this was a queer subject. Some mathematicians refused to believe that true results could follow from such a method. So mathematicians were forced to clear up the confusion, and to find a more exact and logical way of explaining what they meant by speed. In modern books on the calculus, written for professional mathematicians, you will therefore find very long and careful proofs, written in exact, lawyer-like fashion. It is good to understand these proofs, but not when starting calculus. First learn to use calculus, to see what can be done with it, to feel what it is about. In the course of this you will gradually become aware of a need for more exact ideas – then is the time to study the modern treatment, usually known by the name of *Analysis*.

There are other reasons for using the exact speed. For one thing, practical men are not agreed on the shortest amount that need be considered. The carpenter works in hundredths of inches, the engineer in thousandths, the scientist in millionths – microbes, atoms, rays of light. For a locomotive engineer one hundredth of a second is a short time; for the radio engineer, who thinks in terms of so many million cycles a second, a hundredth of a second is an eternity. The pure mathematician, whose results may be used by any of these men, can be sure of saisfying every possible demand only by giving the *exact* result.

Again, the exact result is often simpler than the inexact one. When we studied the speed of a body corresponding to the formula $y = x^2$, we found several rough results. For instance, we found that the speed after one second was between $1\cdot99$ and $2\cdot01$. Suppose we had stopped here, and said $2\cdot01$ is good enough as an answer. This is a more complicated result than the exact value 2. If we had throughout treated one-hundredth of a second as a sufficiently short time for our purposes, we should have been led to the formula $y' = 2x + 0\cdot01$, roughly. This is more complicated than the exact answer, $y' = 2x$. Even engineers use $2x$ as the speed corresponding to x^2. The simpler answer makes up for the more complicated definition.

There is, as you see, much practical justification for the exactness beloved of pure mathematicians. But this is only one side of the question. There are often cases in which the rough idea is very helpful. Often the rough idea of a problem will enable us to see what the problem means, to see the way to a solution. Our answer may be incorrect by a few millionths, but it will be sufficient to give us a general idea of the solution. We may then be able to go over our working, and polish each stage of the work, until the whole thing becomes exact. Or we may rest content with the rough solution of the problem. Many problems which are difficult by exact methods are studied by research workers, by rough methods. The answers are given true to two decimal places, or whatever it may be, sufficient for the purpose required.

Some Examples of Rough Ideas

Suppose, for instance, we were given the problem of finding $\frac{dy}{dx}$ (that is, y') corresponding to the formula $y = \log x$. This is a new problem. We know how to deal with an expression built up from powers of x, but $\log x$ does not belong to this simple type. What is to be done?

Students who have learnt merely to do simple problems by text-book methods are, of course, helpless in face of a new kind of problem. They sit before it, and do nothing at all. I hope readers will not find themselves in this situation, but that they will already see how to experiment with this problem, how to seek for a solution.

Do we know what $\log x$ is? If you had difficulty with Chapter 6 it is not the slightest use going on with this chapter. Obviously, if you have no clear picture of the meaning of $\log x$, it is absurd to expect to reason correctly about the speed of growth of $\log x$. If necessary, then, read Chapter 6 again. Get a table of logarithms, and draw a graph to illustrate the formula $y = \log x$. (By $\log x$ I mean the ordinary logarithm as given in the usual tables. $\text{Log}_{10} x$ is the complete sign. This means – to use the language of Chapter 6 – that 'one complete turn' corresponds to multiplication by 10.) Draw this graph for values of x between 1 and 10, plotting sufficient points to give an accurate graph. You will notice that the graph is most steep at $x = 1$. The larger x gets, the less steep the graph. We shall expect for y' some formula which makes y' get less as x gets larger.

We can obtain a *rough* idea of y' by taking a change of $0 \cdot 1$ in x, and seeing what change this produces in y. Part of the work is shown below. Instead of writing the values of x in rows across the page, it is more convenient to set the work out in columns.

TABLE XIII

x	$y = \log x$	Δy	$\dfrac{\Delta y}{\Delta x}$
1	0·0000	0·0414	0·414
1·1	0·0414	0·0378	0·378
1·2	0·0792	0·0347	0·347
1·3	0·1139	0·0322	0·322
1·4	0·1461	0·0300	0·300
1·5	0·1761	0·0280	0·280
1·6	0·2041		
2·0	0·3010	0·0212	0·212
2·1	0·3222		
10·0	1·0000	0·0043	0·043
10·1	1·0043		

In the first column are values of x. Each number exceeds the previous one by 0·1. So the change in x, Δx, is always 0·1. The second column gives the logarithms of the first column, found from a table of logarithms. The third column gives the changes in the second column, Δy. The fourth column gives a rough estimate of the speed, y'; the change in y, Δy, has been divided by the corresponding change in x, Δx. Dividing by 0·1 is the same as multiplying by 10. The numbers in the fourth column are thus ten times those in the third. The table given above is not complete: the numbers between 1·6 and 2·0 and those between 2·1 and 10 have been omitted, to save space. These gaps should be filled in by the reader.

The numbers in the fourth column give us a *rough* measure of the steepness of the graph of $y = \log x$. It is clear that the graph becomes less steep as x increases – a fact we have already noticed. The next problem is to find a formula for these numbers. Since the numbers are not exact, we shall be content with a formula that fits them reasonably well – we do not expect an exact fit.

Guessing a formula is often difficult. A new discovery usually requires years. No one should be discouraged if he takes a few weeks to solve a problem of this type. One simply has to try one idea after another until one hits on the right result. It helps if one makes a collection of graphs of different functions. One can draw the graph of the table given, and see which graph it most resembles.

One may find a clue, in our problem, by comparing the result for $x = 1$ with that for $x = 2$. Opposite $x = 1$, we have in the fourth column 0·414. Opposite x = 2 we have 0·212. Now 0·212 is roughly half of 0·414. This suggests that $x = 3$ will correspond to one-third of 0·414, $x = 4$ to one-quarter, and so on. $x = 10$ should correspond to one-tenth of 0·414 – that is, 0·0414. The table gives 0·043, which is not much different. To $x = 1 \cdot 5$ should correspond 0·414 divided by 1·5 – that is, 0·276. The table gives 0·280, which is quite close – as close, at any rate, as we can expect with such a rough method.

This work therefore suggests that y' corresponding to $y = \log x$ is *something like* $\dfrac{0 \cdot 414}{x}$.

This result should be regarded as a sort of hint. It suggests that we go back to the explanation of logarithms given in Chapter 6, and try to see if there is some obvious reason why log x should grow at a speed which is proportional to $\dfrac{1}{x}$. Actually, there is, and it can be shown that $\dfrac{0 \cdot 434294}{x} \cdots$ is the true answer to the problem. Our rough method has shown us the *form* of the answer, and has brought us reasonably near to the true value.

(In Chapter 6 we explained the meaning of 10^x. What is the formula for y', if $y = 10^x$?)

You may remember that it was mentioned in Chapter 6 that a slide-rule could be made to any scale we liked. If we mark the number 10 one inch from the end of the scale, the number x occurs at the distance log x inches from the end. But we could take 10 at any other distance, and we could still make a perfectly good slide-rule. Our result for y' corresponding to $y = \log x$ suggests that it might be worth while to alter the scale in a particular way. We found that y' was equal to $\dfrac{0 \cdot 434294 \cdots}{x}$. If we took, instead of $y = \log x$, the formula $y = \dfrac{\log x}{0 \cdot 434294 \ldots}$ we should have a simpler result: y' would then be simply $\dfrac{1}{x}$. This new expression y will do just as well for the distance at which the number x has to be marked. If we mark every number x at a distance $\dfrac{\log x}{0\cdot434294\ldots}$ inches from the end of the scale, we obtain a slide-rule that is on a larger scale, but is otherwise no different from the previous one. 10 now occurs at a distance equal to $\dfrac{\log 10}{0\cdot434294\ldots}$ As log 10 is 1, this can be worked out; it is equal to $2\cdot30258\ldots$ inches. The number which now occurs at a distance of one inch is $2\cdot71828\ldots$ This number is important in mathematics: it is given a special name, and is always spoken of as e. The distance at which any number occurs on this new slide-rule is called the *Natural Logarithm* of the number. The natural logarithm of x is written log x.

When we first explained logarithms in terms of ropes wound on posts, we took the effect of one complete turn to be 10. The only reason for doing this was the accidental fact that we have ten fingers. If we had eight fingers, we would probably take one turn to correspond to 8, and we should get just as good a table of logarithms. For these we should use the sign $\log_8 x$. Any other number could be used. It need not be a whole number. $2\frac{5}{8}$ would do, for instance. All these different numbers would lead to perfectly good slide-rules, but of different sizes. We should always find $y' = \dfrac{a}{x}$, where a stands for 'some fixed number'. It is natural to prefer that system of logarithms for which $a = 1$. For this reason, in theoretical work we usually employ $\log_e x$, the 'natural logarithm'. If $y = \log_e x$, $y' = \dfrac{1}{x}$.

The Cartwheel Problem

We now consider another problem, in which a rough idea is helpful. If a wheel – for instance, a cartwheel – is rolling along a

flat road, how fast do the various parts of it move? They certainly
do not move all at the same speed. You will often notice, when
a motor-car passes, that the lower spokes can be clearly seen, but
the top spokes move so fast that they are invisible. How is this
to be explained?

Many people find a rolling wheel difficult to imagine – not, of
course, difficult to imagine in a vague way, but difficult to imagine

Fig. 11

so clearly that the speed of each part can be seen. Let us therefore
replace this problem by a simpler one. It is fairly easy to imagine
a square rolling, as, for instance, a large log of square section
being pushed along the pavement. It starts with one side flat on
the pavement. Then it turns about one corner, until the next side
is flat on the pavement. Then it turns about the next corner, and
so on. It is easy to see that the corner at the bottom of the square –
the corner about which the whole thing turns – is at rest. The
farther away a point is from this corner, the quicker it moves.

Now let us make our square log rather more like a circle, by four straight cuts with a saw, to remove the four corners of the square, as in Fig. 11. It is still quite easy to imagine the motion. As before, the point which touches the pavement, when the figure rolls, is (at any moment) at rest.

We can continue in this way, cutting off corners, and making the figure more and more like a circle. It will never *be* a circle, but it can be made *as near to* a circle as we like. The figure with 128 corners would make quite a good wheel for most practical purposes.

We are thus led to the conclusion – which every engineer has to know – that a rolling wheel turns about its lowest point, which is (for an instant) at rest.

The same method of approach would enable us to see what curve any point of the rolling wheel describes. The curves known as cycloids, epicycloids and hypocycloids arise in this way.

In the cutting of gear-wheels, a special curve has great advantages. This is the curve described by the end of a cotton thread, as the thread unwinds from a fixed reel. It may help you to see just what the thread does, if you think of the reel as being, not an exact circle, but a figure with corners such as we had above. The more corners you imagine, the nearer you come to the true state of affairs.

In the same way, the motion of a small body rolling down a curved hill can be simplified: we can replace the curve by a figure with corners. If we know all about the behaviour of a small body rolling down a straight line, we can thus build up a picture of a body rolling down a curve.

Again, we can study the behaviour of a hanging string by considering what happens to a hanging chain, made up of straight links like a bicycle chain. The more links we imagine, the nearer we come to a true idea of the string.

All these illustrations use what mathematicians call the idea of a Limit. Mathematicians speak of a circle as being the *limit* of the figures with corners described above: this simply means that you can get *as near as you like* to a circle by making *a sufficiently large number* of straight saw cuts. You can get *as near as you like* to the curve of a string by taking *sufficiently short* links for your chain.

You can get *as near as you like* to the speed $\frac{dy}{dx}$, by taking *sufficiently small* Δx and calculating $\frac{\Delta y}{\Delta x}$.

ILLUSTRATIONS AND EXPERIMENTS

1. The movements of trains on railways are recorded on a graph, when time-tables are being worked out, or emergency trains are fitted in (See J. W. Williamson, *Railways Today*, for a reproduction of such a graph.)

Draw graphs showing the position of the following trains:

(i) Leaves London at 12.00; travels at steady speed of 20 m.p.h.

(ii) Leaves London at 12.00; travels at 30 m.p.h., but stops for 5 minutes every half-hour.

(iii) Leaves London at 12.48 and travels at 50 m.p.h.

In these graphs, have distance going *upwards*, the passage of time towards the *right*. See for yourself that the faster trains have steeper graphs, and that this makes it possible for the express (Number iii) to overtake the goods train (Number i).

2. A cricket ball is thrown straight up into the air. After x seconds its height is y feet, where $y = 40x - 16x^2$. Work out y' and y''. Show that y'' is always minus, and that y' starts by being $+$, but later becomes $-$. At what time is $y' = 0$? Draw the graph for the motion of the ball. When is the ball at its greatest height? What is this height?

3. A piece of wood is hurled downwards into the sea. After 3 seconds it again appears on the surface. A scientist states that during this period its graph had the equation $y = -30x + 10x^2$, where x stands for the time in seconds after it entered the water, and y for its height in feet (measured upwards, so that depths below sea-level are minus). How far is this a reasonable description of what the piece of wood does?

4. A body is shot from a catapult (it does not matter whether it is a pebble or a glider), and its motion is recorded by means of

424

a graph. How would you expect this graph to bend (i) while the body is still in the catapult and gathering speed; (ii) after it has left the catapult?

5. Find out the general appearance of the graphs corresponding to the formulae below, by working out y' and y'' and seeing what signs ($+$ or $-$) they have. Consider x from -10 to 10.

(i) $y = x^2 + x$. (ii) $y = x^3$. (iii) $y = x^3 - x$. (iv) $y = x - x^2$. (v) $y = x^3 - x^4$.

Be careful to note that where $y' = 0$ the curve is, for an instant, *level*. This applies particularly to (ii) and (v).

6. The following example can be dealt with by the method of Rough Ideas.

A man is walking along a straight path, which points due East, at a speed of 5 feet a second. The man whistles to his dog, which is at that moment 30 feet due North of the man. The man does not stop walking. The dog runs, at a speed of 20 feet a second, always facing towards his master. Draw roughly the curve which the dog describes. About how long does the dog take to reach the man? (It is clear that if the dog had given a little more thought to what it was doing it would have run in a straight line, towards a point somewhat ahead of its master, instead of behaving in this way.)

Method. Replace the steady movement of the man by a series of jerks. Suppose the man to remain still for one-tenth of a second, then suddenly to shoot forward six inches. In this way the man will cover 5 feet a second. The dog will run in a chain of straight lines, each 2 feet long, pointing in turn towards the various positions in which the man stands. Drawing this chain we can see roughly how the dog moves and how long he takes to reach the man.

Position of the dog at intervals of $\frac{1}{10}$ second.

Position of man at intervals of $\frac{1}{10}$ second.

CHAPTER 12

OTHER PROBLEMS OF CALCULUS *

'One of the hardest tasks that an expert in any subject can undertake is to try to explain to the layman what his subject is, and why he makes such a fuss about it.'
 – G. C. Darwin, Introduction to *The Story of Mathematics*, by D. Larrett.

THE pioneers of every subject are amateurs. They start with the same knowledge and the same methods of thinking as any other uninstructed person. The early discoveries in any branch of science can be explained in everyday language, and often seem so obvious that the science appears hardly worth studying.

Later generations, building on the work of the pioneers, study more and more complicated problems, and in the course of this introduce new ideas, new words, technical terms which are Greek to the layman. The later discoveries of any science have to be stated in technical terms: they appear remote from ordinary life, and extremely hard to understand. The science now seems so difficult that it appears not worth while to try to master it.

In mathematics, as in other sciences, each generation builds upon the foundation provided by past workers, and adds another storey. By now the building is something of a skyscraper. There are many remarkable books on the eighteenth floor, but they are written in a language which is comprehensible only to those who are thoroughly familiar with the works on the seventeenth floor – and so on, floor by floor, until one reaches the ground floor and the multiplication table.

No living person is familiar with all the mathematical discoveries that are stored in the libraries of the various learned societies throughout the world. Every mathematician has to find out for himself just which parts of the subject are useful for his own purposes, which technical terms and ideas he has time to become familiar with, and to apply to his own problems.

* This chapter may be skipped by those who find it hard.

In this chapter a number of processes will be discussed which are useful to those engaged in the more exact sciences – physics, chemistry, engineering – and to those who use any kind of machine, from a drill to an aeroplane. This type of mathematics is also creeping in to subjects such as biology, economics, even psychology. If you are not interested in such applications, you will perhaps not find this chapter of interest, nor will you find much point in learning calculus at all, unless you belong to the type which is interested in mathematics for itself. If you neither like, nor need, calculus it is a sheer waste of time to study it.

In the course of scientific work it is frequently necessary to find $\frac{dy}{dx}$ for expressions $y(x)$ which are more complicated than any we have so far considered. One might, for instance, come across an expression such as $y = \left(\frac{x}{x^2 + 1}\right)^3$, and wish to know y' corresponding to this. Here a whole series of processes has been carried out. If we start with x, we have to work out x^2 and add 1 to this, giving $x^2 + 1$. Then x has to be divided by this result. The answer to this has to be raised to the power 3.

The problem is dealt with by splitting it up. We bring in new letters, and break up the chain of processes. In calculating y we were first led to calculate $x^2 + 1$. We will call this first result u. $u = x^2 + 1$. How quickly does u grow? We know this from our earlier work: $u' = 2x$. We then calculate $\frac{x}{x^2 + 1}$ ($x^2 + 1$ being the same thing as u). Call this result v, so that $v = \frac{x}{u}$. Now we know that u grows at the rate u', and that x grows at the rate 1. v is obtained by dividing x by u. Since we know x and u, and we know how fast each of them is growing, it ought not to be too difficult to find how fast v is growing. Suppose we solve this problem, and find the answer, v'. We now come to the final stage. y is obtained by raising v to the power 3; that is, $y = v^3$. y is v^3 and v is growing at the rate v'. How fast is y growing?

So far the problem has not been solved. We have simply shown that the one complicated problem can be split up into three simpler ones: I. To find u' when $u = x^2 + 1$. II. To find v' when $v = \dfrac{x}{u}$ and u' is known. III. To find y' when $y = v^3$ and v' is known.

It is because complicated problems can be split up in this way into simple ones that you find certain theorems in every calculus text-book, dealing with the differentiation of a Sum, Product, Quotient, and the Function of a Function. All these theorems have an object – to enable you to find y' corresponding to any formula, however complicated, by splitting the problem into simpler ones.

Differentiation of a Sum

Consider an example – rising prices. Let £y be the price of a watch after x days of war (rising at the rate y') and £z the price of a chain (rising at the rate z'). How quickly does the price of a watch and chain rise? Clearly $y' + z'$. As the price is £$(y + z)$, this shows how easy it is to find the rate of increase of the sum of two changing quantities.

Differentiation of a Product

Let n be the number of men in a town, and p the number of pints drunk daily by each man. Then np is the total number of pints drunk. If n is increasing at the rate n' and p at the rate p', how fast is np increasing? The answer is $p'n + n'p$.

Differentiation of a Quotient

If b barrels of beer are provided for n men, each will receive $\dfrac{b}{n}$ of a barrel. If the number of men increases at the rate n' and the number of barrels at the rate b', how fast does $\dfrac{b}{n}$ change? The answer turns out to be $\dfrac{b'n - n'b}{n^2}$. Notice how this answer compares with common sense. If $n' = 0$, it means that the number of men stays the same, and if b' is $+$, it means that the number of barrels is increasing. In that case, $\dfrac{b}{n}$ is increasing, and its rate of change should be $+$. This is so, for the formula above. If, on the other hand, the number of barrels stays the same, $b' = 0$, while the number of men increases, so that n' is $+$, the formula becomes $\dfrac{-n'b}{n^2}$, which has a minus sign, as it ought to do: the share per man is getting *less*, the change is for the worse, a *minus* sign is to be expected.

Function of a Function

It is well, at this stage, to look back to page 96 and to read again the sentences explaining what is meant by y being a function of x; namely, that y is connected with x by some rule. What now is 'a function of a function'? Consider the formula $y = \log_e (x^2 + x)$. We could make a table of y in the following way. In the first column we could enter the numbers, x. In the second column we could enter the corresponding numbers, $x^2 + x$. In the third column we could put the logarithms (to base e) of the numbers in the second column. This third column would then give the numbers $\log_e(x^2 + x)$. We have x in the first column, y in the third column. Let us call the numbers in the middle column z. The numbers in the second column are found from those in the first column by a definite rule. So z is a function of x. The numbers in the third column are found by a definite rule from those in the second. So y is a function of z. It is this process which gives rise to the name 'function of a function'. In fact, $z = x^2 + x$ and $y = \log_e z$.

Now we know all about the rule connecting x with z, and we know all about the rule connecting z with y. It ought not to be too difficult to find how fast y increases.

It is possible to illustrate this double connexion by a machine. The relation $z = x^2 + x$ can be expressed by means of a graph. In Fig. 12 the curve OB represents a groove cut to the shape of this graph. OA and OC are straight grooves. A represents a small piece of metal sliding in the groove OA. In the same way B

429

slides in the groove OB, and C in the groove OC. A small ring is fixed to B, and through this ring pass the two rods, AB and CB, which are soldered to the sliding pieces A and C in such a way that AB is always upright, and BC is always level. If A moves, B is forced to move, and this in turn forces C to move. The distance OA represents x, the distance OC represents z. Any change in x produces a change in z, and the machine is so designed that $z = x^2 + x$.

In the same way we can express the connexion, $y = \log_e z$. y is represented by the length OE. z is already shown by OC. The curved groove GD is the graph of $y = \log_e z$. The rod CD is always level, while ED is always upright. Both pass through a ring at D.

The whole chain of events can now be seen. If x (OA) changes, z (OC) cannot help changing, and because OC changes, OE (y) must also change.

How fast? We know that z increases $\dfrac{dz}{dx}$ times as fast as x. y increases $\dfrac{dy}{dz}$ times as fast as z. So y must increase $\dfrac{dy}{dz} \cdot \dfrac{dz}{dx}$ times as fast as x. That is, $\dfrac{dy}{dx} = \dfrac{dy}{dz} \cdot \dfrac{dz}{dx}$. This is the theorem about a Function of a Function and its rate of change.

In our particular example it is easy to find $\dfrac{dy}{dx}$. We have to find $\dfrac{dy}{dz}$ and $\dfrac{dz}{dx}$ and multiply these together. There is no difficulty with $\dfrac{dz}{dx}$. $z = x^2 + x$, so $\dfrac{dz}{dx} = 2x + 1$. Now for $\dfrac{dy}{dz}$. $y = \log_e z$. We saw in Chapter 11 that $\log_e x$ grew at the rate $\dfrac{1}{x}$. 'The natural logarithm of any number grows at a rate given by dividing one by that number' is this formula in words. It makes no difference if we call the number z instead of x. So $\dfrac{dy}{dz} = \dfrac{1}{z}$. Accordingly

$\dfrac{dy}{dx} = \dfrac{1}{z}(2x + 1)$. But z is short for the number in the second column, $x^2 + x$. This answer is therefore the same as $\dfrac{2x + 1}{x^2 + x}$ and this formula is the solution of the problem.

By combining the results stated above, it is possible to find $\dfrac{dy}{dx}$ for very complicated formulae.

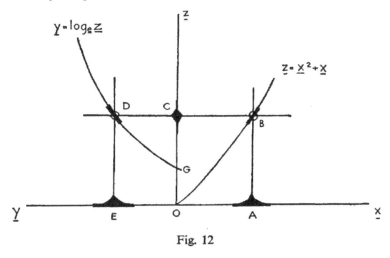

Fig. 12

Integration

We have already considered the problem of differentiation – that is, the problem of finding the speed y' of a body which moves in a manner described by means of a formula for y. The opposite problem frequently occurs: we know the speed at every moment, we have to find how far the body goes after any number of seconds. In other words, we are given a formula for y', and we are asked to find a formula for y. This is the problem of *integration*.

y' need not, of course, be considered as the speed of a moving body. It represents the rate of change of y, whatever y may be. For instance, it is easy to discover *how quickly* the pressure increases as a diver goes deeper into the sea. So y might represent the pressure per square foot on a diver's helmet, when he is at a depth x feet. It is easy to find the rate of increase, y'. In order to find y, the problem of integration (very easy in this particular case) has to be solved. Integration is also used in connexion with the question of air pressure at different heights, a question of interest to mountaineers, airmen, weather experts, and others. There are few, if any, branches of science and engineering in which problems of integration do not arise.

In dealing with any practical problem, a student has to do two things. First, the problem has to be put into mathematical form: then the mathematics necessary to solve the question has to be carried out. The second part is no use without the first. Our study of integration will therefore have two objects: (a) to understand the nature of integration so clearly that we immediately recognize any problem that can be solved by means of integration, (b) to master the mathematical method. The first part, (a), can be understood without any knowledge of the second part, (b). We are at present mainly concerned with (a), though some passing reference may be made to (b). We shall consider a very simple problem – one which can be solved mathematically in two lines – and look at it from all angles. To this simple problem we shall apply methods capable of solving far more difficult questions: we shall use steam hammers to crack a walnut, in fact. The object of this will not be to crack the walnut, but to demonstrate how the steam-hammers work. Our simple problem is the following: if $y' = x$, find a formula for y. This problem is not quite complete, as it stands. We are given y' which might represent the speed of a body after x seconds. Obviously, we must know where the body starts, if we are to work out its position. We will suppose, then, that we are also told that $y = 0$ when $x = 0$. The problem is quite definite. We can think of y as the distance of the body from a fixed point P. To begin with, the body is at P, since the distance y begins by being zero. Then the body begins to move. After 1 second its speed is 1 foot per second; after 2 seconds, its speed is 2 feet per second, and so on. The speed does not grow by jumps, but steadily. For $y' = x$ tells us that the speed after $1\frac{1}{8}$ seconds is

1⅛ feet per second; after 1¼ seconds, y' is 1¼, and so on. We have a complete picture of the motion.

The Method of Rough Ideas

Let us try, first of all, to get a rough idea of the distance which the body would go, for example, in the first second. We will split the second into ten equal parts, and see how much we can find out about the distance which the body travels in each tenth of a second. In the first tenth of a second the body moves with a speed which increases steadily from 0 at the beginning to 0·1 at the end. So the average speed lies between 0 and 0·1. So the distance gone must be more than 0 times 0·1, but less than 0·1 times 0·1. We can apply the same argument to each of the other parts. The distance gone in 0·1 second is more than 0·1 times the least speed, and less than 0·1 times the greatest speed in that part of the motion. We can put the argument in the form of a table.

TABLE XIV

Time	Least Speed.	Highest Speed.	Distance gone At least.	At most.	Differ- ence.
0 to 0·1	0	0·1	0	0·01	0·01
0·1 to 0·2	0·1	0·2	0·01	0·02	0·01
0·2 to 0·3	0·2	0·3	0·02	0·03	0·01
0·3 to 0·4	0·3	0·4	0·03	0·04	0·01
0·4 to 0·5	0·4	0·5	0·04	0·05	0·01
0·5 to 0·6	0·5	0·6	0·05	0·06	0·01
0·6 to 0·7	0·6	0·7	0·06	0·07	0·01
0·7 to 0·8	0·7	0·8	0·07	0·08	0·01
0·8 to 0·9	0·8	0·9	0·08	0·09	0·01
0·9 to 1·0	0·9	1·0	0·09	0·1	0·01
		Total	0·45	0·55	0·10

In the first column we have the ten parts into which the first second is divided. Then follow the least speed and the greatest speed in each part of the motion. We then have two columns showing 0·1 times the least speed, and 0·1 times the greatest

433

speed. In each tenth of a second the body must have gone more than the former, less than the latter. The last column shows the difference between the two previous ones. For instance, we know that, in the time between 0·6 and 0·7, the body goes at least 0·06, at most 0·07. The difference between these is 0·01, so we are left uncertain about the distance gone in this time, to the extent of one-hundredth. The total distance gone in the first second is found by adding up. It must be more than 0·45 foot, less than 0·55 foot.

We now have a rough idea how far the body goes in the first second. The difference between 0·45 and 0·55 is 0·1. This uncertainty of 0·1 is due to the uncertainty of 0·01 in each of the ten rows. If we want a more accurate answer, it will be necessary to carry through the same process, using smaller intervals. We might, for instance, divide one second into 100 parts and then carry out a similar calculation, though of course this would be rather long and boring to do. How close would such a method bring us to the true answer! The difference between the highest and the least speed in any small part would be 0·01, instead of 0·1. The distance gone in 0·01 second is found by multiplying the speed by 0·01. So the uncertainty in the distance gone, in any hundredth of a second, would be 0·01 times 0·01 – that is, 0·0001. But there would be a hundred rows in the table (instead of ten) and the uncertainty in the total distance would be 100 times 0·0001, that is 0·01. (Actually we should find that the distance was more than 0·495 and less than 0·505.) This result is ten times as good as the time before – we are repaid for having to do ten times as much work to obtain it. By taking still more intervals, we could get still better results.

This method is used only when a problem is so difficult that no other method will work. Even then, some shortening of the work would be arranged. The method is not given here as a good way of finding the actual answer, but rather to show what the problem means. The process above will help you to understand the sign used for integration. We have already used the sign $\triangle x$ for the change in x. In the table given above, each row of the first column represents a change of 0·1 – e.g., 0·7 to 0·8. The next two columns tell us the least speed and the highest speed – that is, they help us to see how large y', the speed, is, during this part of the time. In the same way, the fourth and fifth columns give us a number rather less, and a number rather more, than the distance gone during any small part of the time. As distance gone is measured by the speed (y') times the time that passes (Δx), we may think of these columns as representing $y' \Delta x$. Of course there is some doubt about the meaning of y': for instance, as x goes from 0·6 to 0·7, y' also goes from 0·6 to 0·7, and it is not clear whether we should take y' as being 0·6 or 0·7 or some number in between. It is because of this uncertainty that we have the two columns, one headed 'At least', the other 'At most'. This must be borne in mind.

We then estimate the distance gone in the whole of the first second by adding up the fourth and fifth columns. So that the 'sum of $y'\Delta x$' is (at least) 0·45 and (at most) 0·55.

Here we have two estimates – one rather too small, one rather too large. But, fortunately, by taking smaller lengths of time – that is, taking Δx to be 0·01 or 0·001, etc. – these two estimates approach closer and closer to each other. In other words, if Δx is made very small, it matters *very little* whether we take y' to be the highest or the lowest speed that occurs in the interval of time, Δx. The answer will be the same, whichever is taken. If this were not so, we should have to bring in a new sign, such as $y'\Delta x(L)$, to mean 'the *least* speed, y', times the change in x, Δx'. But, as it has turned out, this would be a waste of time. The least speed and the highest speed give answers that draw closer and closer together as Δx gets smaller.

In Chapter 10 it was mentioned that $\dfrac{\Delta y}{\Delta x}$ came nearer and nearer to a certain number as Δx became smaller. The number thus approached was therefore christened $\dfrac{dy}{dx}$. In the same way, the number we have just been estimating – the number which is more than 0·45 and less than 0·55, more than 0·495 and less than 0·505, etc. – is represented by $\displaystyle\int_0^1 y'dx$. The sign $\displaystyle\int$ is an old-fashioned S, S for 'Sum'. The sign is meant to indicate that the number can be found by multiplying y' by Δx for each short part of the time, finding the sum of these, and seeing what happens when Δx gets very small. The numbers 0 and 1 are put in to show that we are interested in the distance gone during the first second – that is, between $x = 0$ and $x = 1$. In other words, the change of x from 0 to 1 has to be split up into little changes Δx, as in the first column of the table. $\int_2^5 y'dx$ would represent the distances gone in the period of time from 2 seconds after the start to 5 seconds after the start. $\int_0^n y'dx$ represents the distance gone in the first n seconds. Since we have supposed y' to be given by the formula $y' = x$, we may replace y' by x, and write $\int_0^1 x\,dx$. It seems likely, from the work above, that the number we are looking for is 0·5, and it can be proved that this is the correct answer. In symbols, $0\cdot5 = \int_0^1 x\,dx$. $\int$ is known as 'the integral sign'. 'To integrate' means 'to make whole': the name, I suppose, is chosen because the process consists in putting together a lot of little bits, all the little changes in y that occur in the brief passing moments of time.

Ways of Seeing Integration

It is useful to know different ways of getting the same result. Then, in any problem, one can imagine the illustration which is most convenient.

We may translate the symbol $\int_0^1 x\,dx$ as the distance gone, in the first second, by a body whose speed is always equal to the number of seconds that have passed (including fractions of a second).

To record such a motion we might use the device illustrated at the beginning of Chapter 11. It would be rather difficult to arrange for the speed y' always to be exactly equal to the number of seconds, x. Let us once more be content with a rough idea. During the first tenth of a second let the pencil-point stay at rest

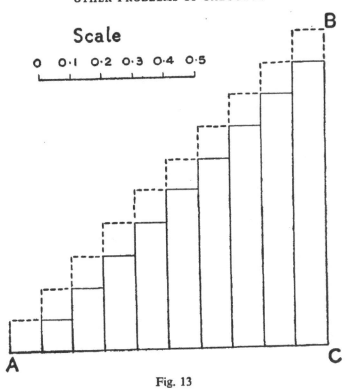

Fig. 13

in the slit *AB*. During the next tenth of a second let it move up-
wards with a speed of $0 \cdot 1$ foot a second: from $x = 0 \cdot 2$ to $x = 0 \cdot 3$,
let the speed be $0 \cdot 2$ foot a second, and so on. In fact, let the speed
during any interval given in the first column of Table XIV be the
number given in the second column of that table. The graph that
results will consist of straight lines, joined together like a chain.
As we saw in Chapter 11, y' measures the steepness of these lines.
As y' increases steadily, each line will be steeper than the previous
one. So we could equally well have explained integration from the
problem: You are told how steep a curve is at every point, draw
the curve.

It is also possible to illustrate Table XIV directly. The numbers
in the fourth column are obtained by multiplying those in the

second column by 0·1. But multiplication – for instance, 0·9 times 0·1 – can be represented by the area of a rectangle, with sides 0·9 and 0·1. The ten numbers in the fourth column can be represented by the area of ten rectangles, as in Fig. 13. The sum of these numbers, 0·45, represents the total area, below the heavy line. In the same figure the area below the dotted line represents 0·55, the sum of the numbers in column five.

Between the dotted line and the heavy line are ten squares, each with an area equal to 0·01. These squares represent the numbers in the last column.

We know that $\int_0^1 x\, dx$ represents a number larger than the area below the heavy line, less than the area below the dotted line. By taking 100 instead of ten steps, we should get an even better idea of the number we want. But however many steps we have, the heavy line always lies below the straight line AB, the dotted line always lies above it. If we draw the line AB, the area of the triangle ABC is always more than the area below the heavy line, less than the area below the dotted line. In fact, the area ABC is equal to the number we are looking for, $\int_0^1 x\, dx$.

This result is quite general. If $f(x)$ is any function of x, then $\int_a^b f(x)$ dx will always represent the area below the graph of $f(x)$, between $x = a$ and $x = b$. *The problem of finding the area inside any curve is a problem in integration.* You should try for yourself to draw an area which represents $\int_0^1 x^2\, dx$.

The connexion between integrals and areas is useful in two ways. We can use an area to illustrate the meaning of an integral, and to help us to understand the behaviour of integrals. Secondly, we can find the actual size of a particular area by working out the value of an integral.

A Shorter Method

The integral, $\int_0^1 x\, dx$, can be found with very little work. We started the problem by trying to find y such that $y' = x$, and $y = 0$

when $x = 0$ (see page 166). But we know that to the formula $y = x^2$ there corresponds the speed $y' = 2x$. $2x$ is just twice the answer we want for y'. We can put this right by taking y half as large – that is, we consider the formula $y = \frac{1}{2}x^2$. This gives exactly the right answer, $y' = x$. Also, $\frac{1}{2}x^2$ equals 0 when $x = 0$, so the condition $y = 0$ when $x = 0$ has been met. So $y = \frac{1}{2}x^2$ is the formula we want. It gives the distance y corresponding to x seconds. Putting $x = 1$, we find $y = \frac{1}{2}$. So the distance gone in one second is $\frac{1}{2}$. This agrees with the result 0.5 which we found by the other method.

Many problems of integration can be solved by this method. The idea is simple enough. We have already learnt how to find y' corresponding to many different types of function, y. We are now asked to do the opposite problem: y' is given, we have to find y. It is natural to turn back to our records of the first problem. If in these we find y' of the type required, the problem is immediately solved. For instance: we have shown that to $y = \log_e x$ corresponds $y' = \frac{1}{x}$. If we are asked to find $\int \frac{1}{x}\, dx$, this is the same as saying: if $y' = \frac{1}{x}$, what is y? Obviously, $y = \log_e x$ gives *an* answer to this question. The complete answer will depend on the other condition: it is not enough to know how fast a body moves, one must also know where it is at some instant.

Differential Equations

Very many practical problems lead to what is known as a differential equation. The nature of a differential equation may best be seen by considering a definite example.

The light from an electric lamp spreads out equally in all directions. Often – as, for instance, in making a motor headlamp or a searchlight – this is inconvenient: we would prefer to have all the light coming out in one direction, and this is achieved by placing a reflector behind the lamp. If the reflected light is to come out in a perfect beam, what shape should the reflector be?

It is known how light behaves when it strikes a mirror. If we take a capital V and underline it, thus V, we have a rough picture of what occurs. The line represents the mirror: the left-hand arm of the V may represent the light striking the mirror, and the right-hand arm the light bouncing off the mirror. The two arms of the V must make the same angle with the line of the mirror. A billiard ball bounces off a cushion in more or less the same way, if it is free from spin.

We shall not get a proper beam if we simply put an ordinary straight mirror behind the lamp. The reflected light will scatter in different directions, as can be seen by drawing a figure.

We might tackle the problem by taking a large number of short pieces of mirror and trying to join them in a chain, in such a way as to get a proper beam. In Fig. 14 P represents the point where the electric lamp is placed. O is some other point, and we want to obtain a beam of light pointing in the direction OP. OA represents a short piece of mirror, so placed that the light from P which

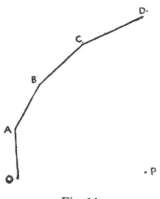

Fig. 14

strikes the mirror at O is reflected back along the line OP. Of course the light from P which strikes the mirror between O and A will be reflected slightly upwards, slightly away from OP, but if the length OA is short, this will not be serious. When we reach A, we join on our next piece of mirror AB, in such a way that the ray of light PA is reflected in the proper direction – that is, parallel to OP. In the same way, we must turn the next piece of mirror, BC, in such a way that the ray PB is reflected parallel to OP. And so the process is continued: each mirror is added in such a way that its lowest point touches the highest point of the mirror before and it is then turned so as to reflect light in the proper direction.

In this way we could build up a mirror which very nearly produces a perfect beam. The shorter the pieces of mirror used, the better the beam would be. We can easily believe that there is a curve which reflects the light exactly in the correct direction. This curve is known as a *parabola*. The mirror built in this shape is called a *parabolic mirror*. Parabolic mirrors are used in some types of telescope, and in beam wireless upright wires arranged in the shape of a parabola are used.

Notice how we built up our chain of lines $OABCD$ ... We started from O, and then, at each stage, we were told *in what direction to go*. Any problem which starts from some rule about the direction to follow at any moment will lead to a differential equation.

For instance, a ship at sea might steer straight towards a lighthouse. It could start wherever it liked, but once it had started the direction it had to follow would be fixed. The lighthouse might be spoken of as a magnet attracting the ship: in the language of magnetism the ship follows a 'line of force'. The problem would become more complicated if we had two magnets, each attracting a moving body. The path of the body would not then be obvious, as it was for the ship and the lighthouse. Differential equations therefore appear in the theory of electricity and magnetism.

What does a differential equation look like in algebraic symbols? We have some rule that gives us the direction of the curve at any point. We might equally well say we have a rule that gives the steepness of the curve at any point. Now, the steepness of the curve is measured by y' and the position of a point on a graph is measured by the two numbers x and y. To every point there corresponds a direction: we might imagine this by supposing the graph-paper to be covered with little arrows, signposts conveying the message, 'If you should arrive at this point, depart in this direction'. By continually following the signposts, one would follow out some curve. The signposts are arranged *according to some rule*: if we have any point (corresponding to any two numbers x and y) we have a rule giving the direction of the signpost, and the steepness of the arrow is measured by y'. So y' is given by some rule – that is, we have a formula giving y' when x and y are known.

For instance, if a lighthouse is placed at the point (0, 0), and all ships sail straight towards it, the formula is $y' = \dfrac{y}{x}$. For the steepness of the line joining any point (x, y) to the point $(0, 0)$ is $\dfrac{y}{x}$, and y' must be equal to this.

You will not be able to follow this argument if you are not familiar with Co-ordinate Geometry: you must master the earlier part of Co-ordinate Geometry (the plotting of points, the steepness of straight lines, the angles between straight lines, the distance between two points, the equation of a circle) before you try to learn the theory of differential equations.

EXAMPLES

The treatment of the subjects in this chapter is too sketchy to justify the setting of examples. Readers who have been able to follow the general ideas of this chapter will find examples in any text-book on Differential and Integral Calculus.

CHAPTER 13

TRIGONOMETRY,
OR HOW TO MAKE TUNNELS AND MAPS

'The utmost care must be taken to avoid errors, and that it is taken is proved by the wonderful accuracy with which the headings driven from opposite ends usually meet ... The Musconetcony Tunnel is about 5,000 feet long. When the headings met the error in alignment was found to be only half an inch, and the error in level only about one-sixth of an inch. In the Hoosac Tunnel, 25,000 feet long, the errors were even smaller.'
A. Williams, Victories of the Engineer.

In this book I have tried to show (i) that mathematical problems can be stated in the language of everyday life; (ii) that any normal person can think about these problems for himself, by using common sense; and (iii) that the methods given in text-books simply represent the improvements on the original common-sense attack, which have gradually been built up by generations of mathematicians.

In no part of mathematics is this easier to show than in trigonometry. Trigonometry arises from very simple practical problems, such as the building of a railway tunnel, for instance. It may be necessary to make a tunnel which is to come out several miles away, on the other side of a range of mountains, at a point which cannot even be seen from this side. It may be necessary to bore the tunnel from both ends, and to meet somewhere far inside the mountain. How are we to find the correct direction in which to bore?

One method is explained in Chapter 4 of *The Railway*, by E. B. Schieldrop. It is illustrated in Fig. 15. The shaded part represents high ground. It is desired to connect the points *A* and *D* by a

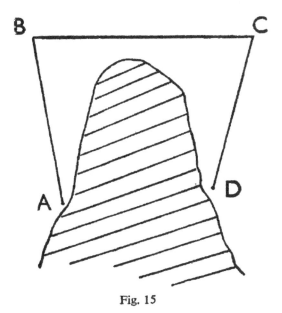

Fig. 15

tunnel. We may be able to find objects B and C, such that B can be seen from A, C from B, and D from C. We measure carefully the length and direction of the lines AB, BC, and CD.

This information is sufficient to fix the position of D. It would enable us to make a map of the district, showing A, B, C, and D on a scale, say, 1 foot to a mile. We start with A, and draw the lines A to B, B to C, C to D, in the proper directions, and to scale. This fixes D. On the map we can draw the line AD, and measure the angles which it makes with AB and CD. We now know in what directions to bore at A and D.

This method shows that the problem can be solved by a common-sense method, though not very accurately. Since we are working to the scale of 1 foot to a mile, an error of $\frac{1}{100}$ inch in our drawing will lead to an error of $1\frac{1}{2}$ yards in the actual work. And in drawing the figure we may easily make several mistakes of $\frac{1}{100}$ inch. Drawing a figure, then, is not sufficient to give a really good answer, but it gives us a general idea of what is needed. First attempts often turn out like this: they give us the germ of an idea: we have to work at this idea until it becomes practical. A mathematical invention goes through the same stages as a mechanical one: first an idea, then a toy, then a commercial proposition.

Trigonometry represents an attempt to improve on the method of drawing. The argument runs rather on the following lines. By drawing the map on a larger scale, we could get a more accurate answer to the tunnel problem. There seems to be no limit to the accuracy we could get by taking our plan large enough. Given the lengths and directions of the lines AB, BC, CD to a high degree of accuracy, we could find (by drawing on an immense scale) the length and direction of AD to a high degree of accuracy. It seems likely that some rule connects the answer with the facts given. We could collect information on the problem, taking A, B, C, and D in different positions, and trying to see how the length of CD, and its direction, depended on the other measurements given. The aim would be to find the rule: once we had this rule, we could work out AD to as many decimal places as we chose, without doing any drawing at all.

444

In trigonometry, then, we consider problems which could be solved by drawing, problems which therefore possess a definite answer (it is a waste of time to try any problem by trigonometry if you are not given sufficient facts to solve it by drawing: trigonometry is not magic): we try to discover *what rule* gives this answer, so that we may be able to find the answer by a formula, instead of by drawing. The aim is therefore to replace drawing by calculation.

Such a question can be tackled, in the first place, only by experiment. Lengths, directions – these are real things. They will not take orders from us: they follow the laws of their own nature. We can find what they do only by *observing* them.

But, of course, we shall not begin by experimenting with such a complicated problem as that of the tunnel and the four points *A, B, C, D*. It is rarely wise to attack a problem of a *new type* directly. It is better to make up a much simpler problem of the same type, experiment with that, and see if the method which solves the simple problem throws any light on the complicated one. In map-making, the simplest problems deal with three points only (hence the name trigonometry, i.e., three-line-ology). In particular, triangles containing a right-angle are easy to study.

The Measurement of Angles

It is easy enough to measure the length of a line. It is not so obvious how an angle is to be measured. Two methods are used.

The first method, measurement in degrees, has something in common with the markings on a clock-face. On a clock the numbers 1 to 12 are evenly spaced out, around the rim of the clock. If the hour-hand goes from 12 to 3, we know it has gone a quarter of the way round. To obtain degrees, the circle has to be divided, not into 12, but into 360 equal parts. Each part is called a degree. There is no deep reason for choosing the number 360. Turning through one quarter of the circle (a right angle) corresponds to 90 degrees, usually shortened to 90°. From 12 to 1 on the clock is 30°.

The second method is known as *radian* measure, and is particularly suitable for questions connected with speed. It may be explained as follows. Suppose we have a wheel, 1 foot in radius, fixed to an axle. A string passes round the rim of the wheel, one end being fixed to the wheel, rather like the rope on a capstan or a crane. By pulling the string, we may cause the wheel to revolve. It is clear that we can measure how much the wheel has turned by measuring the amount of string unrolled. When 1 foot of string has been unrolled, the wheel is said to have turned through *one radian*. When x feet have been unrolled, the wheel has turned through x radians.

It is easy to measure an angle in radians. We take a piece of wood, made in the shape of a circle of 1 foot radius. To measure a given angle, we place the centre of the circle. O, at the point of the angle, and mark the points A and B where the lines cross the rim (Fig. 16). We then wind a tape measure *around the rim* (*not* straight) and measure the distance from A to B. If this distance is $\frac{5}{8}$ foot, the angle is $\frac{5}{8}$ of a radian. If we are told that the hand of a clock turns through 10 radians, we measure 10 feet round the rim. We shall, of course, complete more than one turn: where we end up gives the angle 10 radians. If a wheel, of radius 1 foot, with a fixed centre, is turning at the rate 1 radian a second, any point

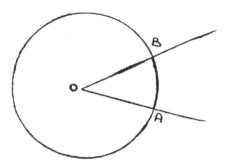

Fig. 16

on the rim is moving at 1 foot a second. Radians are therefore convenient for mechanical problems about ropes being wound on to wheels, for wheels rolling on the ground, and generally for theoretical purposes. If, anywhere in a book on mathematics, you see any statement about 'an angle x' or 'the angle $3\cdot5$', with nothing more said, you must expect this to mean '*x radians*' or '3·5 *radians*', *not* x degrees or 3·5 degrees. 3·5 degrees is always written as 3·5°. If nothing is said about degrees, the angle is in *radian measure*. For mathematicians radian measure is the most natural to use, since it gives the simplest results.

If you measure right round the rim of a circle with the radius 1 foot, you will find the length to be (roughly) 6·28 feet. So one complete turn, 360°, is the same thing as 6·28 radians. This number, 6·28, is not a pleasant number to meet, but we cannot do anything about it. The universe is so made that this number turns up: it is not the fault of mathematicians. We cannot get away from 6·28. If we measure in degrees, so as to make one complete turn a convenient number, 360°, we find that the complication turns up elsewhere. When a wheel turns through 360° a second, the speed of points on the rim (supposing the radius, as before, to be 1 foot) will be 6·28 feet a second. Accordingly, *radians* are used for most questions connected with speed, or with the rims of circles: degrees may be used when we are measuring the angles of things which do not move – fields, for instance.

If you are not familiar with radian measure, you may find it worth while to cut out a large circle, and to mark the two scales around the rim – degrees and radians. Whenever you meet an expression such as 202° or 2·78 radians, you will be able to look at your circle and see what angles these expressions represent. It will be best if you put 0° at the position '3 o'clock', and go anti-clockwise, so that 90° will come at the top (12 o'clock), 180° at 9 o'clock, 270° at 6 o'clock, and 360° back again at 3 o'clock. 0 radians will also be at 3 o'clock, 1·57 at 12 o'clock, 3·14 at 9 o'clock, 4·71 at 6 o'clock, 6·28 at 3 o'clock again. It has become a custom among mathematicians to think of angles in these positions (I do not know why), and it will save misunderstanding if you do the same.

Sines and Cosines

We can now proceed to our experiments on right-angled triangles. It is again to be emphasized that the beginnings of the subject must be experimental. I cannot imagine anyone making any progress who simply sat looking at a right-angled triangle, hoping to be inspired with a method of reasoning out the problem. We must begin with experiments, and then see how much these help us.

Problem: a railway line makes an angle of 5° with the level and is perfectly straight: if a train travels 10,000 feet along the line, how many feet does it rise? No use thinking about it – let us measure and see. We find the answer, correct to the nearest tenth of a foot, to be 871·6 feet (you must take my word for this, unless you are prepared to carry out the experiment for yourself). Nothing particularly simple about the answer: it does not suggest any way of calculating the result without measurement.

But this result does one important job for us: it means that we need not do any more measurements of this particular type, on railways rising at 5°. If we are asked, 'How much does the train rise if it travels 100 feet?' we know the answer immediately. Since the line is straight, the train climbs steadily. In 10,000 feet it will climb 100 times as much as in 100 feet. Therefore, in 100 feet of travel it rises 8·716 feet. In fact, for each foot the train travels, it rises 0·08716 feet (correct to five places of decimals). If it travels x feet, it rises $0·08716x$ feet.

In the same way, to any angle (measured in radians or degrees) there corresponds a number. In travelling x feet along a slope of 13° we rise $0·22495x$ feet: for 30° the formula is $0·50000x$. (Note this, our first simple result, $\frac{1}{2}x$ corresponding to 30°.) It is convenient to have a short way of referring to the numbers that arise in this way. We therefore give them a name, *sines*. (The name goes back to the time when learned men of all countries wrote to each other in Latin: it means a 'bowstring' – the reason for this name may be guessed from Fig. 17.) We say that 0·08716 is the sine of 5° (usually shortened to *sin* 5°), that *sin* 13° = 0·22495 and *sin* 30° = 0·5. 30° is 0·52360 radians, 13° is 0·22689 radians, 5° is 0·08727 radians. (To get these results so accurately we should have to use a circle of 10,000 feet, and measure round the rim). So we may also write *sin* 0·53260 = 0·5, *sin* 0·22689 = 0·22495, *sin* 0·08727 = 0·08716.

Note, in passing, a fact which leaps to the eye: in radian measure, though not in degree measure, the sine of an angle and the angle itself, for fairly small angles, are nearly the same number. The smaller the angle, the nearer it is to its sine. 0·5 is *sin* 0·53260; the two numbers 0·5 and 0·53260 differ by 0·0326. But *sin* 0·08727 is 0·08716. The two numbers here, 0·08727 and 0·08716, differ only by 0·00011. (This fact we have discovered without any effort: you will usually find that, as soon as you start to collect evidence, the discoveries make themselves.) This result suggests that there is some simple law connecting an angle, in radian measure, and its sine. We shall not be surprised when, in Chapter 14, we find a series giving sin x in terms of x. It is important to remember that this series holds *only when the angle is measured in radians, not for degrees*. (Look for the series in Chapter 14, and write a note there, in the margin, to this effect.)

The *cosine* of an angle is defined in a similar way. If an aeroplane starts from an aerodrome and flies 10,000 feet in a straight line at 30° to the level, we know how high it is. It is 10,000 *sin* 30° feet above the ground. Directly underneath the aeroplane there is a certain point on the ground. How far is this point from the aerodrome? By measurement is it found to be 8660·3 feet. Every extra foot the aeroplane flies (still keeping in the original line), this point moves 0·86603 feet further from the aerodrome. If the plane flies x feet, the point moves 0·86603x feet. We call 0·86603 the cosine of 30°, and write, for short, 0·86603 = *cos* 30° = *cos* 0·52360. (The last figure gives 30° in radian measure.)

In short: if we move on a straight line, making any angle t with the level, each foot we travel increases our height in feet by a certain number, called *sin* t, and carries us sideways through a certain number of feet, the number being called *cos* t.

We can easily make a model to demonstrate the meaning of *sin* t and *cos* t. Draw a circle of 1 foot radius, mark around it scales both for degrees and radians. Pin it to a wall or blackboard. Take a strip of cardboard, something over a foot in length. Fasten one end of it by a tin-tack or drawing-pin through the centre of the circle, so that the strip is free to turn. One foot from the centre pierce a small hole in the strip, and hang a plumb-line from this

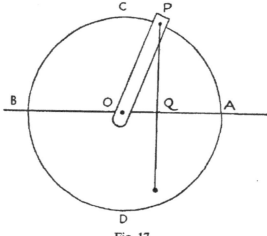

Fig. 17

hole. The arrangement is sketched in Fig. 17. The line *BOA* is level. The thread hanging from the small hole, *P*, crosses *BOA* at the point *Q*. *P* is higher than the line *AOB* by a height *PQ*, and it is a distance *OQ* to the right of *O*. As *OP* is 1 foot in length, the distance *PQ*, measured in feet, is equal to the sine of the angle *AOP*, and the distance *OQ*, also in feet, is equal to the cosine of *AOP*. To make a rough table of sines and cosines it would be better to have *OP* 1 metre long, then, by measuring *OQ* and *PQ* to the nearest millimetre, we should find results certainly true to two places of decimals, perhaps to three.

Actually doing this, or seeing it done, is helpful to the type of person who is good at games but has not a vivid imagination.

We have now explained what sines and cosines are. If you are given any statement about them, you can test for yourself whether it is true or not.

One point is worth mentioning. We have said that *sin t* represents the height of *P* above the line *BOA*. But if *P* is at the angle 270°, which is the same as 4·71 radians, *P* is 1 foot *below BOA*. Being 1 foot below *BOA* we may call being —1 foot above *BOA*. We therefore say that *sin* 270°, or *sin* 4·71, is —1. Similarly, the sines of all the angles between 180° and 360°, between 3·14 and

6·28 radians, have *minus* signs. Also, we take *cos t* to mean the distance Q is to the *right* of O. If Q lies to the left of O, as it does for angles between 90° and 270°, between 1·57 and 4·71 radians, the cosine has a *minus* sign.

Check for yourself the following table.

ANGLE (degrees)	0	90	180	270	360
(radians)	0	1·57	3·14	4·71	6·28
SINE	0	+1	0	—1	0
COSINE.. ..	+1	0	—1	0	+1

An explorer recording his journey will observe in what direction he travels, and for how many miles. If we regard East as corresponding to 0°, North will be 90°, and so on. On a map, North usually means *upwards*, East means *to the right*, so it is easy to apply our railway and aeroplane illustrations to map-making. If an explorer goes 100 miles in the direction 20°, then 50 miles in the direction 40°, what is his new position? 100 miles in the direction 20° is the same as going 100 *cos* 20° East, and then 100 *sin* 20° North. 50 miles in the direction 40° is the same as 50 *cos* 40° East, then 50 *sin* 40° North. If we have tables, we can work out these numbers, and then it is simple to add up, and find the total distance he had gone to the East, and the total distance to the North. Two things to note: (*a*) this method applies to the tunnel problem, Fig. 15, (*b*) it throws some light on the *minus* signs mentioned above. If the explorer, after doing the journey just mentioned, goes a further 30 miles in the direction 135° (i.e., North-West), this *increases* his distance to the North (*sin* 135° is +), but *decreases* his distance towards the East (*cos* 135° is —). In fact, by using the + and — signs in the definition of sine and cosine, we save ourselves the need for any further thought: we just have to write down *distance gone* times *sine*, for each part of the journey. The signs + and —, which then appear, automatically show whether the numbers have to be added on, or taken away.

The Formulae of Trigonometry

Certain other terms, besides sine and cosine, occur in trigonometry – namely, tangent, cotangent, secant, and cosecant.

These are, however, merely abbreviations, and do not bring in any essentially new idea: the subject could be mastered without using these terms at all. We shall therefore not deal with them here, but proceed to study the properties of the sines and cosines.

We shall, of course, try to discover properties of sines and cosines which are useful for our purposes. We have two particular problems in mind, and one rather general use as well.

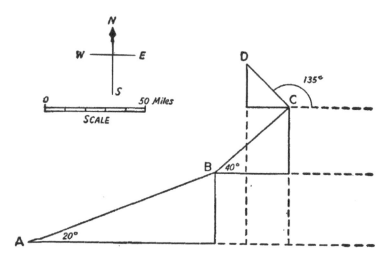

THE EXPLORER'S JOURNEY

The explorer travels from *A* to *B*, from *B* to *C*, and then from *C* to *D*. *AB* is 100 miles, *BC* is 50 miles, *CD* is 30 miles. He records each part of his journey, and works out (by the method explained in the text) how far each part carries him towards the East, how far towards the North. Distances West and South appear with *minus* signs, since 10 miles farther West means 10 miles *less* to the East. The record appears as below:

	Distance.	Direction.	To East.	To North.
A to B.	100 miles	20°	94·0 miles	34·2 miles
B to C.	50 „	40°	38·3 „	32·1 „
C to D.	30 „	135°	−21·2 „	21·2 „
Whole journey A to D.			111·1 miles	87·5 miles

452

The first problem assumes that we have already in our possession satisfactory tables of sines and cosines, and is known as the *solution of triangles*. It is a problem which naturally arises in surveying. We are given certain information about a triangle, sufficient to enable us to draw the triangle, and are asked to find the remaining quantities. For instance, in any triangle *ABC* we might be told the length of *AB*, and the angles *ABC* and *BAC*, and asked to find the lengths *AC* and *BC*. This problem frequently arises in map-making, in the construction of range-finders, in determining the position of a ship at sea by taking the bearings of two lighthouses, in locating submarines, etc.

Surveyors and seamen are in a position to buy printed books of tables, containing sines and cosines and other information. But someone first had *to make these tables* – this is our second problem – and several of the properties of sines and cosines were discovered with this object in view. The interest which mathematicians of the sixteenth century showed in algebra was partly due to the fact that equations had to be solved before trigonometric tables could be made.*

Thirdly, it is desirable to know the properties of sines and cosines on quite general grounds. They arise in many problems, and the work can often be made shorter and simpler if the formulae are known. An example of this will be given later.

Pythagoras' Theorem

In Fig. 17 the sides *OQ* and *QP* have the lengths *cos t* and *sin t*, where *t* is short for the angle ℺*OP*. Students usually find this figure easy enough to grasp, but they do not always recognize it when it occurs in an unusual position, or on a different scale. For instance, in Fig. 18, *DF* makes an angle *t* with *DE*, and *DF* has the length 1. The line *EG* is drawn at right angles to *DF*. It is clear enough that the triangle *DEF* has the same shape as the triangle *OQP*. It may not be so obvious that there are two other

---

* See Zeuthen, *History of Mathematics in the Sixteenth and Seventeenth Centuries*, Chapter II, section 4. I am not sure if this work can be had in English.

triangles in the figure with the same shape. But this is so. If you cut out pieces of paper just large enough to cover the triangles *DEG* and *FEG*, you will find that it is possible (after turning the paper over) to lay these triangles in the positions *LVW* and *LTU*. The triangle *LMN* is exactly the same size and shape as *DEF*. It is now obvious that the three triangles have the same shape, and differ only in size.

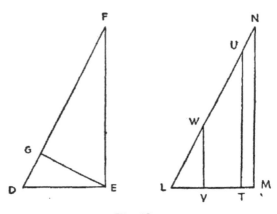

Fig. 18

How long are the lines *DG* and *GF*? The line *DG* can be put in the position *LV*, and is therefore *cos t* times *LW*. But *LW* has the same length as *DE*, which is equal to *cos t*. Accordingly, *DG* must be *cos t* times *cos t*, or *(cos t)²*. In exactly the same way, it may be shown that *GF* has the length *(sin t)²*. But *DG* and *GF* together make up *DF*, which we drew with the length 1 when we began. It follows that:

$$(cos\ t)^2 + (sin\ t)^2 = 1.$$

In Chapter 2 we met a triangle with the sides 3, 4, and 5, and a right-angle between the sides 3 and 4. If we draw this triangle on a scale one-fifth as large, we shall have sides $\frac{3}{5}$, $\frac{4}{5}$, and 1. For this triangle, then, $DE = \frac{3}{5}$ and $EF = \frac{4}{5}$, and $cos\ t = \frac{3}{5}$, $sin\ t = \frac{4}{5}$. The formula given above thus becomes:

$$(\tfrac{3}{5})^2 + (\tfrac{4}{5})^2 = 1,\ \text{or}\ 3^2 + 4^2 = 5^2.$$

It is because of this relation between 3, 4, and 5 that the triangle is right-angled. Another such triangle is 5, 12, 13. $5^2 + 12^2 = 13^2$. If we draw an angle whose cosine is $\frac{5}{13}$, its sine will be $\frac{12}{13}$.

Here we have the answer to the question raised in Chapter 2: the proof given above is, in essentials, that given in Euclid. The result is usually known as Pythagoras' Theorem, and can be stated: if a, b, c are the lengths of the sides of a right-angled triangle, then $a^2 + b^2 = c^2$. This result is essentially the same as the result we have just found. For if t is the angle between the sides a and c, $a = c \cos t$ and $b = c \sin t$. (This result is obtained by enlarging the scale of our standard triangle, OPQ, c times.) So $a^2 + b^2 = (c \cos t)^2 + (c \sin t)^2$. This last expression is equal to c^2 multiplied by $(\cos t)^2 + (\sin t)^2$. By the result proved above, this is the same as c^2 multiplied by 1: that is, c^2. So $a^2 + b^2 = c^2$ follows from our earlier result, by simple algebra.

The Cosine Formula

So far we have considered only triangles containing a right-angle. We will now consider a more general problem. Suppose we have a triangle ABC, and we know the lengths AB and AC, and the size of the angle BAC. How long is BC? (It might be impossible to measure BC directly, owing to mountains, rivers, swamps, etc.)

In books on trigonometry it is usual to write a, b, c for the lengths of the sides BC, CA, AB and to write A, B, C for the three angles of the triangle. Thus, a is the side opposite the angle A, etc. Our problem is: given b, c, A, to find a.

Can this problem be solved at all? Are the facts given sufficient to allow us to draw a plan of ABC? They are. The problem can be solved by drawing: it is a reasonable problem to try.

Can we solve it with the help of tables of sines and cosines without drawing? What are the tables of sines and cosines? They are the result of experiments made on right-angled triangles. Sines and cosines therefore tell us nothing about a figure, unless that figure can be split up into right-angled triangles. Can we split ABC up into right-angled triangles? Very easily indeed. All we have to do is to draw CD at right-angles to AB (Fig. 19). We

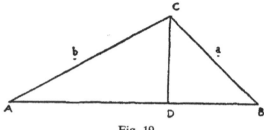

Fig. 19

now have two right-angled triangles, *ADC* and *BDC*. What do we know about these?

Triangle *BDC*: not much hope here. We want to find *BC*, but all we seem to know is that *BDC* is a right-angle.

Triangle *ADC*: quite a different story. We know *AC* = *b*, and we know the angle *CAD* = *A*. In fact, we know everything about this triangle: we have exactly the same information as we had in the railway problem, when we were told the angle the railway made with the level (*A*) and the distance the train travelled (*b*). The height *CD* is therefore *b sin A*, and the distance sideways, *AD*, is *b cos A*.

This new information helps us with triangle *BDC*. It tells us the length *CD*, and shows how *DB* can be found. For *AB* = *c*, and *AD* = *b cos A*. *DB* is what is left when *AD* is taken away from *AB*. So *DB* must be equal to *c* — *b cos A*.

We now know enough about the triangle *BDC* to fix it completely. We know *DC*, *BD*, and the angle *CDB* is a right-angle. *BC* can be found by Pythagoras' Theorem, for $BC^2 = DC^2 + DB^2$. Writing for *BC*, *DC*, and *DB* the lengths found for them, we have:

$$a^2 = (b\ sin\ A)^2 + (c - b\ cos\ A)^2.$$

This formula can be put in a more simple form. Before doing this, we may glance for a moment at the strategy by which we reached this point. The difficult thing in a mathematical problem is *to get started*. Before writing down any calculations at all, one should always prepare a plan of campaign. Otherwise one wanders around like a rudderless ship. While making this plan, forget all the difficulties that may come in the actual calculations. Try

456

simply to build a framework connecting what we know with what we want to know. It is sometimes useful to draw a pencil figure, and to mark with ink those lines whose lengths are given, or angles whose size is known. Then mark with ink lines and angles which can be calculated from those already marked. And so go on, keeping a record of the steps.

For the present problem our plan would be as below.

Line AC and angle DAC given. (Ink these in.)

AD and DC can be calculated. (Ink these.)

AB is given. (Draw a line in ink, just below AB, so as not to blot out the line AD already drawn.)

So DB is found from AB minus AD.

BC is found from DC and DB by Pythagoras.

Do not worry if you have forgotten the formula $AD = b \cos A$, or the exact result of Pythagoras' Theorem. All you need to know in making this plan is that *a formula exists*: that the thing *can* be worked out. In real life (which is more important than examinations) you can always carry a book of formulae with you, and look them up. But no book will tell you on what lines to tackle a problem: that you must learn for yourself, by practice.

Now let us return to the formula we found for a^2. By simple algebra, we can work it out and obtain:

$$a^2 = b^2 \sin^2 A + c^2 - 2bc \cos A + b^2 \cos^2 A.$$

$\sin^2 A$ is the usual way of writing what, until now, we have written $(\sin A)^2$, and $\cos^2 A$ means the same as $(\cos A)^2$. Writing in this way saves a lot of brackets.

We notice that b^2 comes twice in this result. First we have b^2 multiplied by $\sin^2 A$, then b^2 multiplied by $\cos^2 A$. The total amount of b^2 that appears is therefore $\sin^2 A + \cos^2 A$, which is equal to 1. It follows that:

$$a^2 = b^2 + c^2 - 2bc \cos A$$

which is the usual formula given in text-books, and used in problems.

This is an example of the way in which formulae can be shortened by using the properties of sines and cosines. Earlier we promised that such an example would be given.

The Addition Formulae

Now, for some results which arise naturally in connexion with the problem of making tables, though they are also useful for general knowledge.

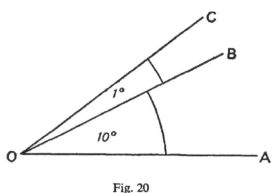

Fig. 20

Suppose that we are setting out to make a very accurate table of sines and cosines, and that (at great labour and expense) we have constructed large triangles and found accurate values for *sin* 1°, *cos* 1°, *sin* 10°, and *cos* 10°. It would be possible to keep on making fresh triangles, and to find by measurement *sin* 11°, *sin* 12°, etc. If carried out on a really large scale, this work would be very troublesome. It would be natural to think, 11° is 10° + 1°. Is it possible to use this fact in some way, and to find *sin* 11° by calculation, from what we know about 10° and 1°? If we can do this it will be very convenient, for the same method will give us information about 12°, since 12° = 11° + 1°, and we may continue thus as long as we care to do.

Our problem is: we have found, by measurement, that *sin* 1° = 0·01745, *cos* 1° = 0·99985, *sin* 10° = 0·17365, *cos* 10° = 0·98481. What are *sin* 11° and *cos* 11°?

The main difficulty in this problem is to draw a figure that brings out the facts clearly, It is easy enough to draw an angle of 10° with a further angle of 1° on top of it, as in Fig. 20. This illustrates the fact that 11° = 10° + 1° all right. But it does not

458

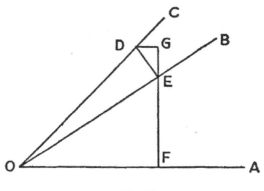

Fig. 21

tell us much about 10° and 1°. We have to take it on faith that
the angles marked 10° and 1° *are* in fact 10° and 1°. There is
nothing in the figure to show that they are: in particular, there is
nothing to link them up with *sin* 1°, *sin* 10°, etc. (Actually, for the
sake of clearness in the figure, it is necessary to draw the angles
rather larger than they actually are.)

We want to bring out the fact that *BOC* is the angle, 1°, whose
sine is 0·01745, and whose cosine is 0·99985. To do this we must
bring in a right-angled triangle. Take *D* at a distance 1 from *O*,
and draw *DE* at right angles to *OB* (Fig. 21). Then we know
$OE = cos\ 1° = 0·99985$, and $DE = sin\ 1° = 0·01745$.

How is *sin* 11° to be brought into the picture? *OD* has the length
1 and makes the angle 11° with *OA*. The height of *D* above *OA* is
therefore *sin* 11°. It is this height that we wish to find.

But this is easy to do: it is exactly the same problem as we had
when the explorer went 100 miles in one direction, and then 50
miles in another. We can get from *O* to *D* by going first from *O*
to *E*, then from *E* to *D*. We know the length and direction both
of *OE* and of *ED*.

Draw an upright line *FEG* through *E*. *F* is on *OA*, and *G* is a
point at the same height as *D*, so that *FG* equals the height of *D*
above *OA*, that is *FG = sin* 11°.

As *FG = FE + EG*, the problem is solved as soon as we can

459

calculate *FE* and *EG*. *FE* presents no difficulties. $OE = 0.99985$ and OE makes an angle 10° with *OA*, so

the height $FE = 0.99985 \sin 10° = 0.99985 \times 0.17365$.

EG can be found from the triangle *EGD*, which has a right-angle at *G*. The triangle *GED* could be obtained by turning the triangle *EOF* through a right-angle, and then making it shrink to a smaller scale. The angle *DEG* is, in fact, the same as the angle *EOF* – that is, 10°. Accordingly, $EG = ED \cos 10° = 0.01745 \times 0.98481$. Adding these two results together, we obtain the length of *FG* – that is, *sin* 11°.

The result we have just found may be written:

$$\sin 11° = \cos 1° \sin 10° + \sin 1° \cos 10°.$$

There is nothing particular about the numbers 1 and 10. The same argument could be carried through for any two numbers, *x* and *y*, and we should find:

$$\sin (x+y)° = \cos x° \sin y° + \sin x° \cos y°.$$

You should find no difficulty in working out *cos* 11°, the distance that *D* is to the right of *O*, and the corresponding general formula for $\cos (x+y)°$.

Other Formulae

The formulae we have considered must be regarded as samples. There are other formulae in trigonometry, which, for the most part, can be found by arguments very similar to those given above. Some books contain vast masses of results. For most purposes, a few formulae and a few straightforward methods are quite sufficient. If you are studying trigonometry for some definite purpose – e.g., surveying, or navigation – you will do well to obtain a book on that subject, and see what formulae of trigonometry are actually used, and for what problems.

Differentiating Sines and Cosines

It often happens that sines and cosines occur in problems about the movement of machinery, the vibrations of some object, or the changes in electric currents. All these, being problems of change of speed, call for differentiation. It is therefore worth while to study the question: how fast do *sin t* and *cos t* change when *t* changes?

We shall study this problem by means of the model illustrated in Fig. 17. We suppose the point P begins at A, and travels round the circle at a steady speed of 1 foot per second. After t seconds it will have travelled t feet, and the angle AOP will therefore be t radians. (The results we shall obtain hold only when the angle is measured in radians.)

We know that *sin t* measures the height of P above AOB after t seconds. This we call, for short, y feet, so $y = sin\ t$. *cos t* measures the distance P lies to the right of O after t seconds. This we call x feet, so $x = cos\ t$. Of course, if P lies below AOB, y will be a number with a minus sign: x will be minus if P lies to the left of O. In the illustration, x equals the length of OQ in feet, y equals the length of PQ in feet.

Note that these signs, x and y have *no connexion at all with any signs x and y that may have been used in other chapters.* For instance, in Chapter 10 x stood for the number of seconds that had passed, and in Chapters 11 and 12 we discussed the expression $\frac{dy}{dx}$. In this section t is the sign used for 'the number of seconds': x and y have simply the meanings given to them in the last paragraph.

The speeds with which x and y change will be $\frac{dx}{dt}$ and $\frac{dy}{dt}$. We shall also write these as x' and y'. So x' is to mean the speed at which the length OQ changes, and y' the speed at which the length PQ changes. (If P lies below AOB, we shall have to continue the line of the plumb-line upwards, until it crosses AOB. This gives Q.) We have already explained carefully what is meant by speed, and how speed can be measured. The meaning of x' and y' should be clear.

There are four points on the circle at which it is particularly easy to see what is happening. These are the highest point, C, the lowest point, D, together with the two points, A and B. At C and D the track of P is level, at A and B it is upright.

As the track is level at C and D, the height of P cannot increase or decrease as it passes these points. As y' measures the speed with which the height of P changes, it follows that y' must be nothing when P passes C or D. It may be easier to see this result if you consider that P is moving upwards just before it reaches C (so y' is $+$), downwards just after it passes C (so y' is $—$). At C, y' is just at the moment of changing from $+$ to $—$, and must be 0. (Compare the remarks in Chapter 11, on the meaning of y'.)

The same argument shows that $x' = 0$ when P is at A or B.

What is x' when P is at C? At C the curve is level. Just for an instant the point P is neither rising nor falling, but is simply travelling towards the left, with a speed of 1 foot per second. In other words, at this instant x is decreasing at the rate 1 per second. That is, $x' = —1$.

At the point D, P is moving towards the right, with a speed of 1 foot a second. So $x' = 1$. In the same way, we may find y' for the points A and B. At A, P moves upwards, y is increasing, $y'=1$. At B, P is moving downward, $y' = —1$.

The points A, C, B, and D are reached after 0, 1·57, 3·14, 4·71 seconds (roughly). We may extend the table given earlier in this chapter, thus:

POSITION				A	C	B	D
t=time in seconds=angle in							
radians ..	..	..	..	0	1·57	3·14	4·71
$x=\cos t=OQ$	..	..	..	$+1$	0	$—1$	0
$y=\sin t=QP$	..	..	..	0	$+1$	0	$—1$
x' ..	..	..	..	0	$—1$	0	$+1$
y' ..	..	..	..	$+1$	0	$—1$	0

This table suggests something. The row y' is the same as the row x: the row x', except for a change of sign, is the same as y. This *suggests* that $y' = x$, and $x' = —y$. These results are, of course, not proved: they are not even made likely. We have taken only four points of the entire circle as evidence. (The law $y' = x^3$ would fit the table equally well.) But, as a bold guess, we might at least *investigate* the results.

It is left to the reader to prepare further evidence, using the points between A and C. A printed table of sines and cosines may be used. Remember to record the angle, *t*, in *radians*. (One degree = 0·01745 radian.) In this way you can convince yourself that the guess was actually correct.

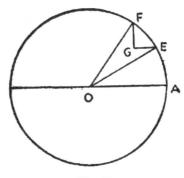

Fig. 22

It is also possible to see this result from a figure. In Fig. 22, *E* represents the position of *P* after any time, *t* seconds. That is, *t* feet of tape, wound round the circle, starting from *A*, would finish at *E*. A little later, *P* will have moved to a point, *F*, a little farther round the circle. The extra piece of tape, *EF*, will have the length Δ*t* feet. If *F* is very close to *E*, the tape *EF* will be very nearly straight, and we shall not be making a serious error if we think of Δ*t* as giving the length of the *straight line EF*.

The line *EG* is level, and the line *GF* is upright. So *GF* represents the increase in the height of *P*, as *P* goes from *E* to *F* — that is, *GF* = Δ*y*. The angle *GFE*, you will find, is very nearly equal to the angle *AOE*, which is *t* radians. Accordingly, *GF* = *FE cos t*, very nearly. (The smaller *EF* is, the nearer this equation comes to the truth.) That is, Δ*y* = Δ*t cos t*, very nearly. When Δ*t* becomes smaller and smaller, we find $\frac{dy}{dt} = cos\ t$.

In the same way, *GE* is equal to the *decrease* in *x*, —Δ*x*, and *GE* = *EF sin t*, very nearly, which leads to the result $\frac{dx}{dt} = -sin\ t$.

As *x* stands for *cos t*, and *y* stands for *sin t*, we may write these results as follows:

$$\frac{d\,(sin\ t)}{dt} = cos\ t \qquad\qquad \frac{d\,(cos\ t)}{dt} = -sin\ t.$$

This is shorter than saying, 'If $y = sin\ t$, $\frac{dy}{dt} = cos\ t$, etc.', and it means the same thing. We shall quote the result in this form in Chapter 14, when we find series for $cos\ t$ and $sin\ t$, or, at any rate, for sine and cosine. I cannot promise that we shall always use the letter t when sine or cosine occurs.

Movement in a Circle

We saw in Chapter 10 that the force acting on a moving weight can be found if we know mx'' and my''. It often happens in machinery that a heavy weight goes round in a circle, as, for instance, any part of a flywheel, or the metal attached to a loco-motive wheel (though this also travels along the line). An aero-plane looping the loop or a motor-car going round a corner raises a similar problem.

We may therefore consider a weight attached to the point P of Fig. 17, and see what force would be required, to make it move in the desired way. Since $y = sin\ t$, $y' = cos\ t$, and y'' (the rate at which y' changes) is therefore $-sin\ t$. In the same manner, we find $x'' = -cos\ t$. There is no difficulty in finding x'' and y'', and the total force acting on the weight at P can be found easily by anyone who has had some practice in the elementary prob-lems of statics and dynamics.

EXERCISES

1. Cut out a circular disc of cardboard, and mark a scale for measuring angles in radians around the edges, by the method ex-plained in this chapter. On the same disc mark a scale for measuring angles in degrees.

Draw on a piece of paper an angle of $\frac{3}{8}$ radian, 1 radian, $2\frac{1}{2}$ radians, 5 radians, 10 radians.

How many radians are 10°, 50°, 95°, 184°?

2. Make an actual model from the design of Fig. 17. From this

make a table giving the sines and cosines of 5°, 10°, 15°, etc. (as far as 90°), to two places of decimals. Check your results for sines from printed tables.

3. Write down, from your results for question 2, *sin* 10°, *sin* 20°, etc. up to *sin* 80°. Write down the cosines in the opposite order: *cos* 80°, *cos* 70° ... *cos* 10°. What do you notice about the two lists? What can you say about *sin* $x°$ and *cos* $(90—x)°$? Can you see any reason for your result?

4. From your model (question 2) find to two places of decimals *sin* 100°, *sin* 110° ... *sin* 170°. Compare these with *sin* 10°, *sin* 20° ... *sin* 80°. What do you notice about the two sets? What formula connects *sin* $(180—x)°$, and *sin* $x°$?

5. Find from your model *cos* 100°, *cos* 110° ... *cos* 170°. (For all of these Q is to the left of O, so the cosines all have a minus sign.) Compare these with *cos* 10°, *cos* 20° ... *cos* 80°. What formula connects *cos* $(180—x)°$ and *cos* $x°$?

Also compare the set just found, *cos* 100° ... *cos* 170° with *sin* 10° ... *sin* 80°. Is there a formula connecting *cos* $(90+x)°$ with *sin* $x°$? If so, what is it?

6. The printed tables give the sines of angles between 0° and 90°. To find the sines of angles between 90° and 180°, and to find cosines, we have to use the results of questions 3, 4, and 5. For example, the tables tell us *sin* $37° = 0·6018$. What are the values of *cos* 53°, *sin* 143°, *cos* 127°?

7. An airman flies 200 miles in the direction 37° North of East. How many miles to the East, and how many miles to the North does his position change? (*Note* – For long flights it is necessary to take account of the fact that the earth is shaped like a ball. All questions in this chapter refer to short journeys, for which the earth may be supposed flat.)

8. Find how many miles East and how many miles North of A is the point C given by the explorer's log below:

A to B 30 miles, in the direction 40° N of E.

B to C 10 miles, due West.

9. Do the same for the journey below:

A to B 40 miles, in direction 70°.

B to C 20 miles, in direction 110°.

10. Also for:.

A to *B* 100 miles in direction 315° (i.e., South-East).

B to *C* 150 miles in direction 80°.

11. An aeroplane has to fly to a town 100 miles away. By mistake it flies in a direction which is 2° off the correct course. When it has flown 100 miles, how far will it be from the town?

12. Ipswich is 65 miles from London, in the direction 36°. Peterborough is 75 miles from London, in the direction 95°. Birmingham is 105 miles from London, in the direction 139°.

How far is Ipswich from Peterborough, Peterborough from Birmingham, and Birmingham from Ipswich?

(This can be done by means of the formula $a^2 = b^2 + c^2 - 2bc.\cos A$. To find the distance from Ipswich to Peterborough, we may take London as *A*, Ipswich as *B*, Peterborough as *C*. A similar calculation gives the other two distances. Remember that $\cos 103°$, which comes in the formula for the distance from Birmingham to Ipswich, has a minus sign. Check your calculations by drawing.)

CHAPTER 14

ON BACKGROUNDS

'Recent workers in the sociology of science have stressed that experimental science arose from the theorists' taking account of the crafts. On the other hand, the crafts have often failed to learn from the theorists almost down to our own day.' – H. T. Pledge, *Science Since 1500.*

STUDENTS of mathematics often have the experience of understanding the proof of some results, but not being able to see what it is all about. The subject remains 'up in the air', a disconnected piece of knowledge. As memory depends on connexions, the result is hard to remember. In ordinary life we remember familiar objects well, because other things continually remind us of them, and thus refresh their images in our mind. Students rightly feel uneasy when they are asked to remember something unconnected with the rest of life: the mind cannot work efficiently unless it is properly treated.

In elementary algebra this 'unearthly' feeling is easily aroused. Many text-books, for instance, explain quite accurately what is meant by an arithmetical progression, or a geometrical progression. The teacher (who may be passionately interested in some other subject, and forced to teach mathematics without understanding it) follows the text-book and teaches A.P.s and G.P.s simply because they are in the book.

We have already (without noticing it) had two examples of arithmetical progressions. The man falling off a house travels 1 foot in the first quarter-second, 3 feet in the next quarter-second, 5 feet in the third quarter-second, 7 feet in the fourth, and so on. The total distance gone in one second is $1+3+5+7$ feet. In the set of numbers, 1, 3, 5, 7, etc., each number is 2 more than the previous one. A set of numbers in which each number is bigger (or smaller) than the number before it by a fixed amount is called an arithmetical progression (A.P.).

The second example was in Chapter 12, when we added together the numbers, 0, 0·01, 0·02, etc., up to 0·09. These numbers also form an A.P. Later in the same section we saw that we could have found a more accurate estimate of $\int_0^1 x \, dx$ if we had divided the first second, not into ten, but into 100 parts. We should then have had to work out the sum of 100 numbers, beginning with 0, 0·0001, 0·0002 ... and ending with 0·0098, 0·0099. Can we shorten the work, so that we shall not actually have to carry out the addition? Yes, this is possible. The first number, 0, and the last number, 0·0099, add up to 0·0099. The second number, 0·0001, and the next to last, 0·0098, also add up to the same amount. Going on in this way, we can arrange all the numbers in pairs, each pair adding up to 0·0099. There will be 50 such pairs. The total will be 50 times 0·0099, that is, 0·495. This result was quoted, without proof, in Chapter 12.

467

Geometrical Progressions

A geometrical progression consists of a series of numbers, each of which is obtained by multiplying the previous one by a fixed number – e.g., 1, 2, 4, 8, 16 ... or 3, $1\frac{1}{2}$, $\frac{3}{4}$, $\frac{3}{8}$ ... Such series can arise in a number of ways.

For instance, there is the well-known question: at what time between 3 o'clock and 4 o'clock is the minute hand of a clock over the hour hand? It is quite natural to begin thinking in the following way. At 3 o'clock the minute hand is 15 minutes behind the hour hand: the hour hand moves slowly, so that in 15 minutes' time the minute hand will nearly have caught up with the hour hand. The hour hand moves through 5 minutes in each hour – one-twelfth as fast as the minute hand. By 3.15 the hour hand will have moved $\frac{15}{12}$ minutes – this is the amount the minute hand still has to catch up. The minute hand will reach this position after an extra $\frac{15}{12}$ minutes. But meanwhile the hour hand will have moved through another $\frac{15}{12^2}$ minutes. In this way we keep revising our original guess of 15 minutes, by adding to it in turn, $\frac{15}{12}$, then $\frac{15}{12^2}$, and so on – each correction being one-twelfth the size of the previous one. In this way we obtain the result $15 + \frac{15}{12} + \frac{15}{12^2} + \frac{15}{12^3} +$ etc., the sum of a geometrical progression. By taking sufficiently many terms of this series, we can get an answer correct to any degree of accuracy: for instance, the four terms actually written above give an answer that differs from the correct answer by less than 0·001.

It is possible to see what the sum of the series is. The hour hand goes only 5 minutes while the minute hand goes 60 – that is, the minute hand gains on the hour hand at the rate of 55 minutes in each hour, or $\frac{55}{60}$ minute in every minute. $\frac{55}{60}$ is the same thing as $\frac{11}{12}$. Accordingly, to catch up 15 minutes on the hour hand, the minute hand will require 15 divided by $\frac{11}{12}$ minutes – that is, $16\frac{4}{11}$ minutes. So the sum of the series must be $16\frac{4}{11}$.

Another problem: if a ton of seed potatoes will produce a crop of 3 tons, which can either be consumed or used again as seed, how much must a gardener buy, if his family want to consume a ton of potatoes every year for ever?

First of all, he must buy a ton to meet his needs for this year. To get a ton for next year, it will be sufficient to plant $\frac{1}{3}$ ton now. To meet the needs of the year after next, $\frac{1}{9}$ ton will be sufficient: for it will yield $\frac{1}{3}$ ton next year, and this planted again will yield 1 ton the year after. And so on. To meet the needs of his family for ever, the farmer must plant $1+\frac{1}{3}+\frac{1}{9}+\frac{1}{27}+\frac{1}{81}+\ldots$ tons.

How much does this series add up to? Let us call the number it adds up to x. We can find x by a simple trick – namely, by working out $3x$ and comparing it with x.

Thus $\qquad\qquad x = 1 + \frac{1}{3} + \frac{1}{9} + \frac{1}{27} + \ldots$

so $\qquad\qquad 3x = 3 + 1 + \frac{1}{3} + \frac{1}{9} + \ldots$

We notice that $3x$ is the same series as x, except that 3 has been added at the front, so $3x = 3 + x$. It follows that $2x = 3$, so x must be $1\frac{1}{2}$.

We can easily see that this is the right answer. If the gardener buys $1\frac{1}{2}$ tons, he needs 1 ton to eat this year, and has $\frac{1}{2}$ ton to plant. The crop will be three times as much as what is planted – this is, it will be $1\frac{1}{2}$ tons – and again he has 1 ton to eat and $\frac{1}{2}$ ton to plant. In this way he and his descendants can continue as long as they care to do.

The same type of series arises in connexion with annuities, compound interest, discount, stocks and shares, etc. Compound interest is one of the main historical reasons why geometrical progressions first came to be studied. To a man making a fortune by money-lending, it is, no doubt, an absorbing subject: for most other people, and particularly for children at school, compound interest is likely to prove deadly dull.

Another application of geometrical series is for the study of air resistance. A body moving through the air is like a man rushing through a crowd. The faster he runs, the more people he knocks into: in other words, the resistance to his progress is proportional to his speed. The same is true for a body moving through the air (provided its speed is not too great): the faster it goes, the more air it has to brush out of its way each second. The result is that it loses a definite fraction of its speed each second. If two-thirds of the speed is lost each second, one-third remains: thus a body might move 1 foot in the first second, $\frac{1}{3}$ foot in the following second, $\frac{1}{3}$ foot in the third second, and so on. The distance gone altogether would be $1+\frac{1}{3}+\frac{1}{9}+\frac{1}{27}+\ldots$, the same series as we had before. It is, of course, taken for granted that no force is acting on the body, apart from the resistance of the air. Thus, the body might be a propeller; if it is properly balanced, and is not connected to an engine, there is no force to make it turn round; if it is given a push, it will start spinning, but will gradually slow down, in the way described.

The connexion between a moving body and geometrical progressions was known already in the seventeenth century. A more modern application of the same idea is to an electric current in a wire: an electron moving inside the wire collides with the atoms composing the wire, just like a man moving in a crowd. If the wire is connected to an electric battery, the problem is altered: there is then a force dragging the electron forward. In the same way, a falling raindrop is subject to the pull of gravitation; for this reason, it is not brought to rest by the resistance of the air. The problem of the way in which a raindrop falls is therefore slightly more complicated, but it too was solved, by means of geometrical progressions, in the seventeenth century.

If x stands for 'any number', we can show (by the method used in the potato problem) that the series $1+x+x^2+x^3+\ldots$ is equal to $\dfrac{1}{1-x}$, provided x is not bigger than 1.

Other Series

We have just seen that $\dfrac{1}{1-x}$ can be expressed in the form of a series, containing the various powers of x. This is not a peculiarity of $\dfrac{1}{1-x}$: almost any function of x you are likely to meet can be expressed in this way. For instance, $\sqrt{1+x}$ is equal to a series which begins with $1+\frac{1}{2}x-\frac{1}{8}x^2 \ldots$ and $-\log_e(1-x)$ is equal to the series $x+\frac{1}{2}x^2+\frac{1}{3}x^3+\frac{1}{4}x^4+ \ldots$ For both these series we suppose x to be less than 1. It is obvious that the series are not true when x is bigger than 1. Of course, we have not *proved* the series

470

to be equal to the functions stated: for proofs you will need to consult text-books.

It is often very convenient to express a function in the form of a series. For instance, while we know from Chapter 12 what is meant by $\log_e 2$, it may not be easy to say just what number this is. By means of the series we can find it. For $\log_e 2$ can be found from $\log_e \frac{1}{2}$. In fact, 2 times $\frac{1}{2}$ equals 1. Taking logarithms, it follows that $\log_e 2 + \log_e \frac{1}{2} = \log_e 1$. But $\log_e 1 = 0$. So $\log_e 2 = -\log_e \frac{1}{2}$. But putting $x = \frac{1}{2}$ in the series given, it follows that $-\log_e \frac{1}{2}$ is equal to $\frac{1}{2} + \frac{1}{8} + \frac{1}{24} + \frac{1}{64} + \ldots$ The terms of this series get small quite rapidly: we do not have to take very many terms to get quite a good value for $\log_e 2$.

Another advantage of such series is that they are easy to differentiate or integrate, since we know how to deal with powers of x. If you differentiate the series for $-\log_e (1-x)$, what series do you get? Is this result reasonable?

Later in this chapter we shall find a series for e^x, and we are now going to find series for $cos\ x$ and $sin\ x$, in order to show how such a question can be tackled.

In Chapter 13 we showed $sin\ 0$ to be 0, and $cos\ 0$ to be 1, also that $\dfrac{d\ sin\ x}{dx} = cos\ x$ and $\dfrac{d\ cos\ x}{dx} = -sin\ x$. It is rather surprising that from this information alone we can find the series we want.

If $cos\ x$ is expressed as a series containing the powers of x, certain numbers will occur in the various terms (as the numbers 1, $\frac{1}{2}$, $\frac{1}{3}$, $\frac{1}{4}$, etc., did in the series for $-\log_e (1-x)$): these numbers we shall call for short $a,b,c,f,g,h,j,k \ldots$ (The numbers d and e are left out, because d is used with a special meaning in $\dfrac{dy}{dx}$ and e also has a special meaning.) So the series will be:

$$cos\ x = a + bx + cx^2 + fx^3 + gx^4 + hx^5 + jx^6 + kx^7 + \ldots$$

Our job is to find out what particular numbers a, b, c, etc., are.

a we can find straight away. If we put $x = 0$, $cos\ 0 = 1$, while the series becomes simply a. It follows that $a = 1$.

If we differentiate the equation above, we find (since the differential of $cos\ x$ is $-sin\ x$):

$$-sin\ x = b + 2cx + 3fx^2 + 4gx^3 + 5hx^4 + 6jx^5 + 7kx^6 + \ldots$$

b can now be found by putting $x=0$. $sin\ 0=0$, so it follows that $b=0$.

We now differentiate the series for $-sin\ x$. The differential of $sin\ x$ is $cos\ s$, so we have:

$$-cos\ x = 2c + 6fx + 12gx^2 + 20hx^3 + 30jx^4 + 42kx^5 + \ldots$$

c is now found by exactly the same method. Put $x=0$. This leads to the equation $-1=2c$, so $c=-\frac{1}{2}$.

It is clear that there is nothing to stop us continuing with this as long as we like, and finding as many of the numbers f, g, h, $\ldots$ as we care to do. The results are (as you can check for yourself):

$$a=1,\ b=0,\ c=-\tfrac{1}{2},\ f=0,\ g=\tfrac{1}{24},\ h=0,\ j=-\tfrac{1}{720},\ k=0:$$

so:
$$cos\ x = 1 - \tfrac{1}{2}x^2 + \tfrac{1}{24}x^4 - \tfrac{1}{720}x^6 \ldots$$

The rule which gives the numbers 1, 2, 24, 720, etc., which appear here, is the following. We start with 1. We multiply this by 1 times 2; this gives the second number, 2. We multiply the second number by 3 times 4, this gives the third number, which again is multiplied by 5 times 6 to give the fourth number: and so on. Differentiating the above series, we find the series for $sin\ x$:

$$sin\ x = x - \tfrac{1}{6}x^3 + \tfrac{1}{120}x^5 - \ldots$$

These are good series for the purpose of calculation, since the terms get smaller very rapidly, and the first few terms of the series give quite accurate answers. These series therefore give an answer to the problem put in Chapter 13, to find a way of making a table of sines and cosines without drawing any figures.

The Dangers of Series

Series played an important part in the early days of the calculus, particularly in the years following 1660. This was a period of great practical activity: men were interested in the new developments of science, and were faced with a great variety of practical problems – the construction of clocks and of telescopes, of maps and ships. If a mathematical method gave the correct answer to a practical problem, people did not bother much whether it was logical or not. In dealing with small changes, Δx, mathematicians followed their own convenience: at one moment they said, 'Δx

is very small, it will be convenient to regard Δx as being equal to 0.' A little later they wanted to divide by Δx, so they said, 'If Δx is 0 we cannot divide by it: we will suppose Δx to be small, but not quite 0.' Whichever was more convenient, that they supposed to be true. If the answer turned out to be wrong, they scrapped their work. As the results were always compared with practice, this rough-and-ready method worked quite well.

Series were treated in this way, too. If it looked reasonable to make a certain step, that step was made. If it gave a ridiculous answer, one soon recognized that something was wrong.

After about 150 years of carefree mathematics, difficulties began to be felt. For instance, in the calculation of logarithms, the series $1-\frac{1}{2}+\frac{1}{3}-\frac{1}{4}+\frac{1}{5}-\frac{1}{6}$ ... arises. Half the terms of this series have a $+$ sign; we will call the sum of these terms a, so that $a=1+\frac{1}{3}+\frac{1}{5}+\frac{1}{7}$ ... We will call b the sum of the other numbers in the series – that is, $b=\frac{1}{2}+\frac{1}{4}+\frac{1}{6}+\frac{1}{8}+$ ... We notice that every number that occurs in b is even. If we double b we thus have $2b=1+\frac{1}{2}+\frac{1}{3}+\frac{1}{4}+$ ...; in the series for $2b$ we have all the terms of the series for a, together with those for b. So it seems that the series for $2b$ should equal $a+b$, so that $2b=a+b$. It follows from this that $b=a$. But b cannot equal a, for every term in a is bigger than the corresponding term in b; 1 is bigger than $\frac{1}{2}$, $\frac{1}{3}$ is bigger than $\frac{1}{4}$, $\frac{1}{5}$ is bigger than $\frac{1}{6}$, and so on. If a equals b, our original series $1-\frac{1}{2}+\frac{1}{3}-\frac{1}{4}$ ... $= a-b=0$. But the sum of the original series is, in fact, just less than 0.7.

In other words, by doing things that *look* reasonable, we have been led to an untrue result. On the other hand, in many cases true and useful results have been obtained by the use of series. It is therefore natural that mathematicians should have begun to inquire more carefully just what is meant by a series, and just what operations may be carried out with series. During the nineteenth century mathematicians carried out such an inquiry. There was a reaction from the carefree attitude of earlier times, and a spirit of caution spread. Mathematicians became rather like lawyers, very concerned about the exact use of words, very suspicious of arguments which merely 'looked reasonable'. Terms such as 'convergence' and 'uniform convergence' were invented, designed to distinguish series which were reliable from those which led to wrong conclusions.

Mathematicians did not only investigate the logic of series: they became uneasy about all the words they were using, and did not become comfortable again until they had given very exact explanations of all the terms they used. Modern books on mathematics are often much longer than the old books, because they spend time explaining and justifying things, which at first sight seem obvious.

There is a fable about a centipede which was asked in what order it moved its feet, and became so puzzled by the question that it was unable to walk at all. Students who begin by studying modern mathematics often suffer from a similar disorder: they spend so much time learning how to criticize, that they never understand how to create. The best policy is to follow the course of history: first to learn to *see* results as the old pioneers were able to see them, only later to examine the weaker points in the natural approach. If there had been no risks taken by the creative mathematicians in the seventeenth and eighteenth centuries, there would have been nothing for the pure mathematicians to criticize in the nineteenth.

The Background of e^x.

Many text-books give explanations of the number e which in themselves are excellent and logical, but leave the reader with the feeling that everything has come 'out of the blue': the argument is logical, but how was it discovered? What is it all about?

We have already had to deal with expressions such as 10^x, a^x, $\log_e x$. We shall now try to collect the facts about these expressions, and to show the connexions between them.

The idea of an exponential function springs immediately from the practice of money-lending. The way in which debt mounts and strangles its victim is an old story, both in fact and fiction. If a money-lender advances £100 now in return for £110 in a month's time, and in a month's time the borrower cannot pay, he finds himself obliged to contract a new loan on the same terms for another month – but the new loan is for £110, not for £100. In a year the debt will become something over £313. The debt for each successive month contains an extra multiplication by $1\frac{1}{10}$. (Compare this with the section 'How Logarithms were invented' in Chapter 6.) 10% a month is the same as 213% a year, much more than 12 times 10%.

We could reverse this and ask: what rate per month is equal to 5% per year? We could try different rates per month, until we found one which worked out (to a sufficient degree of accuracy) to 5% a year. We could ask what rate a week, what rate a day corresponds to 5% a year. If we liked, we could find the rate per hour, or per minute or per second. There would be only one correct answer to any of these questions. By fixing the rate of interest for a year, we automatically fix the rate of interest for any other length of time.

Suppose, for instance, the rate for a whole year to be 100%, and that an inexperienced money-lender charged 40% for six months. Then nobody would borrow money by the year. It would be cheaper to borrow for two periods of six months. £100 now would mean paying £140 after six months. This debt could be met by starting a new loan, for £140. The interest for the remaining six months, at 40%, would be £56, so that £196 would have to be paid at the end of the full year. Borrowing for a year at a time, £200 would have to be paid. In the same way, if the rate for six months were fixed at 50%, it would pay people to borrow money for a year, and lend it out again for two periods of six months: in the first six months, £100 would become £150: in the second six months, £150 would become £225; after paying back £200, a profit of £25 would be left. From practical necessity, then, the rate for six months would be something more than 40%, but less than 50%.

We could make a table showing what £1 would become after any length of time – weeks, days, hours, minutes – once the rate of interest for a year was given. If £1 becomes £a in one year, in n years (n standing for any whole number) it will become £a^n. It is therefore natural to suppose that £$a^{\frac{1}{2}}$ represents the amount that £1 would become after $\frac{1}{2}$ year. A sign such as $a^{\frac{1}{2}}$ has no meaning in itself: in the South of England 'stack' usually means a haystack, in the North a chimney – it is a waste of time to argue which is 'right'. A word is a label tied to a real thing for convenience. It does not matter whether the label is pink or green. A rose by any other name would smell as sweet. If we like to say that $£a^{\frac{1}{2}}$ is going to mean what £1 becomes in $\frac{1}{2}$ year under certain conditions, we have a perfect right to do so. (This definition agrees with that given in Chapter 6, although it uses a different picture.) $£a^x$ will mean what £1 becomes after any number, x, years: x may be a fraction.

As we saw in Chapter 6, the most convenient way of making a table is to start with a small change, and build up from this to larger changes. At whatever rate of interest £1 grows, there will be a time in which it increases by one-thousandth, say, in k years (k may be a small fraction). Every k years that pass, the amount due will be multiplied once again by $1\frac{1}{1000}$. We can thus draw a graph, showing the growth of the debt, by taking upright lines, each separated from the next by a distance k inches. Each line must be longer than the previous line by one part in a thousand. Corresponding to $x=0$ we must have a height of 1 inch: since the sum of money, to begin with, is £1.

Minus Numbers

It is clear that we could extend our graph to minus values of x. Each line is $\frac{1000}{1001}$ of the line to the right of it. So, k inches to the left of $x=0$, we could put a line having the height $\frac{1000}{1001}$, and continuing in this way, we could continue the graph, and find a height corresponding to any distance to the left – that is, to minus values of x. We now have a graph extending as far as we like, both to the right and to the left.

Change of Scale

The distance k depends on the rate of interest. By a suitable choice of k we can get any rate we wish. The distances between our upright lines must remain *equal*, but by altering their size we change the rate of interest. Mechanically this can be done by the arrangement known as 'lazy tongs'. In Fig. 23 we indicate this by a lattice-work of diamond shapes. We suppose a model made to this design, with loosely jointed pieces of wood. Some device (not shown in the figure) will be needed to keep the upright rods in the proper direction. By pulling or pushing at the points A and B, the upright rods can be spaced out, or brought more closely together. In this way, we have one model which represents a^x for *any* number a (within a certain range of values). (In the

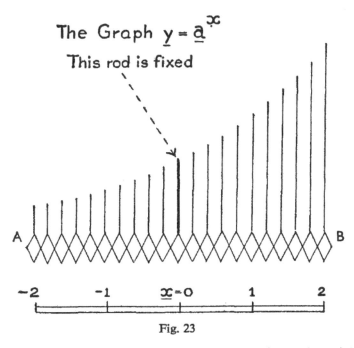

Fig. 23

figure, the rate of change has been exaggerated – each upright stick is actually one-tenth part greater than its neighbour, instead of one-thousandth.) x is throughout measured in inches. When $x=1$, $a^x=a$. Thus a is the length of the rod standing at a distance 1 inch to the right of $x=0$. For example, to obtain the graph of 2^x we must press the points A and B until the rod 2 inches long stands above the point marked 1 on the scale for x. When the model is set in this way, we shall find that 1 inch to the right of any rod there stands a rod twice as high.

The model actually drawn – that is, one in which each rod is $1\frac{1}{10}$ as long as its neighbour on the left – we shall call the *crude* model: the one described in the text, using the ratio $1\frac{1}{1000}$, we shall call the *fine* model. The crude model is suitable for actual construction, and for class work: the fine model should stay in the imagination, for the purpose of argument. As we saw in Chapter 6, the ratio $1\cdot1$ is not sufficiently near to 1 to give accurate values for logarithms.

Logarithms

In Chapter 6 we defined the logarithm as 'the length of rope' needed to multiply one's strength by a given number. In our graph, the distance x corresponds to the length of rope, the height of the rod standing there (y inches, say) measures the multiplying effect. In the crude model we use, in fact, the numbers given in the table on page 75. To get logarithms to base 10, we would need to take $a=10$. But for the moment we are not particularly interested in 10, and we suppose the model set for any number a. Then $y=a^x$, or, to put the same thing the other way round, $x=\log_a y$.

The Number e

If $y=a^x$, what is y'? Consider this with the fine model in your mind. As we go from one rod to the next, x increases by k – that is, $\Delta x=k$. Each rod is $1\cdot001$ times as long as the rod before it; the change in length, Δy, will therefore be $0\cdot001$ times y. So $\dfrac{\Delta y}{\Delta x}$ will be $\dfrac{0\cdot001}{k}y$. This gives us some idea of y': it suggests (what is actually true) that y' is proportional to y. If we take $k=0\cdot001$, we shall have a particularly simple result. $\dfrac{0\cdot001}{k}y$ will then be simply y, and we shall have, very nearly, $y'=y$. (We have to write 'very nearly', because $\dfrac{\Delta y}{\Delta x}$ is 'very nearly', but not quite, y' when $\Delta x=0\cdot001$.)

Taking $k=0\cdot001$ means that the rods are spaced with one-thousandth of an inch between them. In going from $x=0$ to $x=1$, the length of the upright rod will have been multiplied by $1\cdot001$ a thousand times. So a, the length of the rod at $x=1$, will be $(1\cdot001)^{1000}$.

If instead of the fine model we had argued from the crude model, we should have been led to the result $(1\tfrac{1}{10})^{10}$. The fine model gives the better answer, $(1\tfrac{1}{1000})^{1000}$. By taking still larger numbers of rods we could get still better answers. Our result would always be of the form $\left(1+\dfrac{1}{n}\right)^n$. The larger n is, the more nearly would y' be equal to y. As n is made larger and larger, $\left(1+\dfrac{1}{n}\right)^n$ gets closer and closer to the number $2\cdot71828\ldots$, which was mentioned in Chapter 11, and is named e. If $y=e^x$, $y'=y$ exactly.

In Chapter 11, e was found by another method – namely, by choosing a number a which gave the simplest result for the differentiation of the logarithm to base a. As $y=a^x$ means the same thing as $x=\log_a y$, it is not surprising that the same number e should give the simplest answer in both cases. The reader may be able to show that the two methods are really the same. The only complication is due to the fact that the signs x and y have changed places: in Chapter 11, we assumed $y=\log_a x$: here, $x=\log_a y$.

The Series for e^x

We now have enough information about e^x to find a series for it. When $x=0$, $e^x=1$. If $y=e^x$, $y'=e^x$. The method that was used to find a series for $cos\ x$ works equally well for e^x. We find, in fact:

$$e^x = 1 + x + \tfrac{1}{2}x^2 + \tfrac{1}{6}x^3 + \tfrac{1}{24}x^4 + \tfrac{1}{120}x^5 + \tfrac{1}{720}x^6 + \ldots$$

Differentiate this series for yourself, and verify that the series for y' is the same as for y, so that $y' = y$.

This method works also for many other functions, and is associated with the names of Taylor and Maclaurin.

a^x has simple properties, similar to those of e^x, for, as we have seen, the graph of a^x can be got from that of e^x simply by changing the scale of x (in the model, by pushing or pulling the points A and B).

The Applications of e^x

The importance of e^x is due to the property $y' = y$: that is to say, the rate at which it grows is equal to its size. If instead of e^x we take e^{bx}, where b is any fixed number, we have $y' = by$; that is, the rate of growth is proportional to the size.

There are many things which grow in this way. We have already mentioned the example of money-lending. £1,000 grows a thousand times as fast as £1.

Much the same thing holds in business. Within certain limits, the more shops a company owns, the more rapidly can it extend its business.

If a country desires to build up its industry, and starts with very little equipment, it finds that the rate at which it can install new factories is very slow; but the more factories it gets, the quicker it can equip new factories. In a country suffering foreign conquest, the reverse holds: the more factories it loses, the less it is able to replace its losses.

The population of a country, under settled conditions, may grow according to the law e^{bx}. The more people there are in the country, the more children are likely to be born. The population of the U.S.A. between 1790 and 1890 roughly corresponded to the formula $y = 3 \cdot 9 \times 10^{0 \cdot 012x}$, where y is the population in millions x years after 1790.* The formula, of course, ceases to work when a

---

* *Introduction to Mathematics* by Cooley, Gans, Kline, and Wahlert, page 363.

480

country reaches the stage where it cannot support any more people. Rather similar considerations apply to the rate at which microbes multiply in a glass of milk that is going sour, the spread of rabbits in Australia, and other forms of living growth.

There are also conditions in which a new religion or political creed grows by an exponential law. If there are large numbers of people in the mood to accept some new doctrine, once it is put to them, the spread of that doctrine will largely depend on the number of men and women who act as missionaries for it. So long as Mahomet is a lonely man, he can only influence those in his own district. With every convert his power to make himself heard increases. It is possible to find cases where statistics show that a movement has grown according to an exponential law, subject of course to slight variations, due to other causes and particular events which helped or hindered the movement. The fact that a movement grows in this way *during a certain period* tells us nothing at all about its future prospects: it may be smashed by bad leadership, or by disillusion, or by superior force, or by sheer bad luck. When human events show a mathematical law, it means that one or two simple causes were decisive at a certain time: the more different causes are at work, the more complicated will the graph of the movement become.

But the place in which an exponential function really feels at home is far from the complications of human or animal life. In the sciences of non-living matter, exponential functions abound; the speed of a body moving against air-resistance, the pressure of the atmosphere at different heights, the vibrations of an electric circuit, the passage of electrons through a gas, the decay of radium, the speed of a chemical reaction, the current in an electro-magnet, the dying away of any vibration – in these and in countless other problems some quantity grows or shrinks at a rate proportional to its size. It is indeed remarkable how much of the physical world, amid the conflicting action of a great variety of unconnected forces, can be described by the simplest mathematical functions, x^n and e^x.

CHAPTER 15

THE SQUARE ROOT OF MINUS ONE

'The prevalent idea of mathematical works is that you must under-stand the reason why first, before you proceed to practise. That is fudge and fiddlesticks. I know mathematical processes that I have used with success for a very long time, of which neither I nor anyone else understands the scholastic logic. I have grown into them, and so understand them that way.' – Oliver Heaviside.

A T the end of Chapter 5 we saw that the square of every number had a $+$ sign, so that no number could exist with a square equal to -1. One would naturally expect the matter to rest here, and mathematicians to admit that any problem which led to the equation $x^2 = -1$ was meaningless and had no solution.

But a strange thing happened. From time to time mathe-maticians noticed that their work could be much shortened, and the correct answer obtained, if in the middle of the working they used a sign i, assumed i^2 to be -1, and in all other respects treated i just as if it were an ordinary number. This was first done about 1572. The people who did it were very doubtful about the method, but it kept on giving the correct answers. Nobody knew why it should, but the new sign i proved so useful that for two centuries mathematicians used it, without any justification other than success. It was not until 1800 that a logical explanation of the meaning of i was given. (The whole story will be found in Dantzig's *Number, the Language of Science.*)

If, for the moment, we allow i to be treated as an ordinary number, we can see the type of result obtained by eighteenth-century mathematicians.

In Chapter 14 we found series for $e^x \cos x$, and $\sin x$. You may have noticed that the same numbers came into these series. In fact, if you take the series for e^x:

$$1 + x + \tfrac{1}{2}x^2 + \tfrac{1}{6}x^3 + \tfrac{1}{24}x^4 + \tfrac{1}{120}x^5 + \tfrac{1}{720}x^6 \ldots$$

and leave out every other term:

$$1+\tfrac{1}{2}x^2+\tfrac{1}{24}x^4+\tfrac{1}{720}x^6+ \cdots$$

and then make the signs alternately $+$ and $-$

$$1-\tfrac{1}{2}x^2+\tfrac{1}{24}x^4-\tfrac{1}{720}x^6 \cdots$$

you obtain the series for *cos x*. In the same way, *sin x* corresponds to the other half of the terms.

By making use of the sign *i* we can express the relation between the three series in a short formula.

Let us suppose x to have the value *ia*, where *a* may be any number. Putting $x=ia$ in the series for e^x we have:

$$e^{ia}=1+ia+\tfrac{1}{2}i^2a^2+\tfrac{1}{6}i^3a^3+\tfrac{1}{24}i^4a^4+ \cdots$$

i^2 we know is -1, $i^3=i\times i^2=-i$. $i^4=i^2\times i^2=(-1)\times(-1)=+1$. In the same way, all the higher powers of *i* turn out to be 1, i, -1, and $-i$ in turn. Accordingly,

$$e^{ia}=1+ia-\tfrac{1}{2}a^2-\tfrac{1}{6}ia^3+\tfrac{1}{24}a^4+ \cdots$$

If we sort out the terms which contain *i* from those which do not, we see that the terms without *i* give the series for *cos a*, while the terms containing *i* are equal to *i* times the series for *sin a*. In short:

$$e^{ia}=cos\ a+i\ sin\ a$$

This is rather a surprising result. e^x is a simple type of function, like 2^x or 3^x. We meet functions of this type very early – in the arithmetic course, for compound interest. *e* is just a number between 2 and 3, round about $2\cdot7$.

cos a and *sin a* are quite different. We meet them first of all in connexion with geometry, as the sides of a right-angled triangle. We have no reason at all to expect that they will be connected with any of the simpler formulae of algebra: in fact, it is a mystery to most people how the tables for *sin a* are worked out at all.

The formula above shows that *cos a* and *sin a* are in fact closely connected with the simplest type of function. e^x has many simple properties; for instance, $e^p\times e^q=e^{p+q}$, *p* and *q* standing for any two numbers. If we take $p=ia$ and $q=ib$ we obtain the results below:

$$e^{ia}\ e^{ib}=e^{i(a+b)}$$

that is $(cos\ a+i\ sin\ a)\ (cos\ b+i\ sin\ b)=cos\ (a+b)+i\ sin\ (a+b)$. If we multiply out the expression on the left-hand side, and compare the two sides, we see that $cos\ (a+b)$, the part free from i, must be the same as $(cos\ a\ cos\ b—sin\ a\ sin\ b)$, while the number that appears with i, $sin\ (a+b)$, must be the same as the number that appears with i on the other side, $(cos\ a\ sin\ b+sin\ a\ cos\ b)$.

All the formulae given for sines and cosines in books on trigonometry can be obtained, usually without very much work, from the properties of e^x. This fact can be used to take a burden off the memory. Instead of learning the formulae, one can work them out whenever they are needed, by using e^{ia}.

It is easy to find formulae giving $cos\ a$ and $sin\ a$ in terms of e^{ia}. $cos\ a$, in fact, equals $\frac{1}{2}(e^{ia}+e^{-ia})$. We can turn any problem about cosines into a problem about exponentials. For instance, we can immediately find $\int (cos\ x)^6 dx$ by this means, for exponential functions are easy to integrate.

We can regard all problems about sines and cosines as problems about exponentials, thus saving ourselves the trouble of learning special methods for dealing with sines and cosines. i is therefore a very helpful device: as was mentioned in Chapter 5, electrical engineers make great use of it.

What is i?

It seems at first sight very strange that the square root of minus one – something which no one has ever seen, and which seems in its own nature to be impossible – should be useful for such material tasks as the design of dynamos, electric motors, electric lighting, and wireless apparatus.

When some natural fact strikes us as strange, it means that we are looking at it from the wrong point of view. If we find the universe mysterious, it is because we have some idea about what the universe ought to be like, and are then surprised to find it is something different. The fault lies with our original idea – not with the universe.

When we find i mysterious, it is because we are thinking of i as an ordinary number. But there is no *number* x for which $x^2 = -1$. We convinced ourselves of this in Chapter 5.

We have also seen that the sign i, for which $i^2 = -1$ is assumed, leads to perfectly correct results, and clearly has *some* meaning. It is impossible that i should be a *number*; but there is no contradiction at all if we suppose i to be something else. i, in fact, can be interpreted as an operator.

An operation means doing something: 'Turn the piano upside down', 'Move two paces to the right', 'Throw Mr Jones out' are examples of operations applied to a piano, a soldier, and Mr Jones. If we use **U** as an abbreviation for 'turn upside down', and p for 'the piano', **U**p has the same meaning as. the first sentence given above. **U** is called an *operator*. The operation can be repeated. **UU**p would mean 'Turn the piano upside down, and then turn it upside down again', which would, of course, bring the piano back to its original position. Usually **UU** is represented by **U²**, **UUU** by **U³**, etc. Since turning the piano upside down twice leaves it in its original position, **UU**$p=p$, or **U²**$p=p$. It is convenient to use the sign **1** for the operation of leaving something alone. Thus **1**p means the result of leaving the piano alone, which is just the piano in its original position, p. So **U²**$p=$**1**p. This sort of result is not only true for a piano; the result of turning any solid body (not a glass of water, however!) upside down twice is the same as that of leaving it alone. We express this by the equation **U²**$=$**1**.

You will see that it is perfectly possible to argue about operations, and to get results about them, the truth of which can be seen purely by common sense. You will also see that these results, when stated in the shorthand of algebra, *look* like equations for numbers, and might easily be mistaken for statements about numbers. And in fact it is precisely this mistake which has been made in connexion with the equation $i^2 = -1$. To avoid any such misunderstanding, we shall print all signs representing operations in heavy type. From now on, in particular, we shall write **i** instead of i, so as to make it clear that we are *not* dealing with the sign for a number.

While operators are not numbers, they are often closely

connected with numbers. In an adding machine, for instance, we have a number of gear wheels arranged in the same way as the wheels in the mileage recorder of a motor-car. Every time a motor-car goes a mile, the wheel representing units turns through one division, and one is added to the mileage. The turning of the wheels is an operation, and this operation corresponds to adding one to the mileage. It is because of this correspondence between numbers and certain mechanical operations that it is possible to make calculating machines at all.

We shall now find a set of operators **1, 2, 3** ... and **+** which correspond very closely indeed to 1, 2, 3 ... and + in ordinary arithmetic. **1, 2, 3** ... are not numbers, but there are many relations between these operators which correspond to those between ordinary numbers: they have a pattern in common with ordinary numbers, just as a family of father, mother, son, and daughter in a colony of chimpanzees have a pattern in common with a family of father, mother, son, and daughter in Birmingham. This is not to say that everyone in Birmingham is a chimpanzee.

We shall then find it quite natural to bring in an operation, **i**, such that $i^2 = -1$.

The Operators **1, 2, 3** ....

To define the operators **1, 2, 3** ... we begin by imagining a long lath of wood, on which a scale has been marked. O is any fixed point and the figures 1, 2, 3, etc., are marked at distances of 1, 2, and 3 inches to the right. Going to the left from O, we find the figures —1, —2, —3, etc., at distances 1, 2, 3 inches. This is an ordinary scale, such as might be marked on a thermometer.

One end of a wire is fastened to O, and on this slides a bead, A. The wire may point either to the right or the left. The operations we shall consider will consist either in turning the wire from one direction to the other, or in sliding the bead A along the wire.

The operation **2** may now be defined. It consists in moving the bead A to a point on the wire twice as far from O as the former position of A. The operation **2** may be put into words, 'Double the distance OA'. In the same way, the operation **3** means

'Make OA 3 times as long.' $2\frac{7}{8}$ means, 'Make OA $2\frac{7}{8}$ times as long.' **x** means 'Make OA x times as long', where x stands for any positive number. **1** will mean, 'Leave A where it is.'

Several operations may be carried out one after the other. For instance, the operation **(4) (3) (2)** means that the length OA has to be doubled, then trebled, then again made four times as large: in short, OA has to be made 24 times its original length. The three operations, applied in turn, are equivalent to the single operation **24**. **(4) (3) (2)**=**24**. So there is a close correspondence between the doing in turn of various operations and the multiplication of ordinary numbers. We might say that the operations have the same multiplication table as ordinary numbers.

By the operation **−1** we understand that the direction of the wire is reversed, but the distance OA is left unchanged. Thus, if A was originally above the mark 3, the operation **−1** would cause it to come over the mark —3. If A was originally at —3, the operation **−1** would bring it to 3.

By **−x** we understand that the distance OA is made x times as large, and its direction reversed.

Check for yourself that **(−2) (3)**=**−6** and **(−4) (−5)**=**20**. The rules for multiplying **+** and **—** operators are the same as those for ordinary numbers.

Addition

How shall we find a meaning for **2+3** or **2+ (−3)**? We *might* say straight away that **2+3** is to be **5** and that **2+ (−3)** is to be **−1**; that is, we could use ordinary arithmetic as a way of defining addition for operators. But this would have the disadvantage that when we come to consider **i**, which does not correspond to any ordinary number, we should not know what to take for **1+i**.

It is therefore more satisfactory to make use of another method which will apply equally well to operations such as **i**, while agreeing with the first method for operators that correspond to ordinary numbers.

We suppose the bead A to be at any point P, to begin with. Let

Q be the point to which the operation **2** sends A, R the point to which the operation **3** sends A, and S the point to which A is sent by the operation **5**. Then $OQ=2$. OP; $OR=3$. OP; $OS=5$. OP. (OP stands for the distance from O to P, 2, 3, 5 for the ordinary numbers: there are no operators in these equations.) it is obvious that $OS=OQ+OR$, so that we could find the position of S by putting lengths equal to OQ and OR end to end.

In the same way we could find the effect of the operation **2+(−3)**. We must remember that **2** and **−3** will cause OA to point in opposite directions: when we put the two lengths end to end, it must be in such a way that the second length points in the opposite direction to the first. Fig. 24 may help to make this clear.

2+3=5

2+(−3)=−1

−2+3=1

−2+(−3)=−5

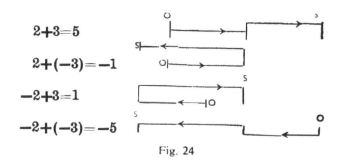

Fig. 24

Accordingly we are led to define addition as follows: if the operation **x** sends A from P to Q, and the operation **y** sends A from P to R, **x+y** is defined as the operation which sends A to S, where S is the point obtained by putting OQ and OR end to end.

We may write **2+ (−3)** more shortly as **2−3**. Be careful to distinguish between **2−3** and **(2) (−3)**. **(2) (−3)** means that the operation **2** has to be applied to the result of **−3** acting on A.

We have now found a set of operators which correspond completely to the ordinary numbers: they can be multiplied and added, and the answers look exactly like the answers for ordinary numbers, except that they are in heavy type. If you picked up a page of calculations, dealing with these operators, you might mistake it for examples in elementary arithmetic, written by someone who pressed very hard on the pen: there would be no way of distinguishing between the two.

The Operator i

The operation **—1** has the effect of reversing the direction of OA, without altering its length – i.e., it rotates OA through $180°$.

Can we find an operation i such that $i^2 = —1$? i^2 means that the operation i is carried out twice. The question asks us to find an operation which, performed twice, turns OA through $180°$.

The question is now ridiculously simple. The mysterious operation i consists simply in turning OA through $90°$! In Fig. 25 A is supposed to start by being at P. The operation i sends A to E, i^2 sends A to F, i^3 sends A to G, and i^4 brings A back again to P. **—1** sends A from P to F, and $i^2 = —1$, as we hoped.

Before we brought i into the picture, the bead A moved on a straight line. It could lie to the right or the left of O, but always

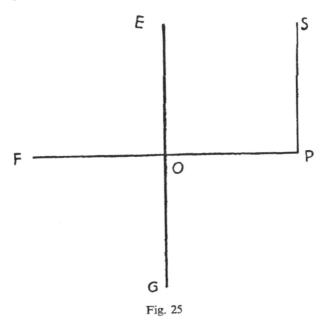

Fig. 25

at the same level as O. Now that i has been brought in, it is possible for A to lie above or below O, and in fact we shall soon have A wandering over the whole surface of the paper.

Addition

The 'end-to-end' method of addition can now be used to give a meaning to expressions such as **1+i** and **2+3i**.

Suppose, as before, that the bead A is at P, and is then acted upon by the operation **1+i** (Fig. 25). Where will **1+i** send it? We have to find the points Q and R to which **1** and **i** send A, and then put OQ and OR end to end. The operation **1** leaves A at P. The operation **i** sends A to E. So Q is P and R is E. We have to put OP and OE end to end. At P we draw PS equal to OE, and having the same direction as OE. This gives us the point S, which we require. The operation **1+i** sends A from P to S. If A starts at any other point, we can find where the operation **1+i** sends it. (For instance, if the bead A were at E to begin with, where would **1+i** send it?)

In the same way, the operation **2+3i** can be studied. The bead A may start at any point of the paper, say at K (Fig. 26). We have to study the operations **2** and **3i** separately, and then to combine them by 'end-to-end' addition.

The operation **2** would send A from K to L. **3i** acting on A means that OA has to turn through $90°$ and become 3 times as long. Thus **3i** would send A from K to M. Now OM has to be put on to the end of OL. We draw LN equal to OM, and in the same direction as OM. N is the point we are looking for. The operation **2+3i** sends A from K to N.

K may be chosen anywhere. We could choose K in different positions, and notice where the corresponding N came. You may notice that the angle KON is always the same, and that ON is always in the same proportions to OK, wherever K may be chosen, In other words, wherever the bead A may be, the operation **2+3i** turns OA through the same angle and stretches the length OA the same number of times.

We may picture any operation **a+bi** as being a turn through

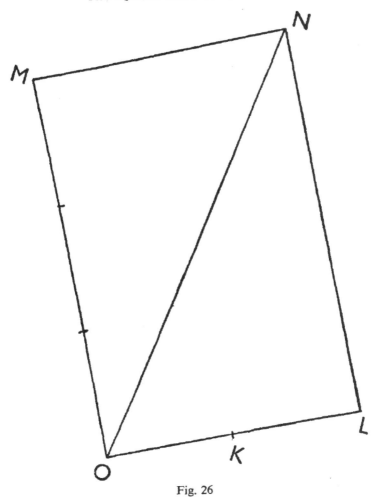

Fig. 26

some angle followed by a stretch. If **a+bi** corresponds to a turn through the angle θ and a stretch r times, it is easy to see that $a = r \cos \theta$ and $b = r \sin \theta$. If we are given a and b, we can find r and θ graphically by drawing a right-angled triangle, with sides a and b. r is known as the *modulus*, θ as the *argument* (sometimes the *amplitude*) of the operation **a+bi**. Special names are given to these two quantities, because they arise naturally and often occur in formulae: we therefore save time by giving them names.

You are now in a position to think about these operations for yourself. We have shown, by the examples $1+i$ and $2+3i$, how to find the operation represented by any symbol of the type $a+bi$. You now understand what the symbols represent, and it is up to you to make yourself familiar with the actual operations, by experimenting with them. What do you understand by the operations $1+2i$, $1-i$, $-3i$? If two operations are carried out in turn, does it matter in which order this is done? Is (2) (i) the same as (i) (2)? Is $(1+i)$ $(1+2i)$ the same as $(1+2i)$ $(1+i)$? By carrying out the actual geometrical operations, find a single operation which has the same effect as $(1+2i)$ $(1+i)$. What is the modulus of i? Of $3+4i$? What operation is $-i$? Does (i) $(i)=(-i)$ $(-i)$? What is (i) $(-i)$? $-i$ means the operation (-1) (i).

Once we have given a definite meaning to the symbols, we lose all control over them. We can decide what name to give any operation, but once we have chosen the name, we have to observe what that operator actually does. We have reached that stage. We have given the names $1, 2, 3 \ldots$ and i to certain operators, and have explained what we mean when two operators are written side by side, or are linked by the signs $+$ and $-$. Division is to mean the opposite of multiplication. The only sign which has not yet been given a meaning is e^x, which we shall come to later. But so far as addition, subtraction, multiplication, and division are concerned, everything is settled. We must not *assume* that these new signs obey the same rules as ordinary numbers: for they are not ordinary numbers. We must try to see whether they do.

For example, we must not *assume* that (2) (i) is the same as (i) (2). Actually (2) (i) is equal to (i) (2), but we must convince ourselves that this is so by trial. There are operators for which the order in which they are performed alters the answer. The effect of being beaten and then beheaded is different from being beheaded and then beaten.

The interesting thing about the operators we are now dealing with is that they behave just like ordinary numbers. If you take any formula which is true for ordinary numbers, it will be true for these operators. For instance, $(x+1)(x-1)=x^2-1$, when x is an ordinary number. If we put any operator $\mathbf{a+bi}$ in the place of x, we find the result (in heavy type) still holds true. For instance, putting i in place of x, it is true that $\mathbf{(i+1)(i-1)=}$ $\mathbf{i^2-1}$. $\mathbf{i^2}$ is $\mathbf{-1}$, so $\mathbf{i^2-1=-2}$. You will find that the result of carrying out the operations $\mathbf{i-1}$ and $\mathbf{i+1}$, one after the other, is to double the length OA, and to turn it through $180°$; that is, to do what the operation $\mathbf{-2}$ does.

You will find, too, that it does not matter in what order multiplication is done, or in what order signs are added to each other. $\mathbf{i2}$ and $\mathbf{2i}$ have exactly the same meaning (multiplication meaning that the operations are carried out, one after the other) and $\mathbf{i+1}$ has the same meaning as $\mathbf{1+i}$ (it does not matter which line is put to the end of the other, in 'end-to-end' addition). In short, any rule which is true for ordinary numbers is true for these operators.

This fact is extremely convenient. Often, when we begin to study a new type of operation, we find laws which are entirely fresh to us. Each type of operation has its own particular way of behaving, which we have to get used to. But we do not have to learn any new rules for the operators $\mathbf{a+bi}$. They behave exactly *as if* they were numbers: while they are not, in fact, numbers, they yet have so much in common with numbers that, *for most purposes*, they can be thought of as numbers. Mathematicians usually refer to them as *complex numbers*, to show that they are close relations of the ordinary numbers. If, in making some calculation, you treat i as if it were an ordinary number, you will obtain the correct result.

On the other hand, by thinking of i as an operator, you can often see results more quickly than by using the methods of ordinary arithmetic. For instance, you may be asked to solve the equation $\mathbf{x^2}=i$. We know that i represents a rotation through a right-angle. We are asked: what operation $\mathbf{x}$, carried out twice, has the same effect as i? The answer is obvious: turn through half a right-angle. This operation does not involve any stretching, so its modulus $r=1$. (*No stretching* does *not* mean $r=0$. The length OA is *multiplied* by r. If OA is unchanged, this means $r=1$.) Since the angle θ is half a right-angle, it is easily seen that the numbers *a* and *b* must be 0·707 and 0·707 (from a table of sines and cosines), and the operation **a+ib**, which represents a turn through half a right angle, is **0·707+0·707i**. (This is an outline only. Draw the figure for yourself. Also check the result by ordinary arithmetic, treating **i** as if it were an ordinary number.)

Complex Numbers and Electricians

It is now easier to see why electricians make such frequent use of the operator **i**. Every generator of electric current contains parts which are rotating, and which every minute pass through many right angles – that is, have the operation **i** applied to them, again and again.

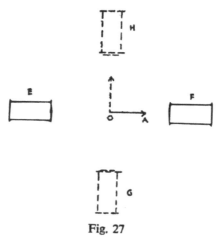

Fig. 27

It would be possible, and for electrical students interesting, to explain **i** entirely in terms of a simple generator of alternating current. For mathematical simplicity, it is best to consider a design of generator very different from that actually used in engineering practice.

We suppose a small coil be be rotating in a magnetic field. The direction of the magnetic field may be represented by means of an arrow, and the strength of the magnetic field may be represented by the length of this arrow. In Fig. 27, OA is an arrow, representing the magnetic field. This arrow, OA, takes the place of the line OA (joining a fixed point O to a bead A). 'Turning OA' means that we change the direction of the magnetic field. 'Stretching OA' means that we make the field stronger. Both operations can easily be done if the magnetic field is produced by electro-magnets, mounted on a bar which can rotate about the fixed point O.

We may take as a standard situation that in which the electro-magnets are at E and F and a current of 1 ampere is flowing through them. The operation **a** is to mean that the current in the electro-magnets is increased until the magnetic field at the centre, O, is a times as strong as before.

The operation **ib** would mean that we start from the standard position, make the field b times its standard strength, and then turn through a right angle. The coils would then be in the positions, shown dotted, at G and H, and the magnetic field would be represented by the dotted arrow.

The operation **a+ib** can be interpreted by supposing we combine the two arrangements. We have coils at E and F, through which there flows a current sufficient to produce a magnetic field of a units at O, and *at the same time* we have coils at G and H with a current strong enough to produce a field of b units at the centre. The *combined effect* will be to produce a magnetic field in a direction which lies between the directions OF and OH. The precise position of the arrow representing the combined effect is given by exactly the same rule as before – 'end-to-end addition', more commonly known as the Parallelogram Law, or the Triangle of Forces.

It will be clear to electricians that the arrow representing the magnetic field can be brought to *any* desired position by suitable choice of the size (and direction) of the currents in the circuits $E - F$ and $G - H$. That is, any operation consisting of 'a turn and a stretch' can be put in the form **a+ib**.

To avoid complicating the figure, the small coil rotating about O has not been drawn. The changes in the direction and strength of the magnetic field will, of course, produce corresponding changes in the phase and amplitude of the alternating current generated. It is natural that the operator i should be used in connexion with alternating currents, to show the changes produced by including extra resistance, inductance, etc. What we really do, in using the sumbol i, is to compare the effect of such changes in the circuit with the effect of certain changes (represented by signs such as $a+bi$) made *inside* the generator which produced the current.

The Further Study of i

One question which has been raised in this chapter, but not yet answered is how to define e^x, when x is a complex number. e^x, in heavy type, is a new label, and we could (if we chose) attach this label to any operation whatever. But this would be very misleading: we should always have to remember that the operation chosen had nothing whatever to do with the ordinary e^x, and we should always be liable to make mistakes through forgetting the difference. On practical grounds it is clearly best not to use the label e^x at all, unless we can find some operation which has properties very similar to those of e^x.

We have already found operations whose claim to the labels of x, x^2, x^3, etc., has been admitted, and we know that e^x can be expressed by means of a series containing x, x^2, x^3, etc. It would therefore be natural to form the corresponding series, in heavy type, and to define e^x by saying:

$$e^x = 1 + x + \tfrac{1}{2}x^2 + \tfrac{1}{6}x^3 + \tfrac{1}{24}x^4 + \tfrac{1}{120}x^5 + \ldots$$

This definition is, in fact, quite satisfactory. It gives us a meaning for e^x which can be proved to have all the properties of the ordinary e^x.

It is important to understand what is implied in this definition. If, for example, we wished to find e^{2+3i} by means of this series, we should have to replace x by $2+3i$, giving:

$$e^{2+3i} = 1 + (2+3i) + \tfrac{1}{2}(2+3i)^2 + \tfrac{1}{6}(2+3i)^3 + \text{ etc.}$$

We should then have to work out $(2+3i)^2$, $(2+3i)^3$, etc., and put the answers in. $(2+3i)^2$ turns out to be $-5+12i$, $(2+3i)^3$ is $-46+9i$, and so on. Taking into account the numbers $\frac{1}{2}$, $\frac{1}{6}$, etc. which occur in the series, we thus find:

$$e^{2+3i}=1+(2+3i)+(-2\tfrac{1}{2}+6i)+(-7\tfrac{2}{3}+1\tfrac{1}{2}i)+\ldots$$

We may now collect together the terms which contain i, and those which are free from i, so that:

$$e^{2+3i}=1+2-2\tfrac{1}{2}-7\tfrac{2}{3}\ldots$$
$$+i(3+6+1\tfrac{1}{2})\ldots$$

This step is justified, because i can be treated just like x in ordinary algebra, as we noted earlier.

But this result will be no use *unless* we find that the series $1+2-2\tfrac{1}{2}-7\tfrac{2}{3}\ldots$ and the series $3+6+1\tfrac{1}{2}\ldots$ settle down to steady values, when sufficiently many terms are taken. Nor will these series be any use if they turn out to be 'dangerous series' of the type described in Chapter 14.

Actually, these two series are very tame and reliable. The later terms in the series for e^x contain numbers such as $\frac{1}{24}$, $\frac{1}{120}$, $\frac{1}{720}$, which rapidly become very small; and at a certain point, the later terms make hardly any difference to the sum of the series. The rule by which the numbers in e^x are formed is the following: $6=1\times2\times3$, $24=1\times2\times3\times4$, and so on. 120 is 5 times 24. 720 is 6 times 120. The farther we go, the more rapidly do the terms of the series decrease.

It can be proved that the series for e^x is all right (in professional language, is *convergent*) whatever x may be. That is, if $x=a+ib$, it does not matter how large the numbers a and b may be: the series will still converge. If a and b are large numbers, we may have to take a large number of terms before we get a good estimate of e^{a+ib}: nevertheless, as the series *does* define e^x, we have a logical foundation on which to build.

Actually, to find e^{a+ib}, it is better to proceed as follows. $e^{a+ib}=e^a \cdot e^{ib}=e^a (\cos b+i \sin b)$. a and b correspond to ordinary numbers a and b. We can look up e^a, $\cos b$ and $\sin b$ in tables. But this procedure is possible only *after* we have proved (by means of the series for e^x) that e^x has all the properties of e^x, so that the steps taken above are justified. If our definition of e^x, by means of the series, is not water-tight, then we cannot trust results obtained from this definition.

Mathematicians are therefore forced to study the convergence of series in which complex numbers occur. They have also studied what meaning can be attached to the sign $\frac{dy}{dx}$ when x and y are complex numbers.

We have already seen that the use of i allows us to show a close connexion between e^x, $sin\ x$, and $cos\ x$, a connexion that is surprising, since e^x appears at first sight very different from $sin\ x$ and $cos\ x$. We have also seen that this connexion is of practical use, as it helps us to see the solution of many problems about sines and cosines.

In the same way, the further study of complex numbers throws light on many problems about ordinary numbers. In fact, the subject of complex numbers is one of the most beautiful and instructive departments of mathematics. It gives one the feeling of having been taken behind the scenes: one sees easily and quickly the reasons for results which had previously seemed quite accidental. It is a subject in which calculation plays a small part: its results frequently take forms which one can *see*, and remember, as one remembers a striking poster. By enabling one to see the inner significance of many practical problems, it is therefore of great value for applied mathematicians.

No one could have foreseen that the study of i would lead to such welcome results, any more than the first men who played with magnets and silk could have foreseen the application of electro-magnetic theory to the invention of wireless. In both cases, it just turned out to be so.

When you first learn to use i, you will suffer from a feeling of strangeness. The subject will seem unreal to you. That is inevitable. Any new subject feels strange at first. When wireless first became popular, people felt it to be strange. But the children who are born today take wireless for granted. If, as a war economy, all wireless were to stop, people would say, 'How strange it is, having no wireless!' But no one had wireless in 1914–18, and no one felt it to be strange. Nothing is either strange or familiar in itself. Anything is strange the first time you meet it: anything is familiar when you have known it five years. The more you use **i**, the more you will come to feel that **i** is a natural and reasonable thing. But this feeling can come only gradually.

Complex numbers show pure mathematics at its best. Pure mathematics is the study of method. Given any problem, we want to know the best way of attacking it. Many problems, at first sight hard, become simple only if one can look at the problem from the proper angle, if one can see the problem in its proper setting. It is the job of pure mathematicians to classify problems, to suggest that this problem is essentially similar that, and likely to yield to a certain type of attack. It may not be in the least obvious that the problems are connected: it is not in the least obvious that the equation $x^2 = -1$ is going to throw light on the question of electric lighting. The less obvious the connexion is the more credit must go to the pure mathematician for discovering it; the harder the problem appears, the greater is the credit due for showing that it is connected with some simpler problem.

Engineers do not need to know more than the most elementary results about complex numbers. The more advanced results are chiefly of interest to professional mathematicians, who are inventing and perfecting new methods, which, when complete, can be used by scientists and practical men. Anyone with a taste for mathematics should try, when as young as possible, to gain some knowledge of complex number theory. Books on the subject have such titles as *The Theory of Complex Variables*, *The Theory of Functions*, etc. Too often, boys at school fail to realize how much mathematics there is to know. Talented boys find themselves ahead of their fellows, and begin to think they have a mastery of mathematics. As a result, they waste their last year at school. The first year at college (for those who are able to go there) they meet the best boys from other schools, and experience a tremendous shock.

Made in USA - Kendallville, IN
1101539_9781938772795
05.08.2020 1000